ιeology of the R Galloway district

The district described in this memoir is covered by Sheets 1 and 3 (Kirkmaiden and Stranraer) of the 1:50 000 geological map of Scotland; its coast provides unparalleled sections through the Southern Uplands accretionary thrust belt. Data from these sections have allowed the detailed determination of Ordovician and Silurian turbidite lithostratigraphy, its integration with graptolite-based biostratigraphy, and elucidation of the thrust-belt geometry by detailed structural analysis. Provenance variation and palaeocurrent trends support a back-arc depositional environment, with sequential southward younging in the onset of turbidite sedimentation above the basin-floor shale sequence. Diachronous deformation propagated southward through the basin as the thrust belt developed from the late Ordovician to the mid-Silurian. As the initial phase of deformation progressively affected sedimentary units at the thrust front, accommodation structures further deformed the thrust hinterland and burial metamorphism was superimposed on the already deformed sequence. Sinistral strike-slip became an increasingly important structural element during the Silurian. Igneous events overlapped the later stages of deformation such that the extensive Caledonian dyke swarm is partly syntectonic and partly post-tectonic; dyke compositions range from lamprophyre to felsite. The Portencorkrie intrusive complex, zoned from a granitic central portion to a dioritic margin, is amongst the youngest manifestations of Caledonian magmatism. Late Palaeozoic extension succeeded Caledonian compression to form the Stranraer basin as a major half-graben containing a very thin Westphalian sequence covered by a much greater thickness of Permian sandstone and breccia. Both this basinal succession and the early Palaeozoic turbidite strata were subsequently intruded by dolerite dykes of Tertiary age. An assessment of the regional geophysical datasets refines the overall shape of the Permian half-graben and allows the identification of likely concealed intrusions of both Caledonian and Tertiary age. The Quaternary glaciation of the district has had a significant effect in terms of landforms and superficial deposits; these, and the limited economic resources of the district, are discussed in the concluding chapters of this memoir.

Steeply inclined greywacke beds of the Kirkcolm Formation north of Salt Pans Bay [NW 962 620]. The beds are slightly overturned, younging northwards from right to left in the photograph (D 4203).

BRITISH GEOLOGICAL SURVEY

P STONE

Geology of the Rhins of Galloway district

Memoir for 1:50 000 geological sheets 1 and 3 (Scotland)

CONTRIBUTORS

Biostratigraphy
A W A Rushton

Portencorkrie complex and Caledonian dyke swarm
J W Gaskarth

Metamorphism
R J Merriman
B Roberts

Geophysics
G S Kimbell

Geochronology
J A Evans

LONDON: HMSO 1995

First published 1995

ISBN 0 11 884513 6

Bibliographical reference

STONE, P. 1995. Geology of the Rhins of Galloway district. *Memoir of the British Geological Survey*, sheets 1 and 3 (Scotland).

Author

P Stone, BSc, PhD
British Geological Survey, Edinburgh

Contributors

A W A Rushton, BA, PhD
R J Merriman, BSc
G S Kimbell, BSc
British Geological Survey, Keyworth

J W Gaskarth, BSc, MSc, PhD
University of Birmingham

B Roberts, BSc, PhD
Birkbeck College, University of London

J A Evans, BSc, PhD
NERC Isotope Geosciences Laboratory

Printed in the United Kingdom for HMSO
Dd 296606 C8 7/95 566 59226

Other publications of the Survey dealing with this district and adjoining districts

BOOKS

British regional geology
The Midland Valley of Scotland, 3rd edition, 1985
The South of Scotland, 3rd edition, 1971
Northern Ireland, 1972, second impression, 1986
Northern England, 4th edition, 1971

Memoirs
Geology of the Whithorn district, 1989
The geology of the Kirkcowan and Wigtown districts, in preparation

Sheet explanation
Geology of the country around Girvan, 1986

Classical areas of British geology
The Ballantrae area, 1988

Reports
See Appendix 1

MAPS

1:625 000
United Kingdom (North Sheet)
Solid geology, 1979
Quaternary geology, 1977
Aeromagnetic anomaly, 1972

1:250 000
Clyde (Sheet 55N 06W)
Solid geology, 1986
Sea bed sediments and Quaternary, 1986
Aeromagnetic anomaly, 1980
Bouguer gravity anomaly, 1985
Isle of Man (Sheet 54N 06W)
Solid geology, 1982
Sea bed sediments and Quaternary, 1985
Aeromagnetic anomaly, 1978
Bouguer gravity anomaly, 1978

1:50 000 (Solid and Drift)
Sheet 1 and 3 (Rhins of Galloway) Solid, 1992
Sheet 1 (Kirkmaiden) Drift, 1982
Sheet 2 (Whithorn) Solid and Drift, 1987
Sheet 3 (Stranraer) Drift, 1982
Sheet 4W (Kirkcowan) Solid, 1992; Drift, 1982
Sheet 7 (Girvan) Solid, 1988; Drift, 1980

1:25 000
Sheets NX08, 18 and 19 in part (Ballantrae) Solid, 1988

CONTENTS

FIGURES

PLATES

TABLES

ACKNOWLEDGEMENTS

The author and contributors to this memoir would like to express sincere thanks to numerous colleagues for assistance with field work, access to unpublished data and the production of technical reports utilised in the preparation of this text. Particular thanks are due to Dr J McCurry (University of St Andrews) and Dr P Davies (University of Keele) for the provision of stratigraphical, structural and sedimentological data collected during postgraduate research and incorporated into BGS technical reports; Dr A A Jackson produced a technical report based on her field survey work and Professor G Kelling (University of Keele) allowed access to his unpublished field maps. The Lower Palaeozoic biostratigraphical work was considerably aided by Dr D E White, Mr S P Tunnicliff and Mr H F Barron whilst Carboniferous floras were reassessed by Mr P J Brand. The concepts and interpretations developed in this Memoir owe much to scientific discussion with many colleagues, particularly the late Dr B C Lintern, Dr J D Floyd and Dr R P Barnes. The text was edited by Dr B C Lintern and Dr D J Fettes, and was produced under the programme management of Dr D J Fettes. Photographs were mainly taken by Mr T Bain and Mr F I MacTaggart, diagrams were produced in the Drawing Office of the BGS, Edinburgh and the text was word-processed by Mrs J M Lumley.

PREFACE

The Rhins of Galloway district lies in the south-west of Scotland and marks the termination of the Southern Uplands against the North Channel. Stranraer is the principal town of the district, serving as the major ferry port for services to Ireland, but elsewhere the population is sparse. Agriculture and forestry are the principal land uses. Based on my own visit to the region I can attest to the magnificence of the coastal scenery and the superb sections through a late Ordovician to mid-Silurian accretionary thrust belt. This controversial part of the Caledonide Orogen is believed to record the development and destruction of a back-arc assemblage at the margin of the early Palaeozoic Iapetus Ocean. The district also contains a Permian half-graben which formed orthogonal to the Caledonian trend as a consequence of late Palaeozoic crustal extension.

This memoir and the accompanying 1:50 000 solid geology map (combined Sheets 1 and 3, published in 1993; drift editions published as two separate sheets in 1982) provide the first detailed subdivision of the Ordovician and Silurian turbidite strata. A combination of biostratigraphy, petrography and structural analysis has been utilised to establish the geometry of the thrust belt and the timing of its development. The conclusions are of significance to the Southern Uplands terrane as a whole and also to its equivalents in Ireland and maritime Canada. Other major sections of the memoir discuss the syn- and post-tectonic intrusive rocks, the development of the late Palaeozoic Stranraer half-graben and the regional structural framework as deduced from geophysical data. The multidisciplinery approach has resulted in a memoir which not only makes a major contribution to our understanding of geological processes within the Southern Uplands terrane but also provides important insights into the development of accretionary thrust belts generally.

Peter J Cook, DSc
Director

British Geological Survey
Kingsley Dunham Centre
Keyworth
Nottingham NG12 5GG

January 1995

ONE
Introduction

GEOGRAPHY

This Memoir describes the geology of a district in the extreme south-west of Scotland covered by the special 1:50 000 Rhins of Galloway Solid Geology Sheet; a combination of Sheet 1 (Kirkmaiden) and Sheet 3 (Stranraer), with small parts of Sheet 4W (Kirkcowan) and Sheet 7 (Girvan). The district comprises the distinctive Rhins of Galloway (rinn = a point or promontary in Gaelic), a north–south strip of moderately high ground joined by the low-lying Stranraer isthmus to the main body of south-west Scotland (Figure 1). The Rhins form the most south-westerly corner of Scotland with the Mull of Galloway the most southerly point. From the Mull a thin ridge of land underlain by Lower Palaeozoic strata trends NNW for 45 km to Milleur Point, separating the Stranraer Permian basin of Luce Bay and Loch Ryan from that of the North Channel. Half way along its length and on its eastern side a 10 km-wide strip of land links with the Scottish mainland and in turn separates Luce Bay from Loch Ryan. The western coastline faces Ireland, about 35 km away and clearly visible on a fine day, but it is also exposed to the south-westerly winds and Atlantic waves. Steep and rocky sea cliffs are therefore common on the western Rhins coast and in some areas, notably near Lagantalluch Head and the Mull of Galloway, spectacularly approach 70 m in height. The more open, sandy bays on this coast have developed where the shoreline intersects lower-lying valleys cutting across the Rhins and probably resulting from glacial erosion along lines of structural weakness. Two such valleys, one linking Chapel Rossan Bay on the east coast and Drumbreddan Bay on the west coast and the other linking Terally Bay on the east coast and Port Logan Bay on the west coast, only rise to a maximum of 25 m above sea level. Elsewhere however the spine of the Rhins is formed by higher ground; in the south, hills to the south-west of Kirkmaiden reach 163 m at Inshanks Fell, whilst in the central part of the peninsula, between Stranraer and Portpatrick, a broad upland area rises to over 180 m at both Cairn Pat and Craigenlee Fell. Portpatrick (population 601 in 1981) is the only sizeable settlement on the west coast and was once the railway terminus and ferry port for Ireland. However, this role was lost to Stranraer when the ferry service was finally withdrawn in 1891, closure of the railway following in 1950. Since then Portpatrick, the only nontidal harbour between North Wales and the Clyde, has served as a small fishing port, a haven for yachtsmen and a tourist centre. The sheltered east coast of the Rhins, on the western shores of Loch Ryan and Luce Bay is low lying and topographically subdued. Extensive raised beaches commonly skirt the shoreline and only locally are relict sea cliffs seen behind them.

The low-lying ground on the eastern side of the Rhins peninsula merges with the low undulating topography of the Stranraer isthmus. The Permian sandstone and breccia underlying this area offered little resistance to glacial erosion and the highest point is only about 40 m above sea level with much of the land surface below 15 m. This is particularly true in the south-east part of the isthmus where extensive areas of raised beach and blown sand fringe a moundy landscape of glacial sand and gravel kames. Farther south-east the raised beaches give way to a wide beach and extensive intertidal mudflats at the head of Luce Bay. The largest town of the district, Stranraer (population 10 872 in 1987), is situated on the north-west side of the isthmus at the head of Loch Ryan. As the principal ferry port for sailings to Northern Ireland it is a busy commercial centre and railway terminus.

North-east of the Stranraer isthmus the topography changes abruptly at the Loch Ryan Fault, the eastern boundary structure of the Permian Stranraer basin. Across the fault the more resistant Lower Palaeozoic strata produce a marked fault scarp trending NW–SE, beyond which the land surface rises to a peneplain at about 230 m above sea level. This is incised by stream valleys draining either south-westerly into Loch Ryan or south-south-easterly feeding into the Water of Luce which flows into the head of Luce Bay. There is very strong structural control of the drainage pattern.

The bleak upland moors in the north-east of the district contrast with the much milder conditions experienced on the south-west coast of the Rhins of Galloway itself. There, despite the strong prevailing south-westerly winds, the benign influence of the Gulf Stream allows the outdoor cultivation of an array of exotic plants from the warm temperate regions of the world in the botanical gardens at Port Logan. Australasian tree ferns, cabbage palms and chusan palms flourish there, but rather more mundane agricultural activity, principally the production of sheep and beef cattle, is the main land use throughout the district.

PRIMARY GEOLOGICAL WORK: 1839–1970

Geologically the district is part of the extensive outcrop of Lower Palaeozoic strata which forms the Southern Uplands of Scotland (Figure 2), an area bounded to the north by the Southern Upland Fault and to the south by unconformably overlying Devonian and Carboniferous strata.

The earliest geological research in the Rhins of Galloway district was carried out by J Carrick Moore who, as early as 1839, reported the occurrence of graptolites in the 'slates and greywackes' (Lyell, 1839) and noted in

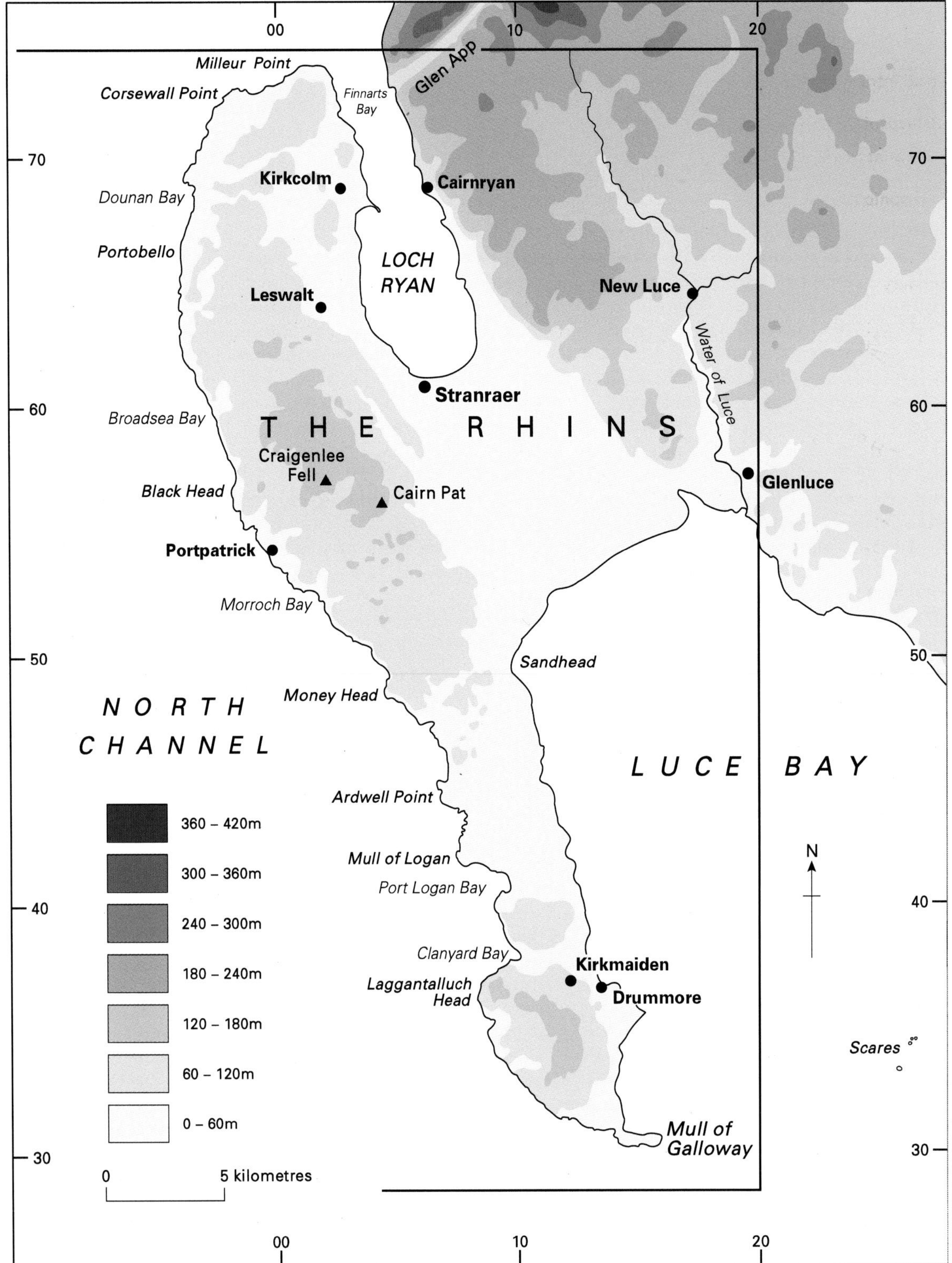

Figure 1 Topography of the Rhins of Galloway district.

subsequent papers details of the various sedimentary lithologies, the uniform regional strike, overturned beds, the presence of intrusive rocks and the unconformably overlying 'coal measures' (Moore, 1842, 1849). In a remarkably perspicacious later paper Moore (1856) produced a structural cross-section from Corsewall Point to the Mull of Galloway as well as several other local sections in greater detail. His account accurately describes

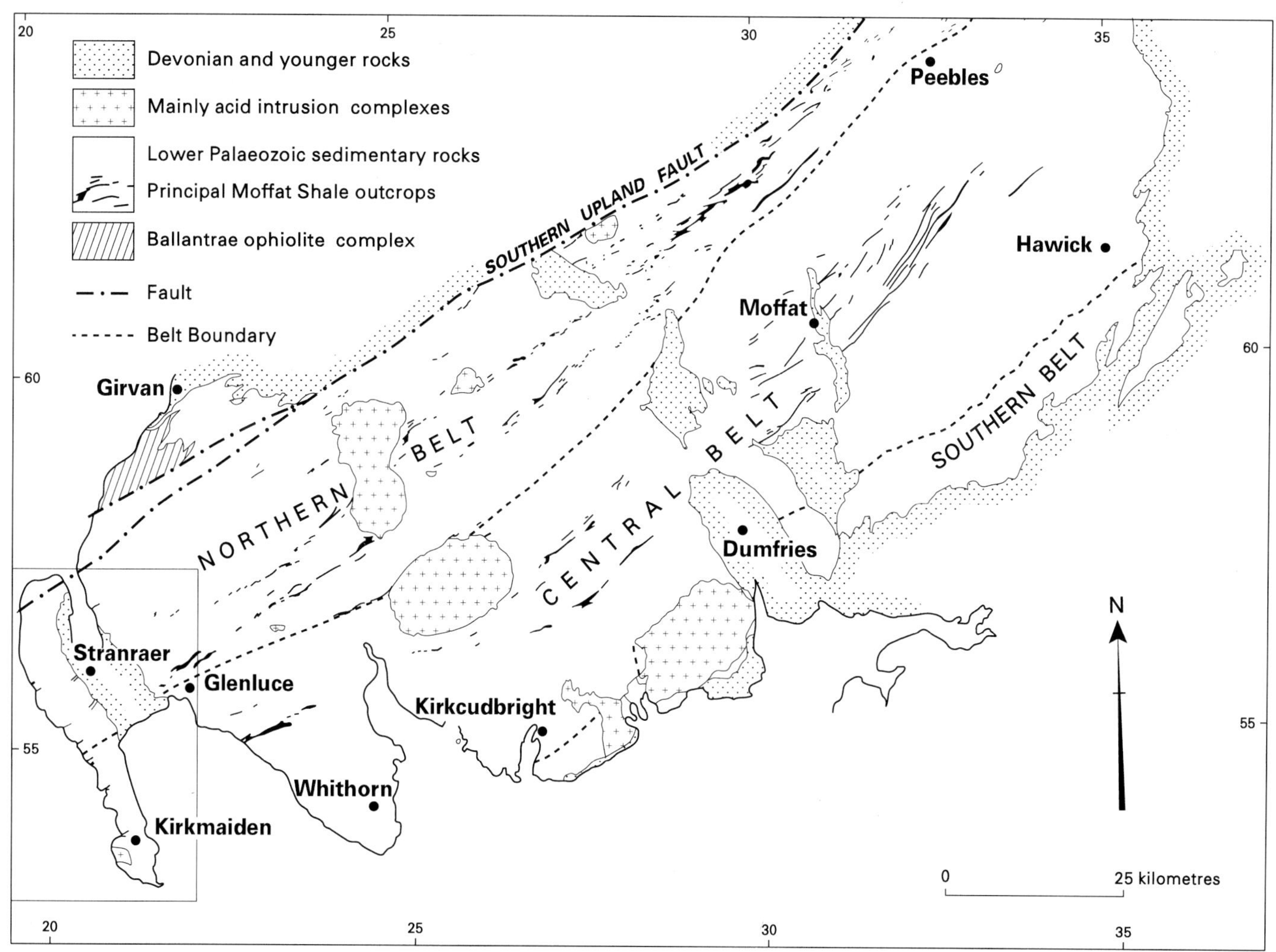

Figure 2 The 1:50 000 Sheet 1 and 3 (Rhins of Galloway) district in its regional geological context within the Southern Uplands terrane.

the dominance of south-verging anticline–syncline fold pairs and illustrates the change in the regional dip at the southern end of the Rhins peninsula. Against this background the first complete detailed Geological Survey mapping of the district at the six-inch scale was carried out by D R Irvine around 1870, although a narrow strip in the extreme north had been surveyed in 1867 by J Geikie and A C Ramsay as an extension of their work farther north. Two map sheets at a scale of one-inch to one mile were published in 1871 to cover the district: Sheet 1 (Kirkmaiden) and Sheet 3 (Stranraer). These were followed shortly thereafter by their accompanying explanations (Irvine, 1872; Geikie and Irvine, 1873).

Although the presence of graptolites in the Lower Palaeozoic succession was known during this early phase of surveying, it was not until 1878 that their stratigraphical significance was established. The pioneering work of Lapworth, in the central part of the Southern Uplands, led to the publication in that year of his seminal work *The Moffat Series* (Lapworth, 1878), which established a regional biostratigraphical zonal scheme based on the widespread graptolite faunas. This new insight demanded a reappraisal of the recently published geological maps and the Rhins of Galloway district, in common with the rest of the Southern Uplands, was rapidly resurveyed by B N Peach and J Horne between 1888 and 1898. The resurvey culminated in the publication of the monumental memoir *The Silurian rocks of Britain, 1: Scotland* (Peach and Horne, 1899) which, following contemporary practice, regarded the Ordovician as the 'lower Silurian'. Three main stratigraphical tracts were recognised: a late Ordovician *Northern Belt*, a Llandovery *Central Belt* and a Wenlock *Southern Belt* (Figure 2). Their structural interpretation, illustrated on the revised one inch to one mile geological maps published in 1923, required tight folding throughout the region. Many fold hinges were certainly observed but Peach and Horne had no way of checking the younging direction in the opposing limbs of folds deduced in zones of uniformly steeply inclined strata. The recognition of sedimentary structures indicative of the younging direction led to the next major advance in the geological understanding of the Southern

Uplands, but this had to await developments in sedimentology during the mid-20th century. Meanwhile the Permo-Carboniferous strata of the Stranraer basin had been re-examined by W Manson and G V Wilson between 1919 and 1921. Their results were incorporated into the revised Sheet 3 (Stranraer) published in 1923.

By the early 1950s the application of sedimentary structures to establish the 'way-up' or younging direction of a sequence was becoming an established technique. Kuenen (1953, pp.44–45) recognised the greywackes of the Rhins of Galloway district as the deposits of turbidity current flow and, using graded bedding as his principal tool, showed that '... the bottom of the graded beds ... lies on their southern side. The northern limbs of the isoclinal structures appear to be entirely suppressed'. Thus was initiated the Southern Uplands paradox: at outcrop the steeply inclined beds young dominantly to the north whereas, in regional terms, the oldest strata are found in the north and the youngest in the south. A further complication became apparent when Lindström (1958) deduced at least two phases of deformation. The regional problem was addressed by Craig and Walton (1959) and Walton (1961) who proposed a model based on large, compound monoclines with steep limb to the north which were cut by northerly dipping, reverse, strike-parallel faults with a very large downthrow to the south. Part of the data on which this model was based was provided by Kelling who made a detailed study of the structure and stratigraphy of the Ordovician strata in the north of the Rhins peninsula (Kelling, 1961, 1962). Although Kelling's overall structural interpretation (in company with that of Craig and Walton) is no longer tenable in detail, the recognition of the interbedding of compositionally different Ordovician greywackes remains an important step in the understanding of the geology of the Rhins of Galloway district. Further information relevant to the structural sequence was gathered along strike to the north-east by Rust (1965) in the Whithorn area and by Weir (1968) in the Gatehouse area.

Following Kelling's work, Welsh (1964) studied the stratigraphy and structure on the east side of Loch Ryan. By comparing their results (Kelling and Welsh, 1970) they were able to confirm the approximate 1500 m westerly downthrow on the Loch Ryan Fault suggested by geophysical modelling of the Stranraer basin by Mansfield and Kennett (1963) and Bott (1964). From this work the asymmetrical structure of the half-graben became apparent.

GEOTECTONIC EVOLUTION: GEOLOGICAL WORK SINCE 1970

The application of plate tectonic theory to the British Caledonides (e.g. Dewey, 1971) led to a general interpretation of the Southern Uplands sequence as the oceanic and trench deposits formed at a continental margin, beneath which an oceanic plate (the Iapetus Ocean) was being subducted north-westwards. This was refined by McKerrow et al. (1977) and Leggett et al. (1979) into an accretionary prism model which proposed that the imbricate thrust system, which built up above the subduction zone, was developed as slices of cover sediment were sheared from the descending oceanic plate and thrust beneath the previously accreted stack of similar slices (Figure 3). Successively younger material would thus be sequentially incorporated at the sole of the developing thrust stack but the dominant north-west-directed younging would be maintained. Continued underthrusting at the trench was thought likely to cause rotation towards the vertical in the older, higher portions of the thrust stack and thus produce the characteristic Southern Uplands tectonostratigraphical pattern. In such a situation the Southern Uplands might be expected to be underlain by oceanic crust. Its apparent absence led Leggett et al. (1983) to modify the accretionary prism model such that continental crust from the southern side of the Iapetus Ocean was thrust beneath the Southern Uplands during the final closure of the ocean. In an alternative interpretation Bluck (1983, 1984) regarded the Southern Uplands as allochthonous, having been overthrust towards the north-west onto the northern continental margin itself. The importance of sinistral strike-slip as a structural component of the accretionary prism was stressed by Anderson and Oliver (1986) who identified the Ordovician–Silurian boundary fault as a locus of such movement.

The accretionary prism hypothesis, although an elegant and popular explanation for the general regional tectonostratigraphical pattern, has not gained universal acceptance. Based on sedimentological and petrographic analyses, which showed andesitic material to be derived from the south (the oceanward side), and on the syntectonic relationships of the regional dyke swarm, Stone et

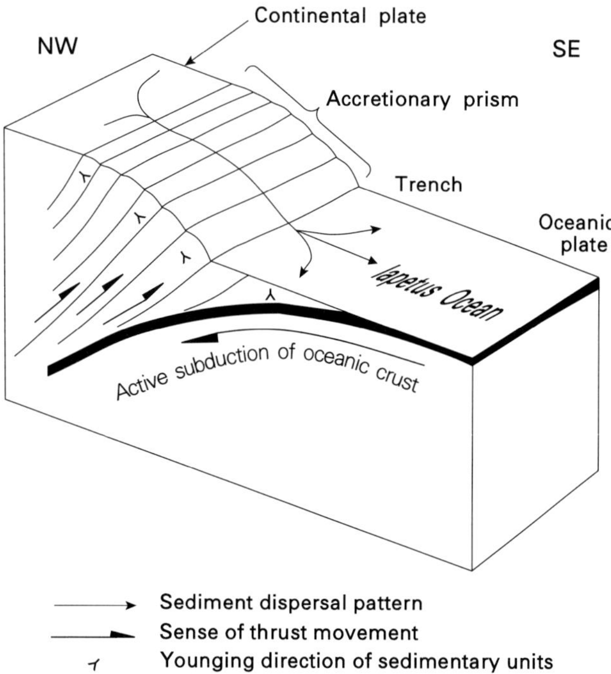

Figure 3 The accretionary prism model for the formation of the Southern Uplands thrust belt.

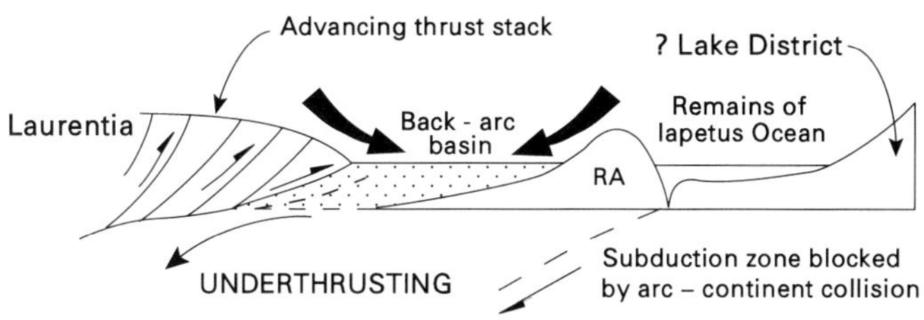

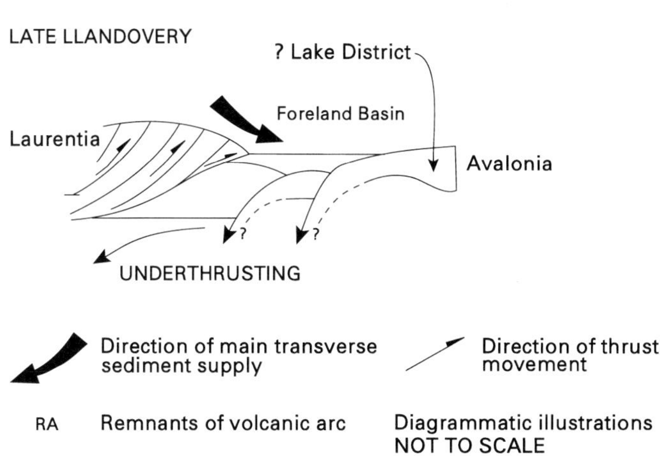

Figure 4 The sequential development of the Southern Uplands thrust belt from a back-arc to a foreland basin.

al. (1987) developed a model initiated in a back-arc basin. Working independently in Ireland Morris (1987) came to broadly similar conclusions. Collision of the southern continental margin of the Iapetus Ocean with this arc (Figure 4) caused compression within the back-arc basin. The resulting thrust system eventually overrode the arc remnants, propagated across the sutured arc-continental basement and developed thereafter as a foreland basin fold and thrust complex. Subsequent NE–SW extension possibly reactivated late Caledonian fault structures and allowed the development of the Permo-Carboniferous Stranraer half-graben.

More recent work in the Rhins of Galloway district has been carried out against a background of these alternative models which both adequately accommodate the regional tectonostratigraphical pattern. A considerable weight of opinion still (1993) favours the accretionary prism interpretation, albeit with some modifications, (e.g. Anderson and Oliver, 1986; Leggett, 1987; McCurry and Anderson, 1989) but a growing body of data is difficult to reconcile with this interpretation and is more compatible with a back-arc-to-foreland-basin hypothesis. In this context relevant studies from the Rhins include the along strike correlation of the Llandovery strata by Barnes et al. (1987) and the detailed sedimentological assessment of the major sand bodies within the Ordovician and early Silurian part of the succession by Kelling et al. (1987). Aspects of the provenance patterns of the greywackes have been investigated in several areas: Elders (1987) considered the boulders of the Corsewall Conglomerate to have a source in Newfoundland; Styles et al. (1989) identified the source of the andesitic detritus as a calc-alkaline island arc; Kelley and Bluck (1989) used ^{40}Ar-^{39}Ar laser probe techniques to date that material at 560–530 Ma; Evans et al. (1991) combined petrographic, sedimentological and Sm-Nd isotope data to confirm the input of juvenile volcanic material from one side of the depositional basin and Proterozoic material from the other. Scrutton and McCurry (1987) described detrital corals from the Llandovery greywackes. Variations in structural style, representing the effects of opposing primary thrust directions, were described from the Mull of Galloway area by McCurry and Anderson (1989), whilst the timing of deformation was partially quantified by Barnes et al. (1989). The Caledonian minor intrusive swarm was included in a regional review by Rock et al. (1986) and some analytical details of Llandovery metabentonites were provided by Merriman and Roberts (1990); a concealed Caledonian intrusion in the Sandhead area has been geophysically modelled by Kimbell and Stone (1992). Generalised structural cross-sections from the west coast of the Rhins of Galloway were figured by Needham (1993) and used to support a reiteration of the accretionary prism model for the origin of the Southern Uplands thrust belt.

This considerable body of research has been utilised in the production of this Rhins of Galloway memoir and the accompanying combined 1:50 000 Solid Geology Sheet 1 and 3 (Rhins of Galloway). The drift geology is published on two separate 1:50 000 sheets. Also available are the British Geological Survey open-file technical reports and Mineral Reconnaissance Programme reports listed in Appendix 1.

TWO
Regional stratigraphical framework of the Lower Palaeozoic succession

TECTONOSTRATIGRAPHY

In the Rhins of Galloway district most of the principal geological boundaries between Lower Palaeozoic stratigraphical units are strike faults trending approximately NE–SW. These are located and named in Figure 5. Commonly the strike faults form the southern margin of inliers of the Moffat Shale Group. In each inlier this assemblage generally youngs northwards, away from the strike fault and is comformably overlain at the northern margin by greywacke-dominated turbidites. The Moffat Shale Group inliers are lenticular and discontinuous (Figure 2) so that for much of their outcrop length the strike faults separate greywacke sequences of different ages. Such strike faults within the Ordovician Northern Belt (Leadhills Group) separate established lithostratigraphical formations which are defined by variations in the composition of the detrital clast assemblage within the greywackes (e.g. Kelling, 1961; Floyd, 1982; Floyd and Trench, 1989). This is also partially true for the most northerly, older units of the Gala Group within the Silurian Central Belt but, farther south, the younger Gala Group stratigraphical units become compositionally similar. Thus they do not carry formal lithostratigraphical status and are distinguished partly on their biostratigraphical position and partly on their tectonic position. The latter relates to the imbricate thrust structure into which the greywackes have been incorporated.

From some time in the late Ordovician or the earliest Silurian, thrusting propagated towards the south-east through the depositional basin and it is the major emergent thrusts which now appear as strike faults with a large downthrow to the south. Initiation of the thrusts was diachronous; the earliest formed in the north-west and subsequent development was sequentially farther south-east, whilst the earlier-formed structures were progressively rotated towards the vertical in the thrust hinterland. The original thrust relationship is now seen as a southerly downthrow across the majority of the steeply inclined strike faults, a downthrow constrained by the age relationship across the faults and, locally, by the interpretation of kinematic indicators. Combining the biostratigraphical and tectonic data it is possible to erect the tectonostratigraphical scheme shown in Figure 6, with biostratigraphy as the consistent link between the fault-defined units.

BIOSTRATIGRAPHY

The biostratigraphy of the Ordovician and Silurian strata in the Rhins of Galloway district is based almost exclusively on graptolites. The coastal sections from Corsewall Point to the Mull of Galloway provide an unrivalled conspectus of the stratigraphy of the Southern Uplands of Scotland, and graptolites were collected from as many of the tectonostratigraphical units as possible. In some instances graptolites obtained from shale interbedded with a greywacke succession gave a direct age for the strata; commonly, however, only a maximum age for greywacke deposition could be inferred from the more extensive graptolite faunas within the underlying Moffat Shale Group.

The faunal lists are summarised in Appendix 2. These are based on recent collecting and re-examination of the material collected for Peach and Horne (1899). All the fossils are housed in the BGS collections at Murchison House, Edinburgh. Details of the fossil localities, specimen registration numbers and faunal lists are held as BGS biostratigraphical records, and are summarised in a series of internal unpublished reports by A W A Rushton, S P Tunnicliff and D E White. These are referenced in Appendix 2. Palynological investigations were carried out in most stratigraphical units by H F Barron. In general only sparse and poorly preserved floras were obtained; the best and most biostratigraphically useful floras were recovered from the youngest part of the Gala Group.

The biostratigraphical zones referred to in this text are listed in Figure 6. They are based very largely on the distribution of graptolites in the Moffat Shale Group, as worked out by Lapworth (1878) and subsequently elaborated by various other authors. The use of the Silurian zones essentially follows the proposals of Rickards (1976), except that the *persculptus* Biozone is now treated as topmost Ordovician rather than basal Silurian. The zones of the Ordovician are more problematical, as discussed by Strachan (1971). Elles and Wood (1901–1918) and Elles (1925) listed the species according to their zonal occurrences. For the lower part of the sequence, from the *gracilis* to the *clingani* Biozone, there is no recent comprehensive revision.

The *Nemagraptus gracilis* Biozone is defined by the range of *N. gracilis* itself (Hughes, 1989). The zone contains a rich assemblage of graptolites but most of the constituent species range up into the overlying zone. Apart from *N. gracilis* itself, *Didymograptus superstes* and *Dicellograptus intortus* are the most diagnostic elements of the fauna.

The definition, recognition and nomenclature of the *Climacograptus 'peltifer'* Biozone are all problematical (Strachan, 1971, p.5; Rushton, 1990). In the Rhins of Galloway district the zone has been recognised,though rather insecurely, where faunas resembling those of the *gracilis* Biozone lack *N. gracilis* itself. Species which, according to Elles (1925) are supposedly confined to the *'peltifer'* Biozone (*Dicellograptus patulosus, Dicranograptus*

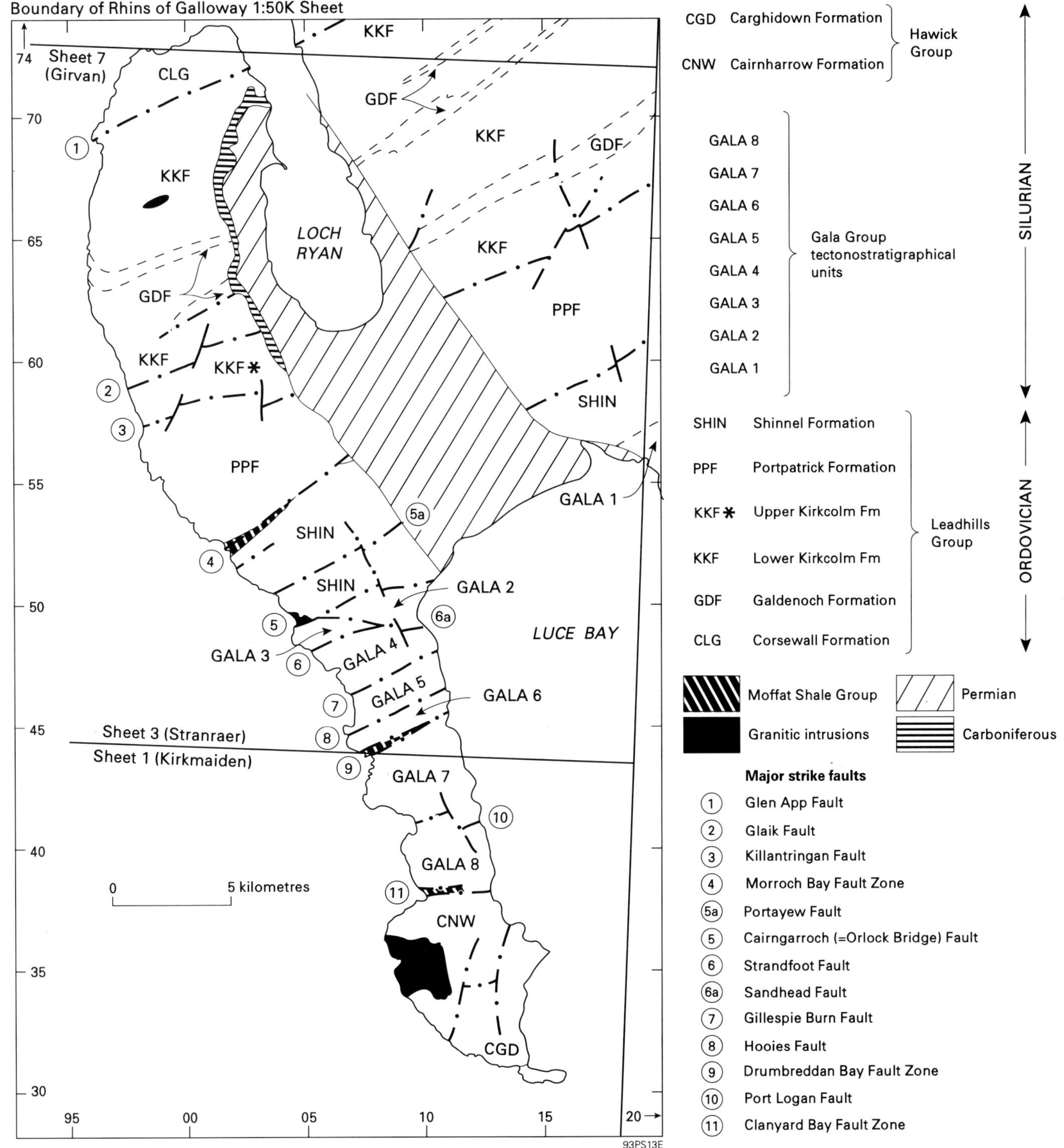

Figure 5 Outline geology of the Rhins of Galloway district.

furcatus minimus), have now been found associated with *N. gracilis*, so their diagnostic value is reduced. *Corynoides calicularis* has been found in beds assigned to the '*peltifer*' Biozone, but not yet in the *gracilis* Biozone.

Compared with the faunas of the underlying zones the fauna of the *Climacograptus wilsoni* Biozone is meagre and lacks distinctive elements. It is recognised by the appearance of *C. wilsoni* and/or *Orthograptus* of the *amplexicaulis* group.

The fauna of the *Dicranograptus clingani* Biozone is diverse and includes several species of *Dicellograptus* (*D. caduceus, D. flexuosus, D. morrisi, D. pumilus*). The appearance of *Dicranograptus clingani* marks the base of the biozone, but this species is absent from its upper part.

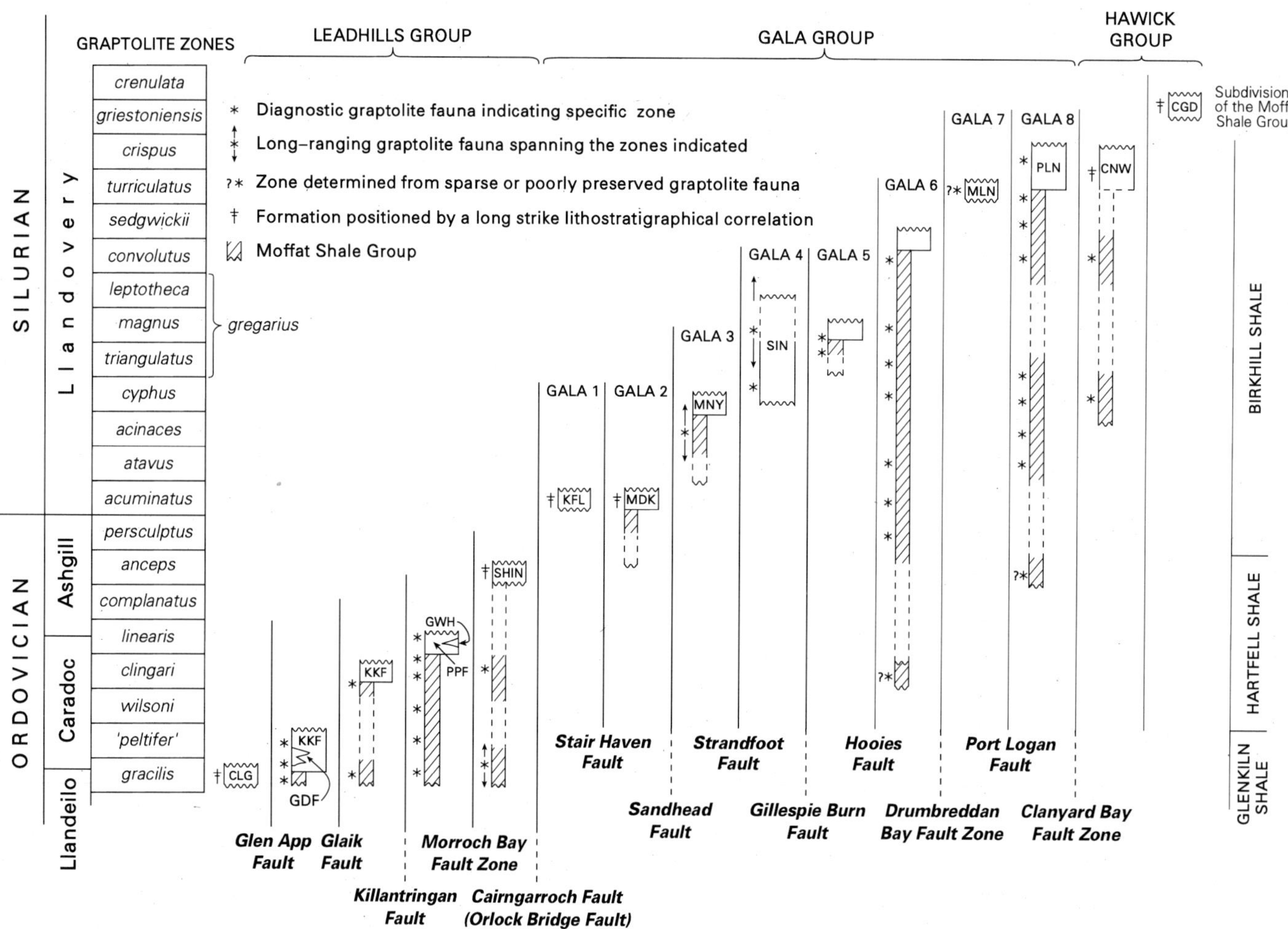

Figure 6 Biostratigraphy of the fault-bounded sedimentary sequences within the Southern Uplands thrust belt.

Climacograptus caudatus also appears low in the zone. Williams (1982a) described the distribution of species in the upper part of the zone as developed at Dob's Linn.

The stratigraphical distribution of higher Ordovician graptolites, from the top of the *clingani* Biozone to the *acuminatus* Biozone, has been recorded in sections at Dob's Linn, Moffatdale, by Williams (1982a, 1982b, 1983, 1987). This potentially gives new precision to the higher zones but the work has yet to be tested in detail at other localities; some discrepancies between Williams' results and Elles and Wood's table have still to be resolved. It is apparent that the stratigraphical ranges of Ordovician graptolites is insufficiently known and introduces a degree of uncertainty into the Ordovician section of Figure 6. Selected graptolites from the Rhins of Galloway district are illustrated in Figures 7 and 8.

Moffat Shale Group

The Moffat Shale Group has been subdivided into three named units (Lapworth, 1878; Peach and Horne, 1899): the Glenkiln Shale at the base, the Hartfell Shale in the middle and the Birkhill Shale at the top. The ranges of these units are shown in Figure 6 and they are more fully described in Chapter Three of this memoir.

There are numerous fossiliferous exposures of Moffat Shale in the Rhins of Galloway district. Several of these have yielded faunas that set a maximum age for the overlying greywacke formations, and these are mentioned below in the context of the tectonostratigraphical units in which they occur. Three localities expose substantial thicknesses of Moffat Shale, where considerable parts of the biostratigraphical succession can be observed: Morroch Bay, Grennan Point and Clanyard Bay. The best known of these is at Morroch Bay [NX 016 525], where the Glenkiln Shale and Lower Hartfell Shale divisions are present and yield evidence of all the zones from the *gracilis* Biozone to the higher part of the *clingani* Biozone (Figure 6). The succession youngs generally from south-east to north-west but is complicated in detail and includes at least one major repetition of the strata (Figure 9a). On either side of Grennan Point [NX 075 438] the Drumbreddan Bay Fault Zone contains complex masses of Birkhill Shale with some Glenkiln Shale or Lower

Hartfell Shale. Several biozones are present in an anticlinal structure near Port Gower (Figure 9b), but elsewhere the structure and stratigraphy within the Moffat Shale outcrops have not been fully resolved. At the northern end of Clanyard Bay [NX 101 381] a complex mass of variegated Moffat Shale Group strata appears generally to young northwards. Several zones of the Birkhill Shale are proved (Figure 6.) and part of the Upper Hartfell Shale (possibly *anceps* Biozone) appears also to be present (Peach and Horne, 1899, p.184).

Leadhills Group

The Leadhills Group contains the Ordovician greywacke-dominated formations exposed in the Southern Uplands north of the Orlock Bridge Fault. Compositional differences allow the recognition of the component formations which become progressively younger from north-west to south-east (Figure 6).

The age of greywackes in the **Corsewall Formation** is inferred from evidence obtained along strike towards the north-east on Sheet 7. The coastal section north of Finnarts Bay [NX 050 728] and south of Nelson's Cove yielded scant faunas, including *Dicranograptus ramosus spinifer* and *Pseudoclimacograptus modestus*, that suggest the presence of the *gracilis* Biozone (Cameron et al., 1986, p.14). A more definite *gracilis* fauna was obtained farther north at Portandea.

South of the Glen App Fault the **Kirkcolm Formation** has yielded graptolites at several localities. Most faunas are not very diagnostic but a few can be assigned to the *gracilis* and '*peltifer*' biozones; the presence of *Amplexograptus leptotheca* at Dounan Bay [NW 966 687] is taken to indicate a late or post-*gracilis* age, probably the '*peltifer*' Biozone (cf. Hughes, 1989). A fauna which included *Climacograptus bicornis* and *Dicellograptus patulosus*, suggesting the presence of the '*peltifer*' Biozone, was collected at Finnarts Bay (Peach and Horne, 1899, p.416) but recent collecting from the south end of Finnarts Bay yielded *Didymograptus superstes* and *Nemagraptus?* fragments, more indicative of the *gracilis* Biozone. Fine-grained interbeds in the Kirkcolm Formation also yield poorly preserved *gracilis* Biozone faunas (including *D. superstes* and *Nemagraptus*) at Polymodie Burn [NX 0585 7030] and Cairnryan quarries [NX 0683 6886]. The Moffat Shale Group exposed below the Kirkcolm Formation near Broadsea Bay [NW 976 589] contains *Didymograptus superstes* and *Nemagraptus explanatus pertenuis*, and is referred definitely to the *gracilis* Biozone.

The **Galdenoch Formation**, a distinctive greywacke unit interbedded with the Kirkcolm Formation, is well constrained biostratigraphically in the Main Water of Luce; rich and typical faunas of the *gracilis* Biozone were collected near Cairnerzean [NX 144 671] and at the Loup of Kilfeddar [NX 152 675]. These faunas occur in shales interbedded with the basal strata of the Galdenoch Formation.

South of the Glaik Fault outcrops of the Moffat Shale Group indicate that the overlying Kirkcolm Formation is substantially younger there than it is to the north. At localities near the Cable House at Knock Bay [NW 980 581] and in Crailloch Burn [NX 033 594] poorly preserved but diagnostic graptolites of the *gracilis* Biozone and/or '*peltifer*' Biozone have been collected (*Dicellograptus exilis, Dicranograptus ramosus spinifer, Didymograptus superstes*). However, at each of these localities a few graptolites have been collected that indicate the presence of the *clingani* Biozone: at Cable House *Corynoides calicularis, Dicellograptus moffatensis?, D.* cf. *morrisi* and *Dicranograptus ramosus longicaulis?*; at Crailloch *Climacograptus caudatus* and *Dicranograptus ramosus* (without spines). The implication of these records is that the Kirkcolm Formation in its development south-east of the Glaik Fault is younger (*clingani* Biozone) than the main development to the north-west, where *gracilis* Biozone and '*peltifer*' Biozone graptolites are interbedded in the formation. Although this conclusion is based partly on poorly preserved specimens (at Cable House) and partly on species whose biostratigraphical range is subject to confirmation (*Climacograptus caudatus*), a comparable stratigraphical relationship has been inferred along strike to the north-east near Tannylaggie [NX 285 715], on Sheet 4W.

The **Portpatrick Formation** is relatively well constrained biostratigraphically (Figure 6). At the northern margin of Morroch Bay [NX 015 527] the base of the formation is clearly interbedded with Moffat Shale Group strata and an abundant fauna, assigned to a fairly high horizon in the *clingani* Biozone, was collected there (Figure 9a). Slightly higher stratigraphically, Peach and Horne's (1899, p.408) record of a *linearis* Biozone fauna from shale laminae interbedded with the Portpatrick Formation greywacke at Bellone Cove [NX 010 527] is represented in the collections only by poorly preserved specimens of *Leptograptus flaccidus macer;* these may be from the *linearis* Biozone but are not decisive. However, farther north at Killantringan Bay [NW 9827 5722] the upper part of the Portpatrick Formation yielded poorly preserved *Leptograptus flaccidus* and a *Pleurograptus* fragment, also suggestive of the *linearis* Biozone. Farther along strike to the north-east exposures of the Moffat Shale Group underlying the Portpatrick Formation in Gabsnout Burn, a tributary of the Water of Luce [NX 193 609], yield faunas suggestive of both the *clingani* Biozone (*Climacograptus caudatus, Neurograptus margaritatus*) and the *linearis* Biozone (*Climacograptus styloideus, Orthograptus quadrimucronatus spinigerus, Pleurograptus linearis?*). Overall, the base of the Portpatrick Formation is thought to be slightly diachronous, because, farther east at Camrie Burn [NX 205 605] on Sheet 4W and at Lamachan Hill [NX 436 760] on Sheet 8E, it overlies Moffat Shale clearly of the *linearis* Biozone and is therefore slightly younger there than at the basal contact at Morroch Bay. However, the degree of diachroneity is not as great as has been illustrated by Kelling et al. (1987, fig. 9).

An acritarch assemblage of probable late Ordovician age was recovered from Portpatrick Quarry [NX 001 537]. It includes *Baltisphaerosum bystrentos, Orthosphaeridium* cf. *ternatum, Peteinosphaeridium trifurcatum trifurcatum, Veryhachium downiei* and *V.* aff. *lairdii.*

The **Shinnel Formation** has not yielded graptolites in the Rhins of Galloway district, but at Portayew [NX 039

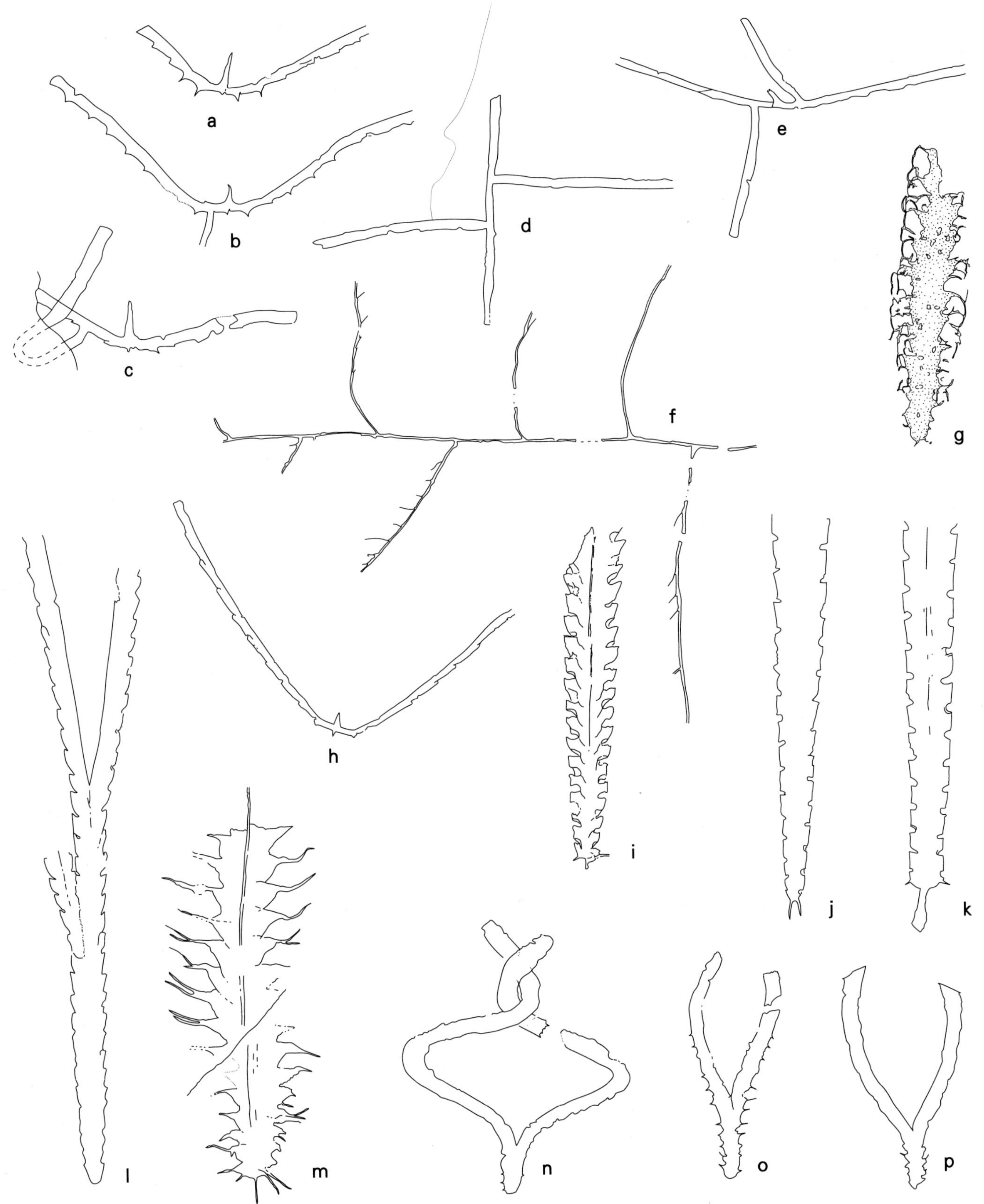
a
b
c
d
e
f
g
h
i
j
k
l
m
n
o
p

Figure 7 Examples of Ordovician graptolites from the Rhins of Galloway district. Locality numbers (e.g. loc. 34) refer to Appendix 2. Specimen numbers refer to material housed in the biostratigraphical collections of the BGS.

a. *Leptograptus flaccidus.* Morroch Bay (loc. 34), *clingani* Biozone. GSE 14907, × 5.
b, c. *Leptograptus flaccidus*, showing a single branch, Morroch Bay, associated with Fig. 7a. GSE 14908 and GSE 14910, × 5.
d, e. *Amphigraptus radiatus*, apparently derived from *L. flaccidus.* Morroch Bay, associated with Figs 7a–c. GSE 14907 and GSE 14923, × 5.
f. *Thamnograptus scoticus.* Morroch Bay (loc. 30), *gracilis* or *peltifer* Biozone. GSE 5479, × 3.
g. *Plegmatograptus nebula.* Morroch Bay (loc. 37), *clingani* Biozone. GSE 14911, × 5.
h. *Dicellograptus angulatus* (topotype). Morroch Bay (loc. 33), *wilsoni* Biozone? GSE 14912, × 5.
i. *Amplexograptus leptotheca.* Dounan Bay (loc. 4), '*peltifer*' Biozone. GSE 14913, × 5.
j. *Climacograptus dorotheus.* Morroch Bay (loc. 37), *clingani* Biozone. GSE 14914, × 5.
k. *Climacograptus wilsoni.* Morroch Bay (loc. 32), *wilsoni* Biozone. GSE 14915, × 5.
l. *Dicranograptus ramosus longicaulis.* Morroch Bay (loc. 38), *clingani* Biozone. GSE 14916, × 3.
m. *Hallograptus mucronatus.* Morroch Bay (northern end), *gracilis* or *peltifer* Biozone. GSE 14917, × 5.
n. *Dicranograptus ziczac.* Morroch Bay (loc. uncertain), *gracilis* or *peltifer* Biozone. GSE 8160, × 3.
o, p. *Dicranograptus furcatus.* Morroch Bay (loc. 30), *gracilis* or *peltifer* Biozone. GSE 8163, × 3.

502], the underlying Moffat Shale Group includes graptolites probably referable to the *clingani* Biozone. The possibility that younger strata may be present is not ruled out, however, and it is noteworthy that beds probably of the *linearis* Biozone are present below the Shinnel Formation in the River Cree, north-west of Newton Stewart on Sheet 4W. Furthermore, along strike to the north-east, in the area north of Moniaive between Dalwhat Water and Shinnel Water, *anceps* Biozone faunas have been recovered from interbeds of mudstone within the Shinnel Formation (Floyd and Rushton, 1993). At Port of Spittal Bay [NX 020 520] one Shinnel Formation sample yielded poorly preserved acritarchs including *Lophosphaeridium* sp. and several indeterminate spore diads. They suggest a probable Ashgill to Silurian age.

Gala Group

The early to mid Llandovery Gala Group is divided by a number of major strike faults into structural tracts (Figure 5). Some of these units have distinct compositional features and may justifiably be regarded as formations. However, others are compositionally similar and are not readily defined in lithostratigraphical terms. The Gala Group is therefore subdivided into structural units and numbered from north-west to south-east (1 to 8) as a series of tectonostratigraphical units or tracts which become sequentially younger towards the south-east (Figure 6).

South of the Cairngarroch Fault (the local extension of the Orlock Bridge Fault) the outcrop of the Gala 1 and 2 tectonostratigraphical units on the Rhins of Galloway have yielded no faunal evidence; their reference to the *acuminatus* Biozone (Figure 6) depends on evidence obtained farther north-east on Sheet 4. At Strandfoot [NX 052 481] the Gala 3 unit overlies an exposure of Lower Birkhill Shale containing *Atavograptus atavus, Dimorphograptus erectus* and *D.* cf. *longissimus*, possibly representing the upper part of the *atavus* Biozone or the *acinaces* Biozone.

South of the Strandfoot Fault the Gala 4 unit has yielded graptolites of the *cyphus* Biozone at Float Bay [NX 062 472] and a triangulate monograptid at the top of the unit, just south of the fault [NX 065 472]. Farther north-east, near Culroy, on 1:50 000 Geological Sheet 4, there is confirmatory evidence that the base of the Gala 4 unit indeed lies within the *cyphus* Biozone.

The Gala 5 unit is interbedded with graptolitic shale at The Hooies [NX 068 446] and at an inlet about 100 m further south. The faunas here include *Monograptus pseudoplanus*, and *M. triangulatus fimbriatus*, typical of the *magnus* Biozone. Deformed black shale, probably part of the Moffat Shale Group, close to the more southerly locality contains a fauna with *M. difformis, M. revolutus* (group) and *M. triangulatus*, suggesting a slightly lower position, probably low in the *triangulatus* Biozone.

The base of the greywacke sequence of the Gala 6 unit has yielded a few graptolites, and the Drumbreddan Bay Fault Zone reveals three outcrops of the underlying Moffat Shale Group, of which the two northerly are shown in Figure 9b. Between Port Gower [NX 075 439] and the north of Grennan Point the *persculptus, acuminatus, atavus* and *convolutus* Biozones were proved (Figure 9b). To the south, in Drumbreddan Bay, the *cyphus* and *triangulatus* biozones were proved in the southern outcrop with the *magnus* and *convolutus* biozones recognised in the north, the latter occurring in the basal beds of greywackes of Grennan Point (Figure 9b). Old collections made for Peach and Horne are not well localised but indicate the presence of Glenkiln Shale or Lower Hartfell Shale, (shown as possible *clingani* Biozone on Figure 6) and also contain excellent specimens confirming the presence of Birkhill Shale as high as the *convolutus* Biozone, e.g. *Monograptus convolutus, M. decipiens, M. limatulus* (Elles and Wood, 1911, pl. 38, fig. 7a) and *Rastrites longispinus* (Elles and Wood, 1914, pl. 50, fig. 2a).

The Gala 7 unit in the vicinity of the Mull of Logan south of the Drumbreddan Bay Fault Zone is dated only by fragments of *Diversograptus runcinatus?* and *M. proteus?* from near Cairnie Finnart [NX 088 415], which suggest the *turriculatus* Biozone, and a derived specimen of the coral *Propora exigua* suggestive of a Telychian (late Llandovery) age (Scrutton and McCurry, 1987). No Moffat Shale Group strata are exposed at the base of this unit within the Rhins of Galloway district.

The Gala 8 unit, south of Port Logan, has yielded good faunas of the *crispus* Biozone at Grennan quarries [NX

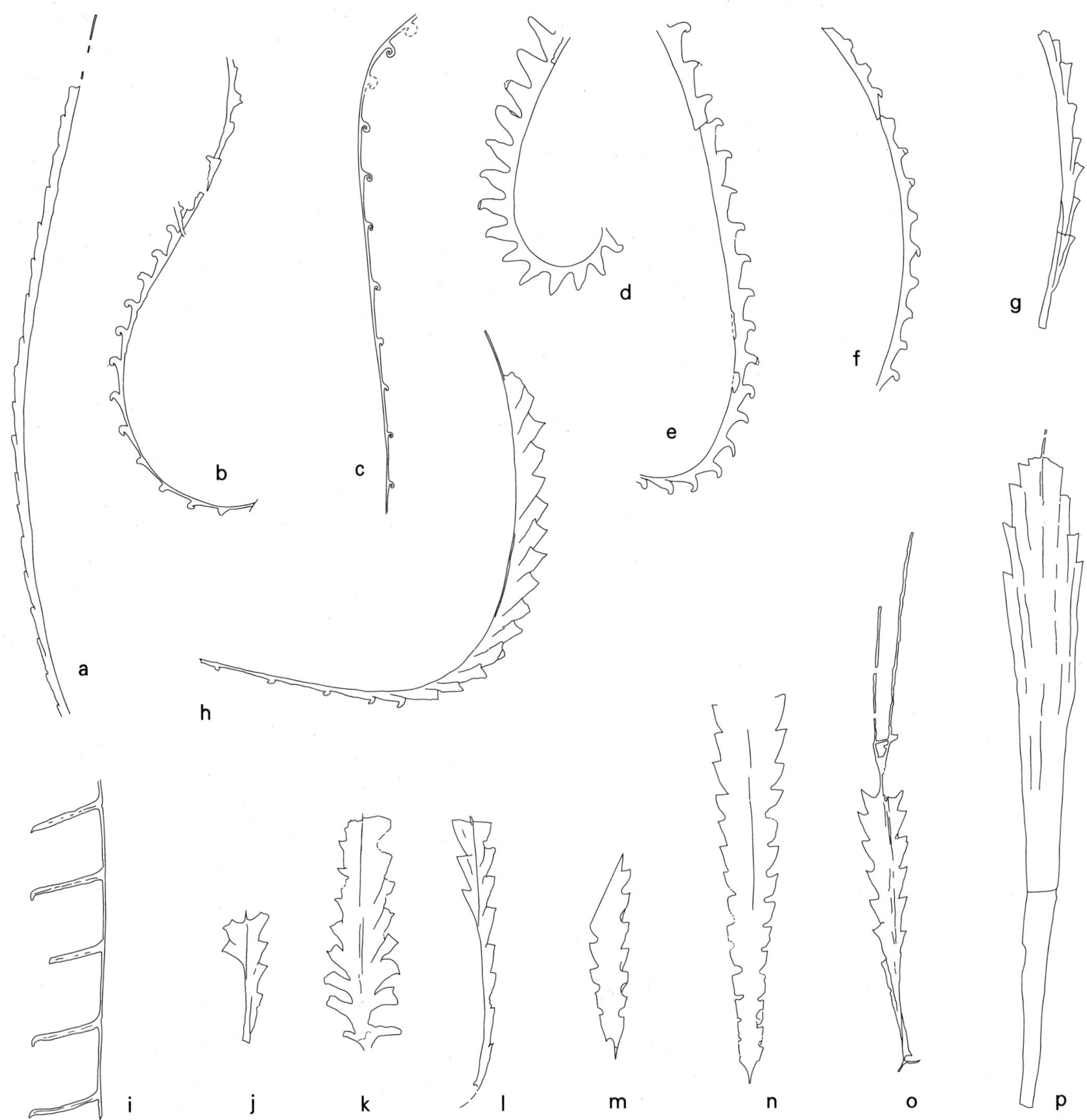

1267 3943 and 1258 3932], where *Monograptus crispus, M. discus, M. marri* and *Streptograptus exiguus* occur, and less definite faunas at Dunbuck sea-stack [NX 0955 3850] and Strones Bay [NX 0951 3866]. Several samples of fine-grained siltstone from the Gala 8 unit proved to contain a diverse and moderately well-preserved acritarch flora. The relative abundance of *Ammonidium* species such as *A. listerii, A. telychense* and *A. wychense* suggests a Telychian (late Llandovery) age supportive of the *crispus* Biozone deduced from graptolites. Derived Ordovician acritarchs and one species indicative of a nonmarine environment suggest a degree of reworking and possible proximity to a terrigenous source. Recent work has confirmed that the Moffat Shale Group underlying the Gala 8 unit ranges from the Ordovician at least up to the *sedgwickii* Biozone at the northern end of Clanyard Bay. However, an old Survey collection that includes *Monograptus involutus, Streptograptus* cf. *nanshanensis minutus, Petalograptus* cf. *palmeus* and *Rastrites abbreviatus* [= *R. equidistans* in Elles and Wood, 1914, pl. 51, fig. 2c] indicates that the *maximus* Subzone at the base of the succeeding *turriculatus* Biozone is also developed there.

Figure 8 Examples of Silurian graptolites from the Rhins of Galloway district. Locality numbers (e.g. loc. 52) refer to Appendix 2. Specimen numbers refer to material housed in the biostratigraphical collections of the BGS.

a. *Atavograptus gracilis.* Port Gower, Grennan Point (loc. 52), *atavus* Biozone? GSE 14918, × 5.
b. cf. *Streptograptus nanshanensis minutus.* Clanyard Bay (north side, loc. 66), basal *turriculatus* Biozone. GSE 14919, × 5.
c. *Monograptus crispus.* Grennan Quarries (loc. 58), *crispus* Biozone. GSE 14902, × 5.
d. *Monograptus triangulatus fimbriatus.* Castle Point (loc. 49), *magnus* Biozone. GSE 14921, × 5.
e. *Monograptus communis communis.* Castle Point (loc. 49), *magnus* Biozone. GSE 14922, × 5.
f. *Monograptus involutus.* Clanyard Bay, as Fig. 8b. GSE 2149, × 5.
g. *Coronograptus gregarius.* Drumbreddan Bay (loc. 54), *triangulatus* Biozone. GSE 14924, × 5.
h. *Monograptus limatulus.* Clanyard Bay (south side, loc. 68), *convolutus* Biozone. GSE 14773, × 5.
i. *Rastrites abbreviatus.* Clanyard Bay (north side, loc. 66), basal *turriculatus* Biozone. GSE 2149, × 5.
j. *Dimorphograptus* cf. *confertus.* Port Gower, Grennan Point (loc. 52), *atavus* Biozone? GSE 14926, × 5.
k. *Dimorphograptus decussatus.* Locality and horizon as Fig. 8j. GSE 14927, x 5.
l. *Dimorphograptus erectus.* Locality and horizon as Fig. 8j. GSE 14928, × 5.
m,n. *Diplograptus elongatus.* Float Bay (loc. 48), *cyphus* Biozone. GSE 14929, GSE 14930, × 5.
o. *Parakidograptus acuminatus.* Port Gower, Grennan Point (loc. 51), *acuminatus* Biozone. GSE 14931, × 5.
p. *Cephalograptus cometa.* The Saddle, Lagantulluch Head (loc. 69), *convolutus* Biozone. GSE 14774, × 5.

Hawick Group

The Hawick Group (*sensu* White et al., 1992) crops out to the south of the Clanyard Bay Fault Zone. Two of the component formations are present at the southern end of the Rhins of Galloway.

The **Cairnharrow Formation** has yielded no macrofossils in the Rhins of Galloway district and its position in Figure 6 is influenced by along-strike correlation to the north-east. The underlying Moffat Shale Group has yielded faunas of the *convolutus* Biozone at the south side of Clanyard Bay [NX 097 377] where *Monograptus convolutus, M. denticulatus* and *M. limatulus* were collected, and at The Saddle near Laggantalluch Head [NX 086 367], where *Cephalograptus cometa* and *M. limatulus* were obtained. Upper Hartfell mudstones on the south side of Clanyard Bay yielded a poor acritarch flora of late Ordovician age, including *Baltisphaerosum* sp., *Baltisphaeridium?, Peteinosphaeridium trifurcatum trifurcatum* and *Stelliferidium?*, together with a possible spore tetrad.

The **Carghidown Formation** has yielded no biostratigraphical evidence in the Rhins of Galloway district and is positioned in Figure 6 on the basis of along strike correlation to the north-east. The trace fossil *Protovirgularia* occurs near the lighthouse on the Mull of Galloway.

Three rock samples collected nearby [NX 1443 3140, 1445 3126, 1560 3055] yielded sparse, poorly preserved acritarchs, including *Oppilatala eoplanktonica?, Diexillophasis denticulata, Moyeria telychensis and Multiplicisphaeridium* cf. *raspum*, the last named indicating a mid-Telychian (late Llandovery) age. This is consistent with the *griestoniensis–crenulata* age indicated on Figure 6.

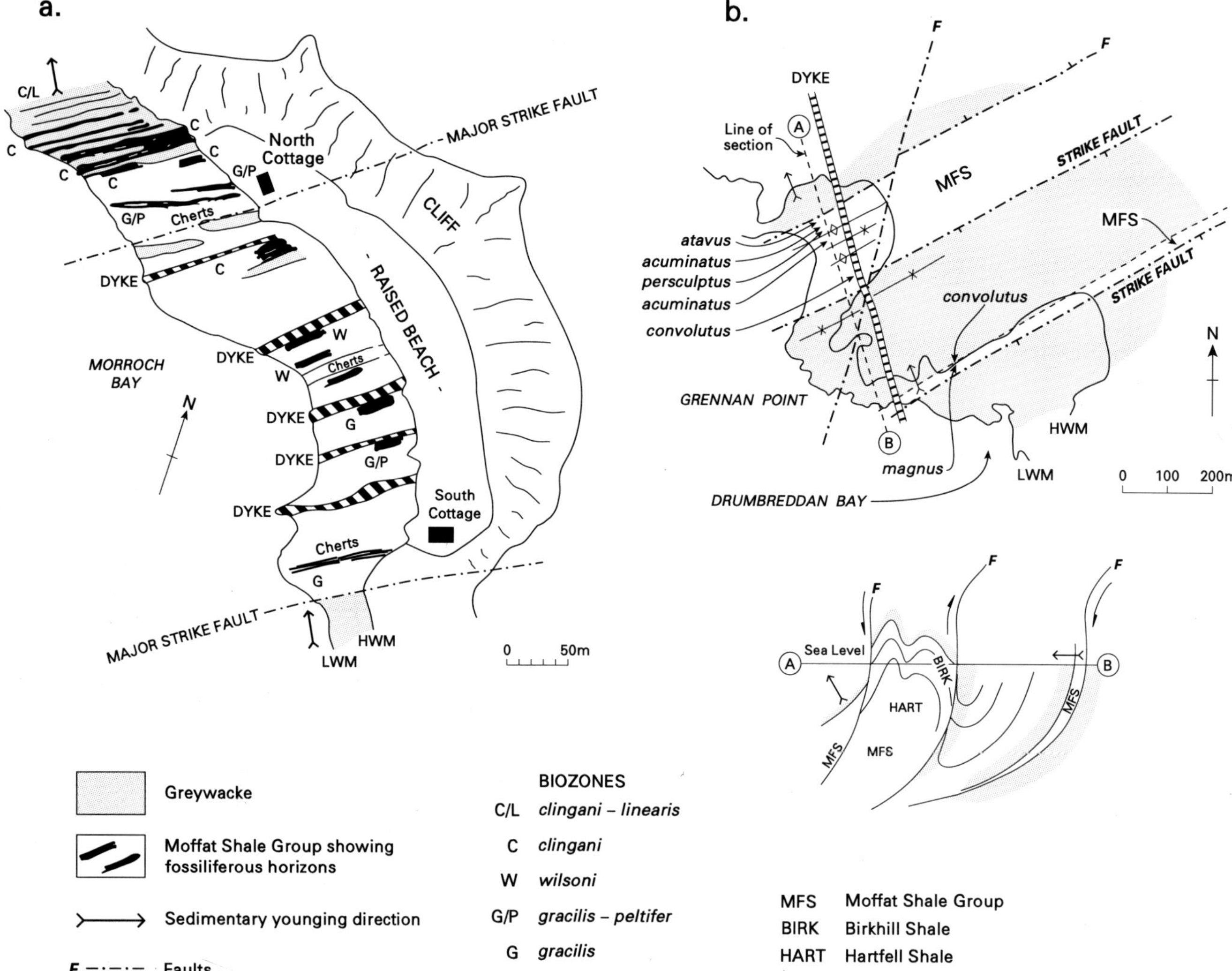

Figure 9 Moffat Shale Group outcrops on the west coast of the Rhins of Galloway.

a. Sketch map of Morroch Bay, after Peach and Horne (1899, fig. 97) showing the distribution of biozones deduced from specimens in the collection of the BGS, Edinburgh.

b. Sketch map of Port Gower, Grennan Point and the north side of Drumbreddan Bay showing the distribution of biozones deduced from specimens in the collection of the BGS, Edinburgh. A sketch cross-section illustrates the structural relationship.

THREE
Moffat Shale Group

The Moffat Shale Group is a condensed sequence dominated by graptolitic carbonaceous black shale (locally pyritous) and siliceous mudstone. It ranges in age from a poorly defined base in the mid-Ordovician to the late Llandovery. The lowermost lithologies are basaltic lavas, often pillowed, associated with mudstone, chert and hyaloclastite; this assemblage may be as old as Arenig in part but is generally associated with a Llandeilo–Caradoc *N. gracilis* graptolite fauna in the immediately overlying black shales. It may be argued that the volcanic rocks and cherts are not part of the Moffat Shale Group *sensu stricto* but they are here informally included for stratigraphical convenience. Above the basal unit, black shale and mudstone, with thin interbedded chert and metabentonite horizons, continue up into the Silurian although a complete succession through the group is not seen. The metabentonites are produced by the diagenesis of silicic vitric volcanic ash and, apart from the discrete horizons, many of the black shales also contain a significant proportion of ash (Merriman and Roberts, 1990). The Moffat Shale Group has been widely described as of pelagic open-ocean origin (e.g. Leggett, 1987), although the large quantities of interbedded ash, the common presence of detrital mica from a terrigenous source (Merriman and Roberts, 1990) and the rare but significant interbedded greywackes (Rushton and Stone, 1991) cast some doubt on this interpretation.

Stratigraphically the Moffat Shale Group can be subdivided into four parts. At the base of the Group a volcanic lava, mudstone, chert and hyaloclastite assemblage is unnamed; above that Lapworth (1878) and Peach and Horne (1899) recognised and named three lithologically distinct shale units (Figure 6). The lowest unit of mainly pale to dark grey shale and mudstone (**the Glenkiln Shale**) includes some black graptolitic mudstones of the Llandeilo–Caradoc *N. gracilis* Biozone and the Caradoc *C. 'peltifer'* Biozone. The middle shale unit (**the Hartfell Shale**) consists, in its lower part, mainly of black graptolitic shale, whereas the upper part consists of grey 'Barren' mudstone with a few thin beds of black shale. The Hartfell Shale ranges up from the Caradoc *C. wilsoni* Biozone to the Ashgill *D. anceps* Biozone, above which a very thin bed characterised by *Climacograptus? extraordinarius* has been recorded farther east in the group's type section at Dob's Linn (Williams, 1983). The uppermost shale unit (**the Birkhill Shale**) consists of black shale or pale grey shale with black graptolitic beds and abundant metabentonite horizons. It continues upwards from the Ashgill *G. persculptus* Biozone to the highest part of the Moffat Shale Group succession seen in the Rhins of Galloway district, the base of the *M. turriculatus* Biozone. It should be stressed once again, following the discussion in Chapter Two, that the complete Moffat Shale Group succession is rarely preserved and may indeed have existed as a single entity only locally. The basal assemblage is seen only in the northern part of the Rhins and the Southern Uplands generally, whilst the top of the Moffat Shale Group ranges progressively higher to the south in successive tectonostratigraphical units (Figure 6).

The Moffat Shale Group forms the stratigraphical base to many of the tectonostratigraphical units cropping out across the Rhins of Galloway (Figure 5). However, the base of the Group itself is never seen since the lowest strata preserved are invariably sited immediately to the north-west of one of the major strike faults, across which they are juxtaposed against younger greywackes. In some parts of the Southern Uplands basaltic pillow lavas form the lowest of the Moffat Shale Group lithologies exposed and, at one locality near Abington, have given a Sm-Nd radiometric age of 490 ± 14 Ma (Thirlwall, in McKerrow et al., 1985). At the same locality the basalts are overlain by a mudstone containing a graptolite fauna ascribed to the Arenig on the basis of identifications listed in Peach and Horne (1899, p.288). Re-examination of this fauna by Dr A W A Rushton has shown that the available specimens are indeterminable but, nevertheless, the general age assignation is confirmed by late Arenig conodonts described from cherts overlying the mudstone (Lamont and Lindström, 1957; Armstrong et al., 1990).

The same authors have obtained Llanvirn and Llandeilo conodonts from cherts elsewhere in the Southern Uplands, including one Llandeilo fauna from Morroch Bay [NX 018 524] on the west coast of the Rhins of Galloway. This was collected from a red mudstone interbedded with grey-green metabentonite horizons, black shale and dark siliceous mudstone, at the southern extremity of the Moffat Shale Group outcrop. The Llandeilo mudstone assemblage is structurally imbricated and sheared but appears to be succeeded conformably by several metres of dark grey radiolarian chert. This relationship is repeated at a locality farther north [NW 976 588] where another outcrop of the Moffat Shale Group occurs on the west coast of the Rhins between Broadsea Bay and Knock Bay immediately to the north of the Glaik Fault. There, a sheared sliver of black shale and hyaloclastite is faulted against the greywacke sequence to the south and is followed northwards by 3 m of thinly and irregularly bedded radiolarian chert (Plate 1a). Structural imbrication precludes a confident assessment of the sequence above the chert but black shale, metabentonite and hyaloclastite are all present and appear to form an interbedded succession in which the proportion of black shale increases upwards before interdigitating with the overlying greywacke. The black shale contains graptolites of the *N. gracilis* Biozone and, at this locality, is conformably succeeded by greywacke of the lower Kirkcolm Formation (Figure 6).

Plate 1 Aspects of the basal Moffat Shale Group underlying the Kirkcolm Formation adjacent to the Glaik Fault. Coast south of Broadsea Bay [NW 976 588].

a. Bedded chert (D 4233).

b. An almost complete pillow of lava in hyaloclastite (D 4234).

a

b

The position of the hyaloclastite horizons within the sequence is thus uncertain; they may occur above and below the chert, be restricted to one or the other of these stratigraphical positions, or indeed the chert itself may not be restricted to a single well-bedded unit. The coarser hyaloclastite beds adjacent to the Glaik Fault contain isolated pillows of altered basaltic lava, pebbles of quartzose greywacke, chert and black shale, together with fragments of vesicular pumice (Plate 1b). The clasts are contained in a metabentonite-rich matrix and the deposits seem most likely to be the products of hyaloclastic debris flows. No such coarse hyaloclastite horizons are seen in the Morroch Bay outcrop of the Moffat Shale Group above the chert. There the black shale and siliceous mudstone stratigraphically overlying the chert range from the *N. gracilis* Biozone up to the *D. clingani* Biozone and contain only rare paler horizons which may possibly be bentonitic.

Structural imbrication of the Morroch Bay sequence can be established from the disposition of graptolite biozones within the coastal outcrop (Figure 9a). Two north-younging repetitions of the *gracilis* to *clingani* Biozone range occur and the abundance of minor faulting and folding suggest a more complex detailed structure. The maximum thickness for the full gracilis to *clingani* development is about 250 m but, in view of the structural imbrication, the true thickness is probably much less. It is worth noting the repeated spatial association of the *gracilis* Biozone shale with the chert. Black shale in the vicinity of the *wilsoni* Biozone graptolite localities also contains conodonts indicative of the same biostratigraphical position (Lamont and Lindström, 1957). Interbedded greywackes first appear in the *clingani* Biozone.

The biostratigraphical range of the Moffat Shale Group at Morroch Bay, and the along-strike outcrops immediately north of the Morroch Bay Fault Zone, is *gracilis* to *clingani* (Figure 6). This contrasts with the restriction to *gracilis* seen farther north adjacent to the Glaik Fault and illustrates the trend, discussed in Chapter Two, for the Moffat Shale Group to range sequentially higher in successive tectonostratigraphical units towards the south. Beneath the Ordovician greywacke formations of the Leadhills Group biostratigraphical evidence from the Rhins of Galloway shows the Moffat Shale Group to range only up to *clingani*, equivalent to the Glenkiln Shale and Lower Hartfell Shale of Peach and Horne (1899). It is possible that a slightly higher unit, within the *complanatus* Biozone of the upper Hartfell Shale, is represented by a unit of grey mudstone within the Moffat Shale Group at Portayew [NX 039 505] (McCurry, 1990). This possibility has not been confirmed biostratigraphically but it would be compatible with the proven *anceps* Biozone age of the overlying Shinnel Formation (Floyd and Rushton, 1993).

South of the Orlock Bridge (Cairngarroch) Fault only the upper part of the Moffat Shale Group is generally seen beneath the Silurian greywacke formations. At two localities only, Drumbeddan Bay [NX 078 437] (Figure 9b) and Clanyard Bay [NX 101 380], have Ordovician graptolite faunas been recovered from black shales, although lithologies suggestive of the upper Hartfell Shale Formation are present in places. Elsewhere the exposed black shales and dark siliceous mudstones contain Llandovery faunas typical of the Birkhill Shale. The black shales and mudstones crop out as inliers up to 100 m across strike but, from the evidence of tight folding and fault imbrication, the true stratigraphical thickness is probably much less. A useful comparison in this respect is with the classic section for the Hartfell Shale and Birkhill Shale at Dob's Linn, near Moffat, where the Hartfell Shale is 37 m thick and the Birkhill Shale (*G. persculptus* to *M. turriculatus* biozones only) is 46.5 m thick.

A common feature of the Birkhill Shale is the interbedding of pale grey-green metabentonite horizons with the black shales and siliceous mudstones. Such horizons are sporadically seen in the Ordovician shale sequences, as described earlier from Morroch Bay and Broadsea Bay and to which can be added several thin (less than 2 cm) examples from the *D. clingani* Biozone at Portayew. However, the frequency of the volcanic activity recorded by the metabentonites increased through the early Silurian so that the pale ash layers are very much more common in the Birkhill Shale. For example, in one spectacular development at Port Gower [NX 076 438] within the Drumbreddan Bay Moffat Shale Group inlier, at least 25 metabentonite horizons occur interbedded with black shale and mudstone containing a graptolite fauna indicative of the upper *C. gregarius* or *M. convolutus* Biozone. The metabentonite beds range from less than 1 cm up to 3.5 cm in thickness, the thicker beds containing occasional small sideritic concretions or spherulitic pyrite nodules (Merriman and Roberts, 1990). In general subalkaline ash falls predominated in the late Ordovician whereas peralkaline ash falls were dominant in the early Llandovery, before giving way to further subalkaline ash falls from about the *M. sedgwickii* Biozone onwards. Merriman and Roberts (1990) relate the ash falls to volcanicity in an ensialic arc transitional to a back-arc setting.

Between the metabentonites the dominant black shale lithology appears to vary very little through the Birkhill Shale sequence. Dark, siliceous mudstone and chert appear sporadically throughout. The only observed major variation occurs at The Hooies [NX 068 446] where ?Moffat Shale Group strata within the lower *triangulatus* Biozone are overlain conformably by a greywacke-dominated sequence containing interbedded black shale and metabentonite within the *magnus* Biozone (Figure 6). The *triangulatus* fauna occurs in dark mudstone laminae interbedded with thin grey and red siltstones and a shaly mélange-like lithology. It is uncertain whether this represents a locally anomalous unit within the Moffat Shale Group or whether the entire assemblage should be regarded as interbedded within the overlying greywacke sequence. The structural complexity does not allow a definitive solution in that case and in general prevents the establishment of a complete Moffat Shale Group stratigraphy on the Rhins of Galloway. However, despite the structural imbrication, the sequence of graptolite Biozones identified in the larger inliers shows that northward younging of stratigraphically intact sections is the norm. Exceptions to this trend are the result of local structural complexity; for example, on the south side of Port Gower [NX 075 438] a south-younging sequence from the *G. persculptus* Biozone to the *M. convolutus* Biozone occupies the south limb of an anticline in a south-verging fold pair, and on the south side of Clanyard Bay [NX 101 377] a south-younging progression from *C. cyphus* to *M. convolutus* Biozone is associated with a change in thrust polarity and fold vergence. This change in trend has fundamental structural implications and will be discussed more fully in Chapter Seven.

FOUR
Ordovician greywacke succession: Leadhills Group

The Ordovician greywacke strata exposed in the northern part of the Rhins of Galloway, and on the east side of Loch Ryan are contained within several tectonostratigraphical tracts which range in age from ?Llandeilo to Ashgill (Figure 6); the tracts are informally associated within the Leadhills Group. A considerable variation in clast composition allows the definition of six formations; these may be structurally separated by major faults or they may exhibit local interbedded relationships. The principal petrographical characteristics of the formations are summarised in Table 1 and are further discussed later in this chapter. An indication of the variation in rock properties imparted by the compositional contrasts is given by the magnetic susceptibility values. Floyd and Trench (1989) showed that greywackes rich in andesitic volcanic detritus such as those from the Galdenoch and Portpatrick formations, had systematically higher susceptibility values. The differences were so marked that susceptibility measurement could be used in the field to map formation boundaries. The same techniques were applied locally on the Rhins of Galloway with similar results. Another indicator of the profound differences in composition between the greywacke formations is the regional geochemical data described by Stone et al. (1991). The data were obtained by chemical analysis of stream sediments collected at a density of about 1 per 1.5 km^2; many single element distribution patterns generated therefrom show a marked NE–SW striping, parallel to both the regional strike and the principal lithostratigraphical boundaries. Some ratios of two or three different elements show the formation-parallel pattern even more clearly and emphasise the normally cryptic variations in the composition of the Ordovician greywackes. The importance of this compositional variation in terms of provenance patterns and palaeogeography of the whole Southern Uplands terrane bears on the alternative models for geotectonic development outlined in Chapter One.

The formations differ to some extent in sedimentological characteristics but these are not sufficiently distinctive or consistent to be definitive. All of the Ordovician greywacke sequences can be related to turbidity current deposition mainly within the B, C and D facies of Pickering et al. (1986). Individual beds frequently show all or some of the characteristic turbidite divisions recognised and described by Bouma (1962). In some specimens the proportion of matrix present is too low (>15 per cent) for the sandstones to be defined as greywacke *sensu stricto*. These examples are quartz and/or lithic arenites but for convenience the general term greywacke is retained in this account. Representative modal analyses are given in Appendix 3.

CORSEWALL FORMATION

The Corsewall Formation crops out on the northern end of the Rhins of Galloway and to the east of Loch Ryan on the north-west side of the Glen App Fault (Figure 5) which marks the base of the unit. Two subdivisions are recognised: an older greywacke-dominated sequence and a younger spectacular development of coarse boulder conglomerate. No lithologies of the Moffat Shale Group are seen beneath the greywackes which are locally sheared and brecciated adjacent to the Glen App Fault. The vergence sense of steeply plunging minor folds and

Table 1 The principal detrital components in the Ordovician Leadhills Group greywackes of the Rhins of Galloway district, after Floyd (1982) and Evans et al. (1991).

Formation	Lithic fragments	Mineral grains*
Corsewall	granodiorite, quartz-porphyrite, chlorite schist, microgranite, rhyolite, felsite, andesite, gabbro, spilite, serpentinite, chert	quartz (14%), feldspar, apatite clinopyroxene, hornblende, spinel, epidote, biotite
Kirkcolm	spilite, quartzite, garnet schist, biotite schist	quartz (45%), feldspar, garnet, zircon
Galdenoch	andesite, dacite, rhyolite, spilite, chlorite schist	quartz (18%), feldspar, hornblende, augite, epidote, apatite
	Total 'andesitic' may exceed 25%	
Portpatrick	hornblende-andesite, dacite, rhyolite, spilite glaucophane schist, garnet schist, shale, gabbro, diorite, granite	quartz (15%), feldspar, clinopyroxene, hornblende, garnet, epidote, glaucophane, spinel
	Total 'andesitic' may exceed 25%	
Glenwhargen	quartzite, mica schist, spilite, chert	quartz (67%) feldspar
Shinnel	granodiorite, granophyre, rhyolite, felsite spilite, quartzite, shale	quartz (57%), feldspar, zircon, apatite

* Average quartz content shown %.

S-C fabrics show that the latest movement on this fault was a sinistral shear with a possible dextral overprint. The fault zone is well exposed at Dounan Bay on the west coast of the Rhins, Lady Bay on the east coast and Finnarts Bay on the east side of Loch Ryan. The absence of underlying graptolite-bearing Moffat Shale Group strata means that a maximum age for the greywacke sequence is not available. No determinable macrofossils have been recovered from the Corsewall Formation on the Rhins of Galloway but along strike correlation with fossiliferous localities to the north-east suggests a position within the *N. gracilis* Biozone.

The lower, greywacke member of the Corsewall Formation (the Flaggy Division of Kelling, 1961) is some 750 m thick and consists principally of parallel-bedded, fine- to medium-grained turbidite units interbedded with units of interlaminated fine-grained greywacke and siltstone. The greywacke turbidite beds are mostly of the T*abc* or T*bc* type; they may reach 2 m in thickness but in general are in the 25–75 cm range. The fine greywacke and siltstone interlaminated units range up to about 3 m in thickness and represent a very large number of thin T*bc* and T*bcd* turbidite deposits. A typical section through the greywacke member of the Corsewall Formation is shown in Figure 10a. The sedimentology of the member was thought by Kelling et al. (1987) to indicate distal turbidite deposition in a basin-plain environmental setting. The thicker greywacke beds, which occur either singly or in groups within the otherwise relatively thinly bedded sequence, can be related to Facies C (principally C2.2) of the Pickering et al. (1986) classification; the units of very thinly bedded greywacke and siltstone relate more to the C2.3 or D2.3 subfacies. The alternation of these two types suggests deposition from alternating periods of high-density and low-density turbidity current flow.

Sedimentary structures from which a reliable indication of palaeocurrent flow can be deduced are sparse in the Corsewall Formation's greywacke member. Groove casts recorded from several localities all have a general NE–SW trend but Kelling (1962) has reported evidence from one locality of current flow from the north-west.

The composition of the Corsewall Formation greywackes is characteristically mixed, with a high proportion of rock fragments, quartz generally less than 20 per cent and feldspar about 15 per cent. Modal analyses are presented in Appendix 3 and summarised diagramatically in Figure 11a. The most striking feature is the great variety of rock fragments present, most commonly of acid igneous lithologies ranging from granodiorite to felsite but also including abundant spilitic grains (Plate 2a), some andesite clasts and rare fragments of serpentinite (Kelling, 1961; 1962). Metamorphic lithologies present include quartzite and low-grade micaceous schist together with rare glaucophane schist grains reported by Kelling (1962). Single mineral grains of apatite, spinel, augite, hornblende and epidote are common but never abundant. The exceptionally high magnetic susceptibility of greywackes from the Marchburn Formation, the along-strike correlative of the Corsewall Formation, was linked by Floyd and Trench (1989) with a high magnetite content. The high magnetic susceptibility of the Corsewall Formation greywacke suggests a similarly high magnetite content and much of the identified 'spinel' may well be magnetite.

The greywacke sequence is overlain quite abruptly by the Corsewall conglomerate which crops out at the northern end of the Rhins peninsula. Individually the beds of conglomerate range from 0.5 to 5 m thick but they combine to form packets up to 25 m thick which are interbedded with massive coarse greywacke beds and finer-grained thinner-bedded units reminiscent of the underlying greywacke sequence. The conglomerates are spectacularly coarse in places with boulders up to 1.5 m in diameter. The conglomerate beds are lenticular in along-strike section with markedly erosive bases. These coarse rudites may be either clast supported or matrix supported and are disorganised sequences of facies type A1 in the Pickering et al. (1986) classification. A minority show either normal or inverse grading. They were deposited from debris flows and high-density turbidity currents flowing from the north-west through a braided submarine channel system (Kelling et al., 1987) which cut down into the underlying greywackes. The channel-fill deposits were themselves eroded by subsequent channel development. These laterally supplied channelised complexes are interpreted by Kelling et al. (1987) as proximal or inner fan sediments deposited in a laterally migrating channel with a minimum width of 2 to 3 km. The size of the component boulders would seem to preclude long-distance transport but, since the majority of them, irrespective of size, are quite well rounded, they have clearly spent some time in a high-energy environment before being swept into the submarine channel.

A wide range of lithologies is present in the boulder suite, broadly comparable with the clast assemblage in the underlying greywacke. Various granitic and granodioritic types are the most abundant but felsitic and spilitic boulders are also common, whilst sedimentary clasts include boulders of greywacke, chert, and pre-existing polymict conglomerate; more extensive lithological descriptions are provided by Kelling (1961, 1962). Rb-Sr whole rock isochrons obtained from several of the granite boulder suites by Elders (1987) gave groups of ages around 1200 Ma, 600 to 700 Ma and 470 to 490 Ma. These were correlated by Elders with a possible provenance terrane in Newfoundland from which intrusive rocks of similar age and lithology were known; this implied extensive sinistral strike-slip movement during the latter stages of Caledonian orogenesis. Correlation of the 600 to 700 Ma group is the most tenuous since this age group is not well represented in Newfoundland. The older (Grenville) ages are the most contentious. If the 1200 Ma age is indeed correct foliated metamorphic lithologies might be expected as the country rock to the foliated ?Grenville granite. No such Precambrian metamorphic rocks are seen in the Corsewell conglomerate boulder suite. However, a mixed provenance is certainly implied with a dominantly acid to intermediate plutonic basement overlain by a clastic sedimentary sequence and, probably, an ophiolitic assemblage.

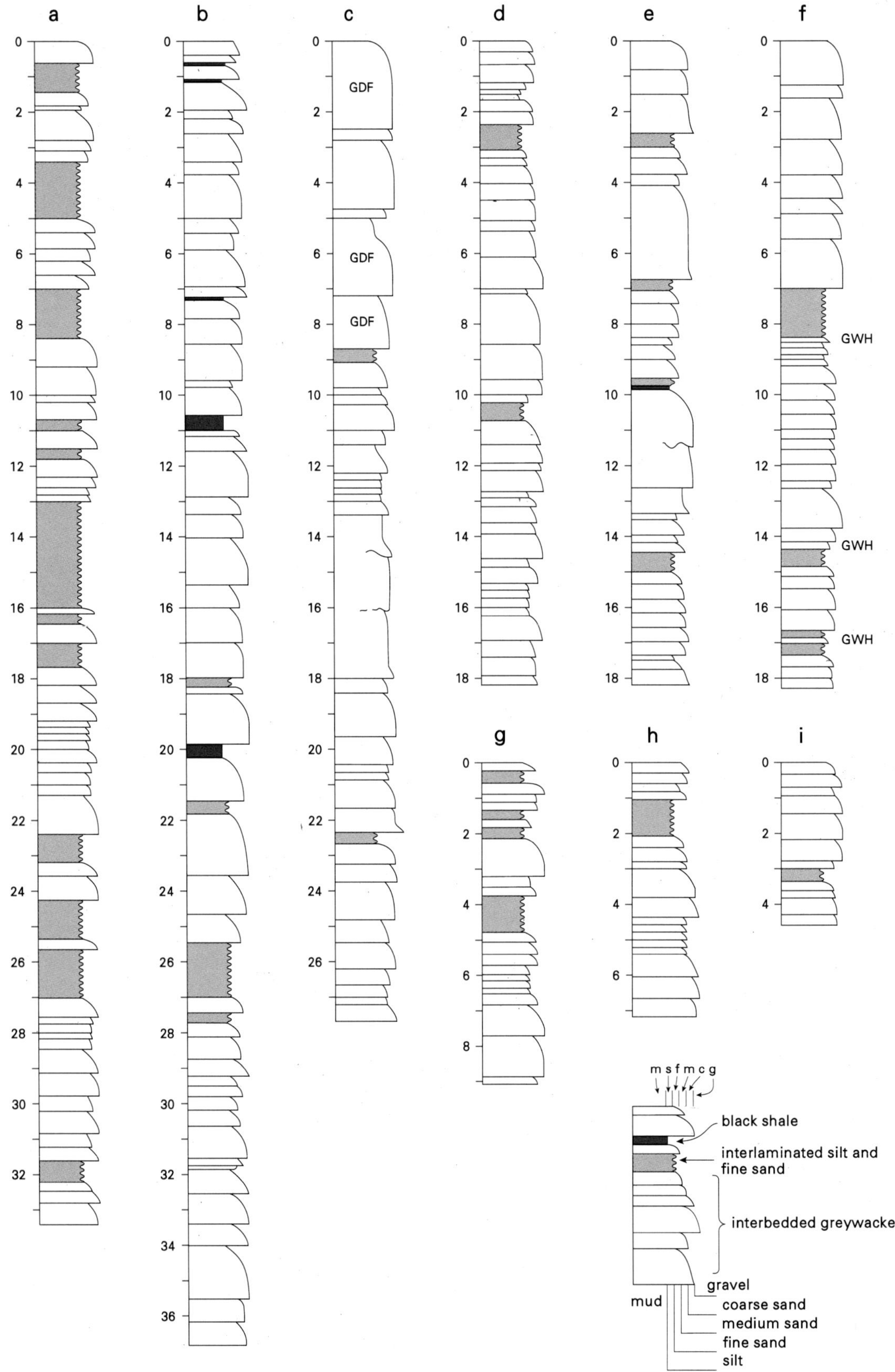
a
b
c
d
e
f
g
h
i
GDF
GWH
m s f m c g
black shale
interlaminated silt and fine sand
interbedded greywacke
gravel
mud
coarse sand
medium sand
fine sand
silt

Figure 10 *left* Representative measured sections illustrating lithological variation within the Leadhills Group.

a. Corsewall Formation. Top at NX 0276 7193.
b. Kirkcolm Formation. Top at NX 0547 7161.
c. Kirkcolm and Galdenoch formations. Top at NW 9599 6346 (GDF = Galdenoch Formation).
d. Portpatrick Formation. Top at NW 9802 5646.
e. Portpatrick Formation. Top at NX 0006 5371.
f. Portpatrick and Glenwhargen formations. Top at NX 0190 5219 (GWH = Glenwhargen Formation).
g. Shinnel Formation. Top at NX 0225 5142.
h. Shinnel Formation. Top at NX 0299 5079.
i. Shinnel Formation. Top at NX 0262 5102.

For more detailed analysis of sections d, e, g, h and i see Davies (1990):

KIRKCOLM FORMATION AND GALDENOCH FORMATION

The Kirkcolm and Galdenoch Formations are interbedded units of markedly different greywacke compositions which crop out in a NE–SW belt spanning Loch Ryan from the mainland to the northern part of the Rhins of Galloway (Figure 5). The base of the main sequence is exposed south of Broadsea Bay on the west coast of the Rhins [NW 976 588] where the greywacke turbidites of the Kirkcolm Formation overlie black shale of the Moffat Shale Group containing a *N. gracilis* Biozone fauna (Figure 6). Northwards (and up the succession) several more fossiliferous interbeds occur within the greywacke sequence and all, with one exception, can be assigned to the *N. gracilis* Biozone. The most northerly (and therefore probably youngest) outcrop of the Kirkcolm Formation, at Dounan Bay [NW 965 688] immediately to the south of the Glen App Fault, contains interbedded shales with a *C. 'peltifer'* Biozone fauna. Thus the top of the main Kirkcolm Formation sequence is of Caradoc age, although the base may well be within the Llandeilo. However, south of the main Kirkcolm Formation outcrop the same lithologies with the same composition are seen to the north of Knock Bay [NW 980 582], overlying black shale of the Moffat Shale Group containing graptolite faunas of both the *N. gracilis* and the *D. clingani* biozones. This younger Kirkcolm Formation section is in all other ways similar to the older main part of the outcrop. The two units, differentiated in Figure 6, are separated by the Glaik Fault and may be conveniently referred to as the upper and lower Kirkcolm Formation.

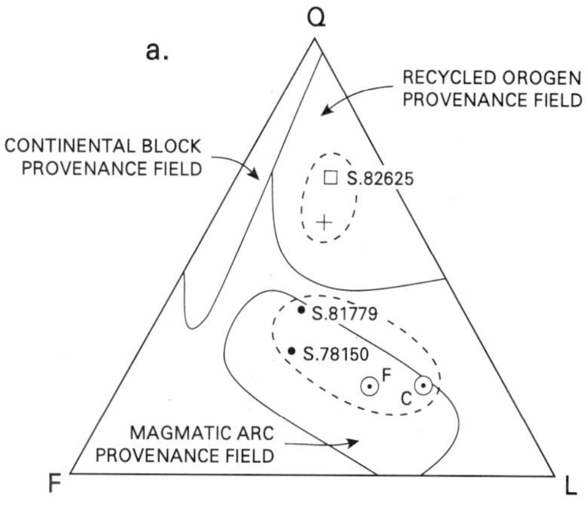

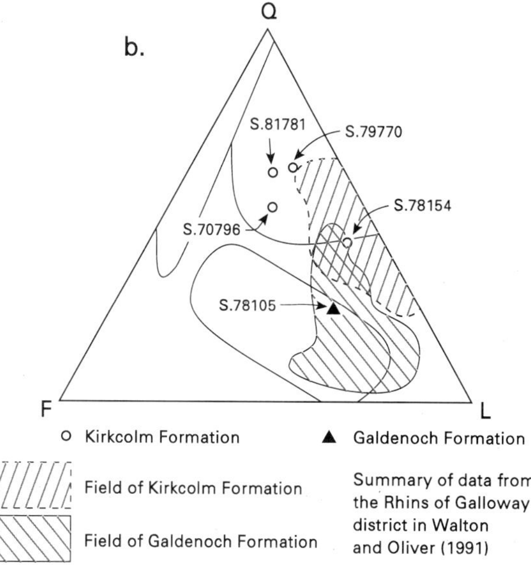

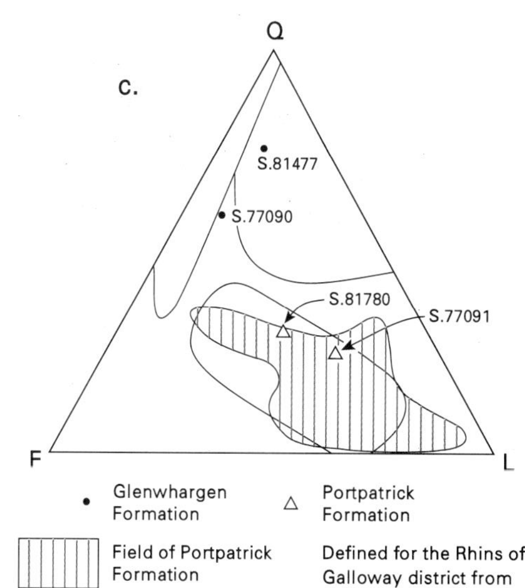

Figure 11 Summary of the compositional characteristics of greywackes from the Leadhills Group in terms of quartz (Q), feldspar (F) and labile components (L).

a. Corsewall and Shinnel formations.
b. Compositional contrast between the interbedded Kirkcolm and Galdenoch formations.
c. Compositional contrast between the interbedded Portpatrick and Glenwhargen formations.

Provenance fields from Dickinson and Suczek (1979).

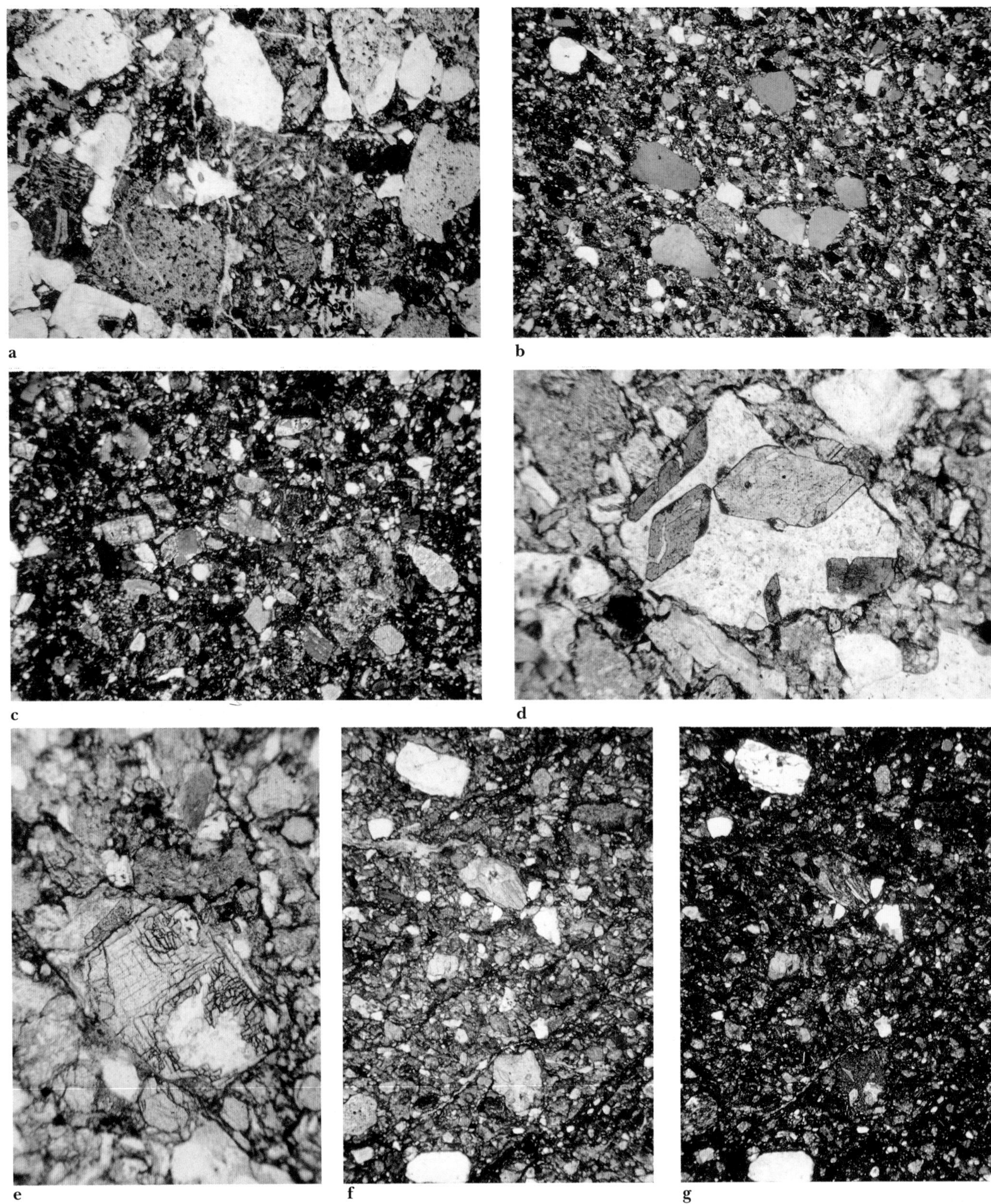

Interbedded with the lower Kirkcolm Formation are the distinctive andesite-rich greywackes of the Galdenoch Formation. These were recognised by Kelling (1961) who considered that on the Rhins of Galloway peninsula the Galdenoch Formation strata were conformably above those of the Kirkcolm Formation which was divided into three: an upper and a lower unit divided by a middle unit markedly richer in metamorphic detritus. On the

Plate 2 Representative photomicrographs illustrating compositional aspects of the Leadhills Group greywackes.

a. Mixed clast assemblage including spilite grains in a Corsewall Formation greywacke. S78150. Plane polarised light. Crossed polarisers ×12 GN01.
b. A quartz-rich Kirkcolm Formation greywacke. S78112. Crossed polarisers ×12 GN02.
c. Andesitic-rich greywacke of the Galdenoch Formation containing abundant detrital pyroxene and amphibole. S77044. Plane polarised light. Crossed polarisers ×12 GN03.
d. Amphibole phenocrysts in an andesitic clast from a Galdenoch Formation greywacke. S80294. Plane polarised light ×25 GN04.
e. Pyroxene grain from a Galdenoch Formation greywacke. S80294. Plane polarised light. Crossed polarisers ×25 GN05.
f. and g. Andesite-rich greywacke of the Portpatrick Formation containing abundant detrital pyroxene and amphibole. S78887. Plane polarised light (f) and crossed polarisers (g) ×12 GN06.

east side of Loch Ryan, Welsh (1964) described four stratigraphical units of similar compositon to the Galdenoch Formation and regarded them as a transitional member at the top of the Kirkcolm Formation marking a fundamental change of provenance. The current structural interpretation for the area is incompatible with the original proposals of Kelling and Welsh but the greywacke compositional variations they observed are real and emphasise the complexity of provenance contributing to the sequence.

The recent survey results show that at least two major units of Galdenoch Formation greywacke, each up to about 250 m thick, are interbedded with the lower Kirkcolm Formation sequence and occupy the same stratigraphical position on either side of the Loch Ryan Upper Palaeozoic basin (Figure 5). The internal variability of the Kirkcolm Formation, defined principally by the proportion of metamorphic detritus, is more difficult to quantify and in places reflects a bed-by-bed variation. The combined Kirkcolm and Galdenoch formations may exceed 2500 m in thickness but the estimate is beset by uncertainties over the full extent of structural imbrication.

Throughout the Kirkcolm Formation, both in its upper and lower components, T*a*, T*ab* and T*abc* greywacke turbidite units combine to form well-bedded sequences up to several hundred metres thick (Frontispiece). Within these sequences, principally facies C2.2 of the Pickering et al. (1986) classification, bedding thickness varies from a few centimetres to 1.5 m with the sporadic thicker bed. A typical measured section is shown in Figure 10b. Alternating with the greywacke-dominated sequences are packets of very thinly bedded fine-grained greywacke, siltstone and shale (Plate 3) forming T*c* and T*cde* turbidite units within facies D of Pickering et al. Individual units of D facies lithologies range from a few centimetres to about 20 m in thickness but in total form probably less than 5 per cent of the complete Kirkcolm Formation sequence, randomly distributed. They were erroneously allocated to the Moffat Shale Group by Peach and Horne (1899) but are clearly interbeds of the Kirkcolm Formation. Their presence shows that periods of low-density turbidity current flow or overbank deposition alternated with the more abundant high-density flows which deposited the greywackes. These thinly bedded sequences are highly deformed and some of that deformation may be the result of slumping of soft unconsolidated sediment (Plate 3a). However, in places, diagenetic concretions preserve regular bedding lamination, whilst being surrounded by intensely disrupted strata (Plate 3b and c). This suggests that much of the deformation seen is in fact tectonic.

From a consideration of the sedimentological characteristics Kelling et al. (1987) described the Kirkcolm Formation as the deposits of non-channelised or open-sheet turbidity flows, of high and low concentrations, with sporadic poorly channelised high-concentration turbidity and debris flows. The last are present in both the lower and upper Kirkcolm Formation divisions south of Broadsea Bay as matrix-supported conglomerates containing clasts of greywacke generally similar in lithology to those elsewhere in the Kirkcolm Formation but with the addition of a carbonate cement.

The Galdenoch Formation tends to be more thickly bedded than the Kirkcolm Formation with individual T*abc* greywacke units commonly in the 0.5–1 m range and locally exceeding 2 m, although the apparently very thick beds may be the result of amalgamation. The bulk of the formation falls in the C2.1 subfacies as defined by Pickering et al. (1986) with the occasional run of thinner beds having more affinity to the C2.2 subfacies. Kelling et al. (1987) considered the Galdenoch Formation to have been deposited in a series of relatively small and overlapping depositional lobes constructed by high-concentration turbidity currents.

Sedimentary structures are abundant within the Kirkcolm Formation and palaeocurrent trends can be deduced from flute and groove casts on many bed bases (Plate 4). The simplest flow pattern appears in the south-west part of the outcrop on the Rhins of Galloway, where an axial flow from the north-east is predominant. However, farther north in the Rhins outcrop and on the eastern side of Loch Ryan, the axial flow is both from the north-east and from the south-west with an equally important transverse flow from the south. Farther north-east in the Southern Uplands the flow pattern seems to become more variable (Evans et al., 1991). Palaeocurrent trends in the Kirkcolm Formation are summarised in the rose diagrams (Figure 12). Palaeocurrent data for the Galdenoch Formation is very sparse. Kelling (1962) reported flow from the south near Port Vad [NW 960 633] on the west coast of the Rhins but the examples cited are in a complex structural zone and, depending on the structural interpretation, could equally well be unfolded to indicate flow from the north-east.

Deduction of original palaeocurrent flow directions is complicated in areas of complex structure and thus the only data utilised was derived from relatively simple structural zones with uniform bedding attitude and sub-horizontal plunge of minor fold hinges. Strike ranges

Plate 3 Thinly bedded, siltstone-dominated facies of the Kirkcolm Formation at Finnarts Bay [NX 052 724].

a. Fine bedding lamination disrupted by some soft sediment deformation (MNS 5753).
b. Characteristic intense disruption of the bedding (MNS 4541).
c. Late diagenetic concretion preserving original planar bedding (MNS 4538).

a

b

c

from 045° to 085° and each measurement was corrected to a regional trend of 060° before unfolding to enable an overall comparison to be made (Figure 12). The same procedure was followed for all of the palaeocurrent data presented elsewhere in this account which should therefore be consistently comparable.

The composition of the greywackes comprising the two interbedded formations is markedly different (Plate 2b and c, Figure 11 and Appendix 3). The Galdenoch Formation is relatively quartz-poor and contains abundant feldspar and andesitic detritus. This contrasts with the Kirkcolm Formation greywackes in which quartz grains

Plate 4 Flute casts indicating palaeocurrent flow direction in the Kirkcolm Formation at Finnarts Bay [NX 053 722] (D 3743). Bedding strike is approximately 060°, dip is subvertical and the younging is towards the NW.

typically form 40–45 per cent of the rock and feldspar (mostly sodic plagioclase) about 20 per cent. Lithic clasts in the Kirkcolm Formation greywackes include fine-grained acid igneous felsitic rocks, spilitic basalt and various metamorphic lithologies such as foliated quartzite, mylonite, mica- and garnet-bearing schists and very rare clasts of glaucophane schist (cf. Kelling, 1961). Kelling also comments that most of the quartz has undulose extinction and is probably metamorphic in origin. Detrital pyroxene, hornblende and andesite grains, characteristic of the interbedded Galdenoch Formation, are all notably absent from the Kirkcolm Formation greywackes. In the Galdenoch Formation greywackes quartz is probably of mainly igneous origin (Kelling, 1961) and typically does not exceed 25 per cent. Feldspar, mostly sodic plagioclase, is usually in the 20–25 per cent range. The lithic and mafic clasts are dominated by broadly andesitic detritus which includes abundant and remarkable fresh pyroxene and hornblende grains together with fragments of andesite and dacite (Plate 2d and e). The andesite clasts contain phenocrysts of plagioclase and either one or both of augite and hornblende; the dacites may have biotite phenocrysts (Styles et al., 1989). Some spilitic basalt and fine-grained felsitic grains are also present, as is metamorphic detritus, generally chlorite schist with sporadic garnetiferous schists (Kelling, 1961).

The marked compositional differences between the two interbedded formations requires a different provenance area for each. The Kirkcolm Formation was derived from a plutonic–metamorphic basement area with a possible cover of sedimentary strata and ?ophiolitic spilites. The isotopic characteristics (Evans et al., 1991) indicate a Proterozoic age but rule out the Dalradian as a possible source. Nevertheless the palaeocurrent indicators show that much of the Kirkcolm Formation detritus was derived from the north of the Southern Uplands terrane, (Kelling et al., 1987, Table 1) although a similar basement may have been present on both sides of the depositional basin (cf. Stone et al., 1987). The incompatibility of the clasts and the Dalradian assemblage presently exposed to the north of the Southern Uplands, supports the concept of large-scale postdepositional strike slip movement along

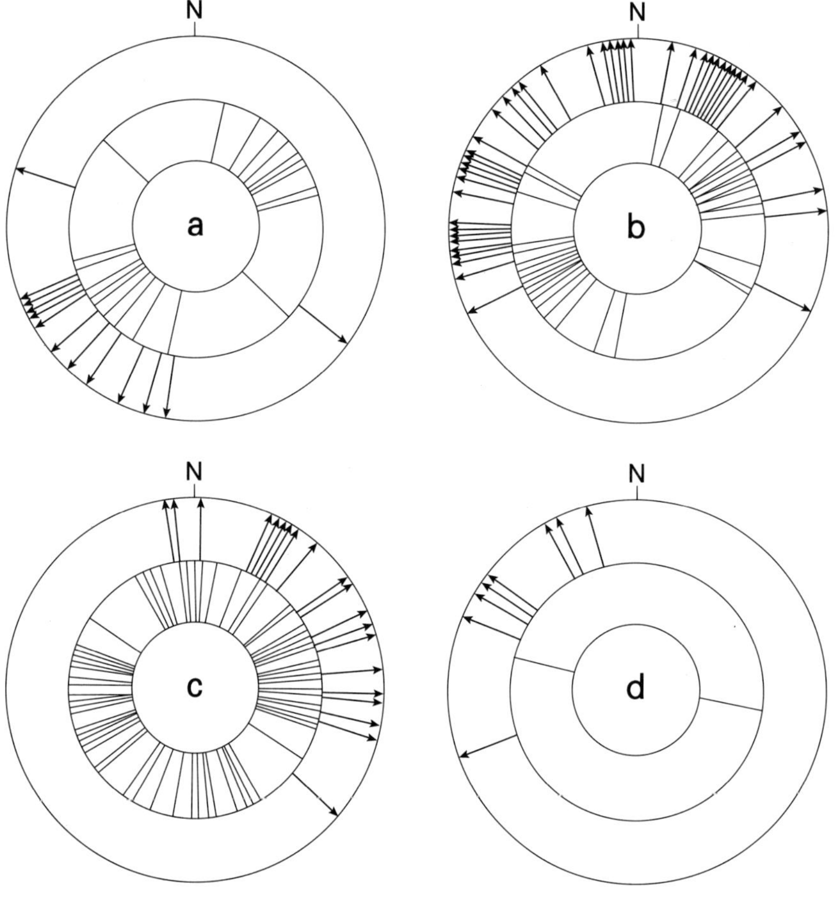

Figure 12 Palaeocurrent data from the Leadhills Group structurally corrected and rotated to regional strike of 060°.

a. Kirkcolm Formation south of Galdenoch [NW 970 630] on the Rhins peninsula.
b. Kirkcolm Formation north of Galdenoch on the Rhins and east of Loch Ryan.
c. Portpatrick Formation, main part of outcrop.
d. Portpatrick Formation, Port of Spittal Bay [NX 019 521].

the Southern Upland Fault and/or along a parallel structural lineament farther north. The composition of the Galdenoch Formation andesitic clasts requires a provenance within a transitional moderately evolved calc-alkaline island arc, probably founded on continental crust (Styles et al., 1989). Palaeocurrent evidence is not available for the Galdenoch Formation in the Rhins of Galloway district and is ambiguous elsewhere in the Southern Uplands (Evans et al., 1991). Nevertheless, the back-arc models (e.g. Stone et al., 1987) predict a southerly provenance.

PORTPATRICK FORMATION AND GLENWHARGEN FORMATION

These interbedded Ordovician greywacke formations occur in a NE–SW belt spanning the central part of the Rhins of Galloway district and crop out on both sides of the Stranraer Upper Palaeozoic basin (Figure 5). The andesitic-rich Portpatrick Formation is by far the dominant partner with only sporadic beds of the distinctive quartz arenite of the Glenwhargen Formation present within the district, although it is more fully developed along strike to the north-east. The base of the Portpatrick Formation is well exposed on the north side of Morroch Bay [NX 014 626] where the greywackes are interbedded with and overlie black shale of the *D. clingani* Biozone from the Moffat Shale Group. The upper age range of the Formation (Figure 6) is indicated by a possible *P. linearis* Biozone graptolite fauna recovered near the top of the exposed sequence at Killantringan Bay [NW 983 570]. Thus, on the Rhins of Galloway, the Portpatrick Formation may be restricted to the Caradoc or may just extend up into the early Ashgill. However, there is a suggestion that the base of the Portpatrick Formation may be diachronous. Farther north-east in the Southern Uplands the underlying Moffat Shale Group strata range up to the *P. linearis* Biozone and Kelling et al. (1987) suggest that to the south-west, in County Down, the lithologically similar Grey Point Formation rests unconformably on *N. gracilis* Biozone shale.

The Portpatrick Formation is of the order of 1500 m thick and for the most part consists of the C2.1 and C2.2 subfacies of Pickering et al. (1986). The greywacke beds are usually in the range 0.5 to 1 m but sporadic beds up to 2 m thick are not uncommon. Bed thickness can be very variable in any one section and interbedded laminated siltstone intervals, usually in the 2–20 cm range, may be as much as 75 cm thick. Most of the greywacke beds are T*a*, T*b* or T*abc* turbidite units with well-developed internal structure, although grading appears absent from many of the beds and amalgamation is probably widespread. Some of the basal greywackes in the T*a* division are very coarse and gravel pockets are seen locally together with common rip-up clasts of shale and siltstone. Typical sections are presented in Figure 10(d, e and f). The proportion of interbedded siltstone increases and the average thickness of the greywacke beds decreases abruptly towards the top of the Portpatrick Formation which presents a very much more distal appearance than the main part of the sequence. The overall sedimentological characteristics led Kelling et al. (1987) to suggest that much of the deposition was from high-density open sheet-flows and subordinate channelised flows. A higher proportion of low-density or overbank flows make up the higher part of the formation. The variability of the sequence suggests a range of depositional environments including non-channelised slopes, channels, interchannel areas and minor lobes. These probably occurred in a sandy 'apron' of small, coalescing depositonal fans.

Interbedded with the Portpatrick Formation greywackes are thin interbeds of the siliceous greywackes related to the Glenwhargen Formation. These are normally about 2–20 cm thick but rarely range up to nearly 1 m. Their distinctive composition produces a marked colour variation such that they stand out as pale horizons within the generally darker Portpatrick Formation greywackes (Plate 5). Most are T*bc* or T*bcd* turbidite units which are relatively matrix poor and should properly be classified as quartz arenites rather than greywackes. They are best developed at two localities, both on the west coast of the Rhins. On the north side of Port of Spittal Bay [NX 020 522] the interbedded Portpatrick and Glenwhargen formations are contained within a lower structural imbricate beneath the Morroch Bay Moffat Shale Group outcrop. The greywackes overlie a probable *P. linearis* Biozone shale sequence and the Glenwhargen Formation interbeds occur only a few tens of metres above the base of the Portpatrick Formation. In contrast, near Killantringan lighthouse [NW 982 564], the Glenwhargen Formation interbeds are very much higher in the sequence, close to the locality containing a *P. linearis* Biozone fauna. A section showing the style and scale of the interbedding is presented in Figure 10f.

Plate 5 Quartz-arenite horizon of the Glenwhargen Formation (pale) interbedded with Portpatrick Formation greywacke (dark) at Port of Spittal Bay [NX 019 521] (D 3756).

Palaeocurrent flow patterns derived from the Portpatrick Formation greywackes are quite consistent in showing flow from the south-west quadrant. Flute and groove casts are a common feature of the greywacke beds and allow a sizeable dataset to be assembled (Figure 12c) which compares well with the results of Davies (1990) and Kelling (1962). One slightly anomalous area is the section north of Port of Spittal Bay contained within the lowest imbricate slice beneath the main part of the sequence where the consistent palaeocurrent flow is from the south-east quadrant (Figure 12d). Despite the consistent palaeocurrent evidence there is a common presumption in the literature that the Portpatrick Formation was derived from the north-east. In a recent example McKerrow et al. (1991) propose a distant source in the early Cambrian Mongolian arc.

Kelling (1961, 1962) subdivided the Portpatrick Formation on the basis of compositional variations into a lower 'acid-clast' division and an upper 'basic-clast' division. The 'acid-clast' greywackes contain more quartz, acid igneous and metamorphic grains but less feldspar, andesitic and basic igneous and ferromagnesian mineral grains than do the 'basic-clast' greywackes. Whilst the basis of this separation remains sound, the change from one type to another is more of an overall transition than the abrupt switch implied by Kelling. The basal beds overlying the Moffat Shale Group mudstones are the most quartzose. From there an upward increase in the proportion of 'basic-clast' components is interrupted by greywacke beds showing the extreme characteristics of either type. As a result most of the greywackes south of Portpatrick are of 'acid-clast' type whereas those to the north are 'basic-clast'. The characteristic features of the Formation as a whole are low quartz, rarely exceeding 15 per cent, but feldspar (dominantly plagioclase) usually in excess of 20 per cent. Andesite, dacite and pyroxene grains are abundant with felsitic and spilitic clasts common (Plate 2f and g). Similar compositions were reported by Welsh (1964) from the east side of the Stranraer isthmus. Typical modal analyses are summarised in Figure 11c and listed in detail in Appendix 3. The andesite grains have phenocrysts of plagioclase with usually either augite or hornblende. In some samples both are present and in a few it appears that amphibole was forming at the expense of pyroxene. Some grains contain serpentine pseudomorphs, thought to be after orthopyroxene rather than olivine, as they replace elongate rather than equant grains (Styles et al., 1989). Other rock types sporadically present in the clast assemblage are gabbro, diorite and granite together with various metamorphic lithologies. These latter include quartzite, mica, chlorite and garnetiferous schists and, very rarely, glaucophane schist (Kelling, 1961). Garnet also occurs as a detrital mineral grain. In marked contrast the clast assemblage of the Glenwhargen Formation is dominantly quartzose, with the quartz content commonly exceeding 60 per cent. Very little feldspar is present and the lithic grains are mostly of quartzite or chlorite schist. Typical modal analyses are summarised in Figure 11c and listed in detail in Appendix 3.

The volcanic detritus within the Portpatrick Formation was derived from a calc-alkaline volcanic arc built on a continental crustal basement. Consistent palaeocurrent evidence places this provenance to the south and/or south-west of the depositional basin. The detrital pyroxenes indicate a rather more evolved calc-alkaline source during Portpatrick Formation deposition than the more transitional affinities of the slightly older, but lithologically similar, Galdenoch Formation (Styles et al., 1989). This, and the freshness of the pyroxenes, led Styles et al. (1989) to the conclusion that the volcanic arc provenance was active (and evolving) during deposition. However, Kelley and Bluck (1989), using ^{40}Ar–^{39}Ar laser probe techniques, obtained cooling ages in the 530–560 Ma range from detrital volcanic clasts in the lower part of the Portpatrick Formation; this suggests a provenance volcanically active in the early Cambrian. The source direction of the interbedded Glenwhargen Formation horizons is not established by data from the Rhins of Galloway. Elsewhere in the Southern Uplands there are some indications of derivation from a westerly quadrant (Evans et al., 1991) but the marked compositonal differences with the dominant Portpatrick Formation requires a very different provenance terrane. The Glenwhargen Formation greywackes were derived from a quartz-rich basement area devoid of basic volcanic rocks.

SHINNEL FORMATION

The Shinnel Formation forms a NE–SW belt on either side of the Stranraer Upper Palaeozoic Basin north of Luce Bay (Figure 5). Its outcrop is divided into northern and southern units by a major strike fault, the Portayew Fault. The two units are compositionally very similar and are taken to be imbricate thrust repetitions of the same Shinnel Formation strata. The northern unit was previously called the 'Portayew Rocks' by Kelling (1961; 1962) and by Kelling et al. (1987). The correlation with the more widely recognised Shinnel Formation suggested by Floyd (1982) has been adopted (Table 2). The northern unit has been informally termed the Portayew Formation and the southern unit the Cairngarroch Formation by McCurry (1990) and Davies (1990).

The base of the Shinnel Formation is best seen at Portayew [NX 039 504] on the west coast of the Rhins where greywacke overlies graptolitic shale and mudstone of the Moffat Shale Group to the north of the Portayew Fault (Figure 5). This is the base of the northern imbricate unit of the Shinnel Formation. No age evidence has been forthcoming from the southern unit which is terminated on the south side by the major strike-parallel Orlock Bridge Fault (Anderson and Oliver, 1986) locally known as the Cairngarroch Fault. At Portayew, however, the graptolite faunas include some typical of the *D. clingani* Biozone and others suggestive of the *N. gracilis* Biozone. On this basis the Shinnel Formation is very similar in age to the Portpatrick Formation and the upper Kirkcolm Formation to the north. However, McCurry (1990) has suggested that unfossiliferous grey shales at Portayew can be correlated with the upper Hartfell Shale lithologies elsewhere in the Southern Uplands; hence the Shinnel Formation could be as young as the *D. complanatus* Biozone. Comparison with other Shinnel Formation localities along strike to the north-east is similarly ambiguous; the post *D. clingani* age is certain but there is also evidence for an age as young as the *anceps* Biozone (Floyd and Rushton, 1993). This uncertainty is reflected in Figure 6.

Each of the two presumed tectonic repetitions of the Shinnel Formation contains something in excess of 650 m of strata. Although they are sedimentologically similar, there are some contrasts, notably the increased proportion of thickly bedded greywackes and the corresponding lower proportion of laminated siltstones in the northern unit (Portayew Formation). It contains coarse- to medium-grained, variably bedded greywackes; some sections are thinly bedded but elsewhere bedding may be thick with some individual T*abc* units in excess of 2 m. Grading is not always well developed, however, and amalgamation is common. Alternating with the greywackes are intervals of laminated siltstone and very fine-grained greywackes which form about 10 per cent of the total succesion. Deposition in this sequence can be related to the C2 and D2 facies of Pickering et al. (1986) and is illustrated by the sections in Figure 10(g, h and i). South of the Portayew Fault (the Cairngarroch Formation) a more generally distal aspect prevails with fewer thick greywacke beds and a much higher proportion of laminated siltstone which locally forms 25 per cent of the sequence.

Kelling et al. (1987) envisaged the Shinnel Formation being deposited by low- to high-density open sheet flows, with ephemeral subordinate channelised flows. The thicker, coarser greywacke beds may represent a proximal lobe deposit, particularly those showing tabular, parallel-sided bed geometry with occasional thickening- and coarsening-upwards cycles. Greywacke beds related to channel-fill deposition more frequently show erosive bases and thinning- and fining-upwards cycles.

The Shinnel Formation outcrop in the Rhins of Galloway district contains few reliable paleocurrent indicators but those which have been recorded consistently show palaeocurrent flow towards the north (Davies 1990). However, this is diametrically opposed to the trend deduced elsewhere in the Southern Uplands from equally sparse data (Evans et al., 1991) and may not reflect the true sediment-distribution pattern.

The Shinnel Formation greywackes are uniformly quartz rich in composition; generally the quartz content is in excess of 50 per cent. Feldspar, usually a sodic plagioclase, is relatively sparse. The lithic clast assemblage is dominated by acid igneous rocks including granodiorite, granite and felsitic lithologies. Low-grade chlorite schists and metaquartzite are well represented, with detrital grains of zircon and apatite present in most thin sections. A provenance area composed mainly of low grade metamorphic rocks and acid plutonic lithologies is indicated. Modal analyses are summarised in Figure 11 and listed in detail in Appendix 3.

FIVE

Silurian greywacke succession: Gala Group

Within the central part of the Rhins of Galloway a number of tectonostratigraphical units contain greywacke sequences overlying Moffat Shale Group strata of Llandovery age. Where graptolites have been recovered from shale laminae interbedded with the greywackes they show that the turbidite deposits are either of the same age as the underlying shale or in some cases are one graptolite zone younger (Figures 5 and 6). Together these Llandovery greywacke-dominated turbidite sequences form the Gala Group. Formal lithostratigraphical subdivision of the group is not possible because there is no systematic sedimentological or compositional variation between the sequences which lie in fault-defined tracts. The greywackes within each tract are of slightly different age, becoming sequentially younger southwards (Figure 6), and are separated from adjacent tracts by major strike faults. For this reason they are referred to as numbered tectonostratigraphical units (Gala 1, Gala 2, etc.) in the subsequent discussion and on the accompanying 1:50 000 geological map. The locations of the units and their boundary faults are shown in Figure 5 and correlated in Table 2 with local lithostratigraphical terminology previously used. For ease of comparison previously published or informal lithostratigraphical terms are also quoted in the subsequent section headings.

Some Gala Group sandstones contain less than 15 per cent matrix and so are not greywackes *sensu stricto* but quartz-lithic-arenites. However, for convenience the term greywacke will be used in this account to include all of the Gala Group clastic lithologies. All the Gala Group greywackes are relatively quartz rich, total quartz content ranging from about 30 per cent in the Gala 2 unit to about 55 per cent in some Gala 8 greywackes. A trend of increasing quartz content into the younger strata has been described from the eastern Southern Uplands Gala Group outcrop (Casey quoted in Walton and Oliver, 1991) but this is less apparent in the Rhins of Galloway. Plagioclase and K-feldspar are both present in the northern units, Gala 1 to Gala 6, mostly in about the same quantity, each forming 10–15 per cent of the rock; the lowest K-feldspar: plagioclase ratio is seen in the Gala 2 and 3 units both of which contain up to 15 to 20 per cent of andesitic detritus as rock fragments, hornblende and pyroxene grains. K-feldspar is not a significant component of the Gala 7 and 8 greywackes wherein plagioclase forms about 15 per cent of the rock. In the other northern Gala units apart from Gala 2 and 3, the andesitic detritus is a minor constitutent forming about 3–5 per cent. Andesitic material, with the exception of the occasional accessory grain, is absent in the southern Gala units 6 and 8; some parts of the Gala 7 unit contain a little an-

Table 2 Stratigraphical correlation of the Leadhills and Gala groups in south-west Scotland.

Rhins of Galloway This memoir		Rhins of Galloway Kelling (1961)	East of Loch Ryan Welsh (1964)	Nithsdale Floyd (1982)	Tectonostratigraphic tract numbers Leggett et al. (1979)
Corsewall Formation	Leadhills Group	Corsewall Group		Marchburn Formation	1
Kirkcolm Formation		Kirkcolm Group	Lochryan Rocks	Afton Formation	2
Galdenoch Formation		Galdenoch Group	Cairnerzean Rocks	Blackcraig Formation	
Portpatrick Formation		Portpatrick Group	Glenwhan Rocks	Scar Formation	3
Glenwhargen Formation					
Shinnel Formation		Portayew Rocks*	Boreland Rocks	Shinnel Formation	
Rhins of Galloway This memoir		**Rhins of Galloway Davies (1990) and McCurry (1990)**		**Wigtown peninsula (Sheet 4W) British Geological Survey (1992)**	
Gala Group unit 1				Kilfillan Formation	4
Gala Group unit 2				Mindork Formation	
Gale Group unit 3		Money Head Formation		not present	
Gala Group unit 4		Float Bay Formation		Sinniness Formation	
Gala Group unit 5		Stinking Bight beds		Garheugh Formation	5
Gala Group unit 6		Grennan Point Formation		unnamed	
Gala Group unit 7		Mull of Logan Formation		Mull of Logan Formation	6
Gala Group unit 8		Port Logan Formation		Port Logan Formation	

* Term introduced by Floyd (1982) for a sequence included by Kelling (1961) within the Acid-Clast Division of his Portpatrick Formation.

desitic material but levels are low and variable. However, in these three units detrital mica, predominantly muscovite, increases from the accessory trace seen elsewhere to 15 per cent in some Gala 8 samples. Fine-grained, acid igneous lithologies, spilitic basalt, sedimentary intrabasinal clasts and low-grade schistose rocks all contribute a small but fairly uniform proportion, only rarely exceeding 5 per cent, to all of the Gala Group greywackes. A summary of modal analysis results from typical Gala Group greywackes is shown in Figure 13 and representative photomicrographs in Plate 6. Four potentially important trends can be identified:

1. Overall increase in quartz content with decreasing age of Gala Group tectonostratigraphical units.
2. Decrease in the andesitic component. This occurs irregularly southwards falling from a maximum of about 25 per cent in Gala 2 and 3 to virtually zero in Gala 6 and 8.
3. Loss of virtually all K-feldspar in Gala 7 and 8. Farther north K-feldspar contributes between 10 and 20 per cent to the Gala 4–6 greywackes, approximately equal to the plagioclase content. K-feldspar levels are lower in Gala 5 and 3. The plagioclase content remains much the same in all of the Gala Group units.
4. Southward increase in the abundance of detrital muscovite. Muscovite becomes an important accessory in Gala 5 and 6, increases to about 5 to 10 per cent in Gala 7, and increases further to 15 per cent in some samples from Gala 8.

Field of Gala Group greywacke compositions obtained by Casey as reported by Walton and Oliver (1991); arrow indicates increasing quartz content with decrease in age of strata

Tectonostratigraphical unit
2 : S.81788
4 : S.81782
5 : S.80350
6 : S.81787
7 : S.81783
8 : S.78890
8' : S.78891

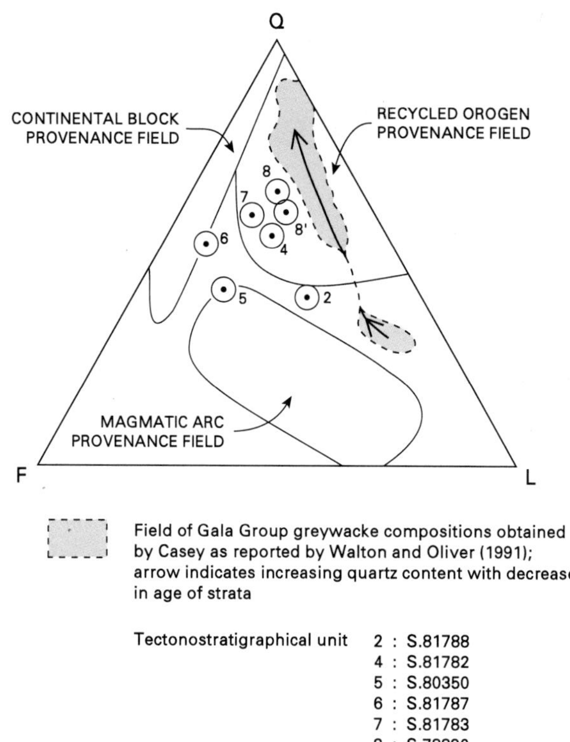

Figure 13 Compositional range of the Gala Group greywackes in terms of quartz (Q), feldspar (F) and labile components (L).
Provenance fields from Dickinson and Suczek (1979).

GALA 1 (Kilfillan Formation)

This tectonostratigraphical unit is only present in the mainland part of the district between Glenluce [NX 200 575] and Luce Bay (Figure 5). Within the district exposure is very poor but along strike the Gala 1 tract consists of about 2000 m of regularly bedded quartzose greywacke with bed thickness ranging from about 20 cm to 2 m. Rare interbedded units of laminated siltstone generally do not exceed 5 m and the sporadic development of coarse greywacke beds up to 4 m thick may well be the result of amalgamation. The greywacke beds are generally of the T*ab* or T*abc* type and fall into the B2 or C2 subfacies of Pickering et al. (1986), although in many greywacke beds grading is either absent or only poorly developed. Age control is provided by a *P. acuminatus* Biozone fauna recovered from the laminated siltstone interbeds farther north-east on Sheet 4W. The assemblage of sedimentological characteristics suggested to Kelling et al. (1987) that Gala 1 deposition occurred in an essentially channelised environment; palaeocurrent indicators suggested turbidity current flow towards the south-west.

GALA 2 (Mindork Formation)

Outcrop of this tectonostratigraphical unit is restricted to the area west of Sandhead [NX 097 500] in the central part of the Rhins of Galloway (Figure 5). The base of the greywacke sequence conformably overlies black shale of the Moffat Shale Group in the Cairnweil Burn [NX 089 494] south-west from Sandhead. However, this zone is severely tectonised and no determinable graptolites have been recovered. The age of the Gala 2 greywackes is suggested as *P. acuminatus* Biozone from along-strike correlation to the north-east where faunas of that age occur in interbedded siltstones.

Plate 6 Representative photomicrographs illustrating compositional aspects of the Gala Group greywackes.

a. Gala 2 greywacke containing abundant andesitic clasts and detrital pyroxene and amphibole in addition to quartzofeldspathic detritus. S81788 crossed polarisers ×20 GN08.
b. Gala 4 greywacke, quartz-rich with a prominent granitic clast. S81782 crossed polarisers ×20 GN09.
c. Gala 6 greywacke, quartz-rich with a scattering of feldspathic clasts and rare, accessory spilite grains. S81787 crossed polarisers ×20 GN010.
d. Gala 7 greywacke with polycrystalline quartzite, strained quartz and feldspathic clasts accompanying the commoner monocrystalline quartz grains. S78889 crossed polarisers ×20 GN011.

a
b
c
d

Gala 2 greywackes are generally medium to coarse grained and may be very thickly bedded. A bed thickness range of 50 cm to 3 m is commonly seen but some more massive units do occur, possibly as a result of amalgamation. Units of thinner-bedded greywacke (less than 50 cm) are often associated with laminated siltstone intervals 1–2 m thick. The greywackes contain a variable proportion of andesitic detritus with the total of pyroxene, hornblende and lithic andesite clasts reaching 25 per cent in some samples. However, other interbedded greywackes are almost devoid of andesitic material and no formal lithostratigraphical definition is possible. There seems to be no relationship between composition and lithofacies. The greywackes are generally T*a*, T*ab* or T*abc* greywacke units, sometimes with grading very poorly developed, in the B2.1 or C2.1 and C2.2 subfacies of Pickering et al. (1986). A generally channelised depositional environment seems likely with palaeocurrent flow dominantly towards the south-west. A total thickness of about 1000 m is likely for this unit.

GALA 3 (Money Head Formation)

Thick beds of coarse-grained greywacke characterise this tectonostratigraphical unit which is present on the west side of the Rhins of Galloway (Figure 5). A conformable base above Moffat Shale Group strata is seen in the Cairnweil Burn [NX 085 495] and on the coast at Strandfoot [NX 052 482]. At both localities the Strandfoot Fault forms the structural base and in the Cairnweil Burn tectonism is sufficiently severe to prevent the recovery of any graptolite faunas which may have been present. However, at Strandfoot the shales contain graptolites suggestive of the *acinaces* Biozone which provides a maximum age for the overlying greywacke sequence.

Thick greywacke beds are characteristic. They range up to 5 m thick and alternate with laminated siltstone intervals which range from 10 cm to 1.5 m thick. Rarely a thicker (up to 8 m) development of laminated siltstone occurs in association with very thin greywacke beds ranging from 2 to 30 cm. The lithofacies style and variation are illustrated in the measured graphic log (Figure 14a). Many of the thicker greywacke beds are poorly graded with strongly erosive bases and amalgamation seems very likely; other greywacke beds are more tabular. Most greywacke beds are T*a*, T*ab* or T*abc* turbidite units with low-angle cross-stratification well developed locally and rippled tops seen on some beds. Several beds of slump breccia, up to 2–3 m thick, contain only intrabasinal clasts and are thought to represent channel wall collapse episodes. The whole sedimentological assemblage was interpreted by Kelling et al. (1987) to indicate deposition within a channel and channel margin environment.

In total the Gala 3 sequence is about 900 m thick with the more andesitic-rich greywackes found in the lower half of the succession. Palaeocurrent flow indicators are abundant with flute casts consistently indicating turbidity current flow towards the south-west (Figure 15a), parallel to the main groove cast trend. The sand-rich sedimentary system probably developed as an axially diverted low-efficiency fan.

GALA 4 (Float Bay Formation)

The structural base of this unit on the Rhins of Galloway is marked by the major strike-parallel Gillespie Burn Fault (Figure 5). No Moffat Shale lithologies are preserved in its vicinity but graptolite faunas from siltstone and shale interbedded with the greywackes suggest an age range from the *C. cyphus* Biozone to the succeeding (and composite) *C. gregarius* Biozone. Graptolites from several localities near Float Bay [NX 064 472] are indicative of the *cyphus* and lowermost *gregarius* biozones (*triangulatus*). Farther north a fragmentary graptolite fauna near the top of the preserved Gala 4 sequence, just south of Strandfoot [NX 053 480], suggests a level within the *gregarius* Biozone. The range overlap of these faunas is such that all of the Gala 4 greywacke sequence could be assigned to the lower *gregarius* (*triangulatus*) Biozone but equally the top of the unit could be as young as the upper *gregarius* (*leptotheca*) Biozone (Figure 6), while the base may well be as old as the *cyphus* Biozone. The more northerly of these fossiliferous localities was originally interpreted as Moffat Shale Group by Peach and Horne (1899) but is now considered to lie within a sequence of dark grey shales and laminated siltstones interbedded with Gala 4 greywackes.

Bedding in the greywackes is generally in the thickness range 20 to 75 cm with the sporadic appearance of more-massive greywacke beds up to 1.5 m thick. Commonly interbedded with the greywacks are up to 50 cm of laminated siltstone. Thin greywacke beds, 3–10 cm thick, may be included within the laminated siltstones which become more abundant northwards into the younger part of the sequence. T*ab* and T*abc* turbidite units are most common. The uppermost 200 m which contains the *gregarius* graptolite fauna, is dominated by the laminated siltstone lithofacies which, at that level, contains much interbedded grey shale. The characteristics of the Gala 4 succession are shown in Figure 14b. Kelling et al. (1987) deduced deposition of the greywackes from unconfined sheet flows with only minor channelised beds; the laminated siltstone units were related to deposition in the interlobe and channel areas. The total thickness of the Gala 4 unit has been estimated at 1500 m by McCurry (1990). Palaeo-

Figure 14 Representative measured sections illustrating lithological variation within the Gala Group.

a. Gala 3: Money Head. Top at NX 0485 4832.
b. Gala 4: Float Bay. Top at NX 0635 4704.
c. Gala 5: Ardwell Point. Top at NX 0665 4483.
d. Gala 6: Drumbreddan Bay. Top at NX 0748 4368.
e. Gala 7: Daw Point member, Mull of Logan. Top at NX 0811 4165.
f. Gala 7: Cairnie Finnart member, Cairnie Finnart. Top at NX 0873 4155.
g. Gala 7: Chair member, Port Gill. Top at NX 0767 4307.
h. Gala 8: Cairnywellan Head. Top at NX 0911 4015.

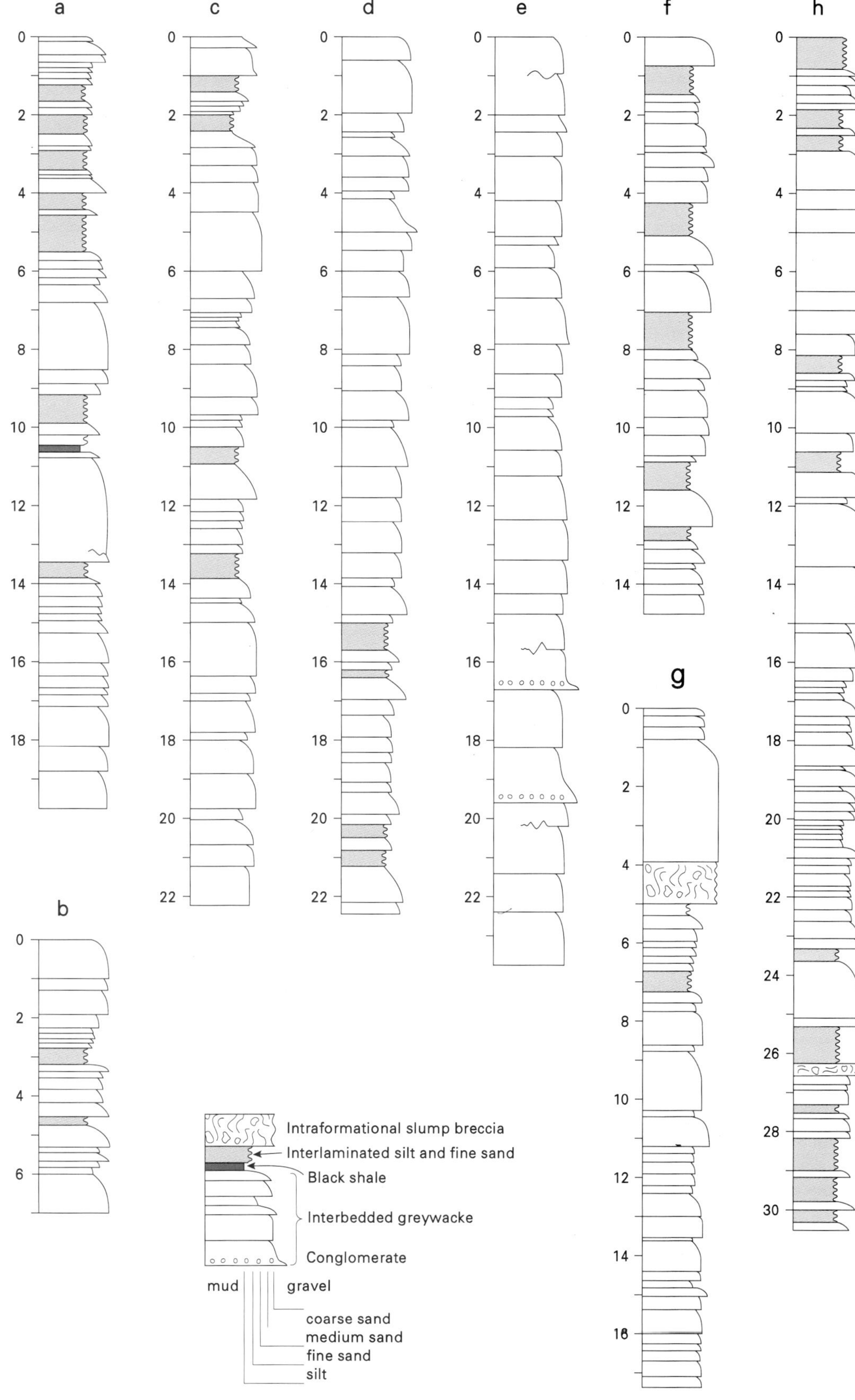
a
b
c
d
e
f
g
h
Intraformational slump breccia
Interlaminated silt and fine sand
Black shale
Interbedded greywacke
Conglomerate
mud
gravel
coarse sand
medium sand
fine sand
silt

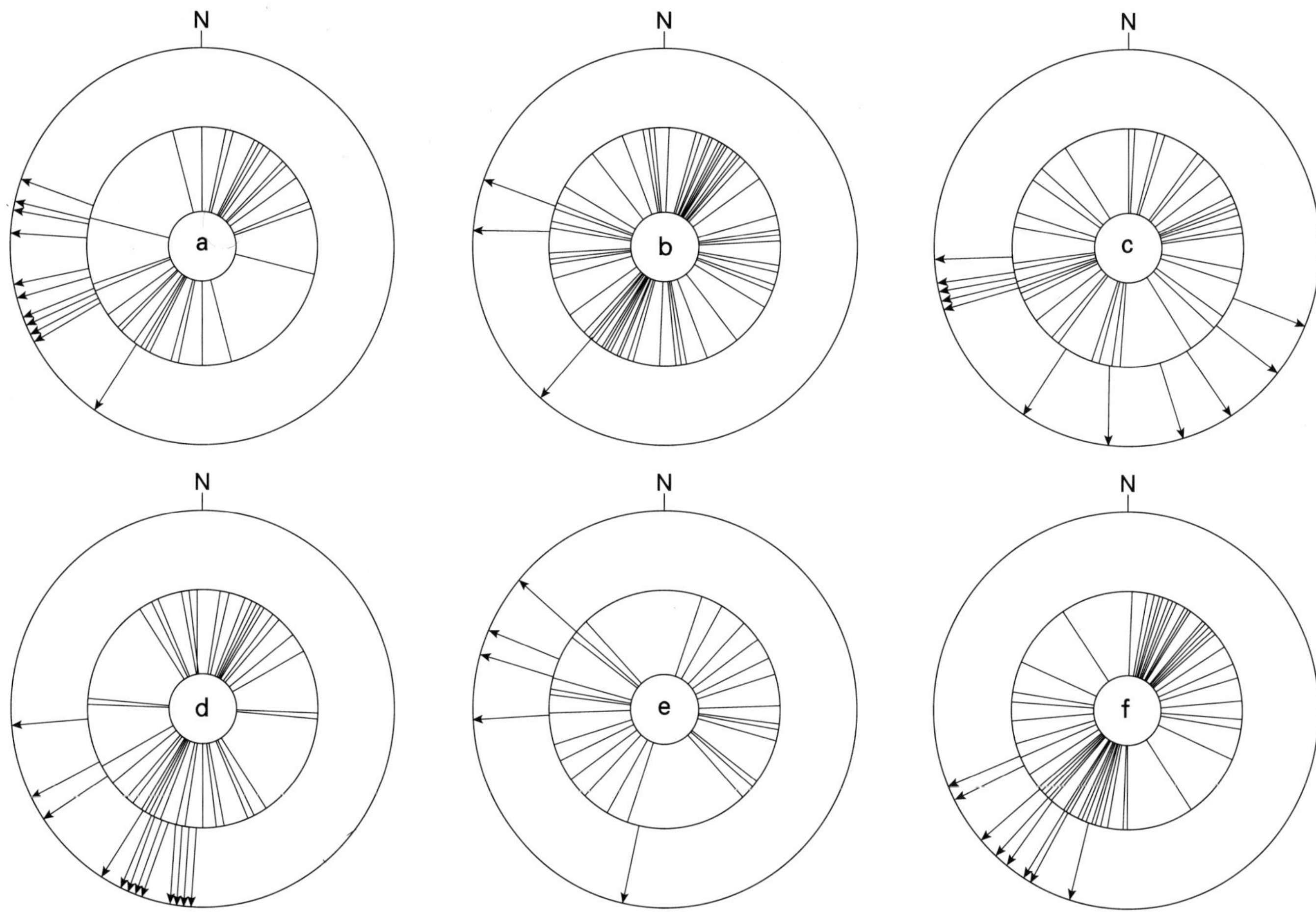

Figure 15 Palaeocurrent data from the Gala Group structurally corrected and rotated to regional strike of 060°.

a. Gala 3
b. Gala 4
c. Gala 5
d. Gala 6
e. Gala 7
f. Gala 8

(a–f: Tectonostratigraphical units)

Data after Davies (1990) supplemented by information in McCurry (1990) who provides a broadly comparable palaeocurrent pattern.

current flow indicators are variable but generally indicate turbidity current movement towards the west and southwest, axial to the depositional basin (Figure 15b). An elongate sedimentary system of sheet flows and minor channels seems the most likely environment.

GALA 5 (Stinking Bight beds)

The base of this unit is a structurally complex zone exposed on the west coast of the Rhins (Figure 5) adjacent to the Hooies Fault [NX 068 446]. Immediately to the north of the fault a black and red shale and mélange sequence, interbedded with very thin red siltstone beds, is intensely sheared but appears to be conformably overlain northwards by thinly bedded greywackes. The shale and mélange is thus tentatively assigned to the Moffat Shale Group and the graptolite fauna it contains is indicative of the *triangulatus* Biozone. Farther north the sequence is repeatedly faulted and is largely southward younging, with a pervasive sinistral shear superimposed on earlier structures. Another graptolite fauna, from Hooies cove about 100 m north of the Hooies Fault, indicates the *magnus* Biozone, one zone above that seen adjacent to the Fault. This biostratigraphical change is consistent with the northward younging of the steeply inclined greywackes adjacent to the Hooies Fault but contradicts the southward younging seen in the vicinity of the Hooies cove and in the fossiliferous sequence itself. The *magnus* faunas were recovered from Moffat Shale-type black shale lithologies interbedded with bentonite horizons which, despite the locally intense deformation, appear to be interbedded with the Gala 5 greywackes. Northwards from the Hooies and its complex faulting the greywacke sequence is overturned and consistently north younging. It is dominated by thickly bedded greywackes with interbedded units of laminated siltstones and thinly bedded greywackes. The greywackes are dominantly T*ab* and T*abc* turbidite units with individual beds in the thickness range 20 cm to 3 m. Erosive bases to the greywacke beds are common and amalgamation and cross-stratification are widely developed. Slump folding and intraformational conglomerates are sporadically present and the extensive assemblage of sedimentary features suggests the B2, C1 and C2 subfacies of Pickering et al. (1986). A characteristic measured section is shown in Figure 14c. Deposition within a system of channels and sheet flows was deduced by Kelling et al. (1987). The exposed Gala 5 sequence is about 900 m thick (McCurry, 1990) and the palaeocurrent pattern, although quite variable, suggests that turbidity flow was predominantly to the south-west, axially along the depositional basin (Figure 15c). A palaeontological curiousity of the Gala 5 sequence is the detrital coral clast described from one of the greywacke beds by Scrutton and McCurry (1987) as *Ceriaster* sp., a form previously known only from the late Llandovery of Asiatic Russia and China.

GALA 6 (Grennan Point Formation)

A complex fault zone approximately 1 km wide marks the structural base of the Gala 6 unit (Figure 5). Within this fault zone, best exposed on the west coast of the Rhins at Drumbreddan Bay [NX 078 437] after which it is named, inliers of Moffat Shale Group strata are tectonically imbricated with the base of the greywacke sequence (Figure 9b illustrates the outcrops of the two northernmost inliers). The black shale and interbedded chert and bentonite horizons range in age from the late Ordovician *persculptus* Biozone to the mid-Llandovery *convolutus* Biozone; the latter provides a maximum age for the overlying Gala 6 greywackes (Figure 6). The Ordovician strata (Hartfell Shale) are contained within the northernmost inlier and are exposed in the bay north of Grennan Point [NX 0750 4385] as part of a faulted anticline surrounded by sheared and tightly folded Llandovery (Birkhill Shale) strata. Here the Moffat Shale outcrop is about 150–200 m wide although much of its thickness is probably due to repetition of the shale sequence by imbricate thrust faulting and tight folding. Both north and south margins of this shale sequence are probably faulted. However, at the northern end of Drumbreddan Bay [NX 0775 4377] 12 m of Birkhill Shale are conformably overlain to the north by Gala 6 greywackes and are only intensely faulted along their southern margin. The two more southerly Moffat Shale outcrops [NX 0777 4360 and 0779 4300] are both about 10 m wide and are not sufficiently well exposed to allow deduction of the stratigraphical relationships with the associated Gala 6 greywackes. However, from the overall relationships it appears that a few metres of grey shale and laminated siltstone overlie the Moffat Shale lithologies. These in turn are conformably succeeded by greywackes, with bedding thickness in the range 10 cm to 1.5 m, and interbedded units of laminated siltstone up to about 75 cm thick. Rarely the siltstones contain thin beds of pale grey and red shale. A representative section through the greywacke sequence is shown in Figure 14d. The greywackes are only moderately well graded and erosive bases are no more common than planar bases to the thicker beds, most of which are T*ab* or T*abc* turbidite units of the C1 and C2 subfacies defined by Pickering et al. (1986). The Gala 6 greywacke sequence has been estimated at between 300 and 600 m thick by McCurry (1990). The assemblage of sedimentary features suggested to Kelling et al. (1987) that deposition was predominantly from sheet flows with some minor channeling. Palaeocurrent evidence (Figure 15d) suggests that turbidity flow was predominantly towards the south-west.

GALA 7 (Mull of Logan Formation)

The Gala 7 tectonostratigraphical unit is the most variable within the Group; four distinct members have been recognised and described by Davies (1990) and McCurry (1990). No Moffat Shale lithologies are exposed at the presumed base of the sequence which extends northwards from the 700 m wide bay of Port Logan (Figure 5). A major back thrust (the Port Logan Fault) is believed to underlie this bay and mark the southern margin of the Gala 7 unit. Age control is provided by a sparse graptolite fauna from near Cairnie Finnart [NX 088 415] assigned to the *turriculatus* Biozone.

The four members of the Gala 7 unit form a northward younging conformable sequence internally disturbed only locally by minor faulting. The oldest Cairnie Finnart member is about 350 m thick and is composed dominantly of graded greywacke beds 5 to 50 cm thick, with sporadic intercalations of siltstone. Associated with these are thin shale laminae which may be grey, reddish purple or green. The greywacke beds are generally tabular or broadly lenticular and only rarely are their bed bases strongly erosive. There are many features indicative of dewatering, such as sand volcanoes, and slump structures are sporadically developed. Palaeocurrent indicators show turbidity flow towards the west (Figure 15e). A representative section through the 'Cairnie Finnart member' is shown in Figure 14f. The assemblage of sedimentary features suggests deposition in the C2 subfacies of Pickering et al. (1986) probably as part of a suprafan lobe (Kelling et al., 1987).

On the west coast of the Rhins in the vicinity of Yellnowte Isle [NX 082 417] the thin- to medium-bedded greywackes of the 'Cairnie Finnart member' are overlain conformably by about 500 m of coarse-grained, very thickly bedded to massive greywackes locally termed the 'Daw Point member'. Bedding in this sequence is not always readily apparent and ranges up to almost 8 m in thickness, probably as a result of amalgamation. Erosive bed bases are common, particularly in the lower part of the sequence, and the base of the member is marked by a thin intraformational conglomerate. Higher in the member there is a marked decrease in the average bed thickness and units of laminated siltstone appear interbedded with the greywackes. The overall assemblage of sedimentary features, illustrated in the representative section (Figure 14e), indicates deposition in a channelised environment. The lower part of the 'Daw Point member' has thickly bedded and coarse-grained greywacke units representing the fills of stacked channels. In the upper part of the member the laminated siltstone units are representative of channel and interchannel or overbank deposits. The overall sedimentary association can be linked to the B2 subfacies described by Pickering et al. (1986).

The 'Daw Point member' is overlain abruptly by about 550 m of exceptionally coarse, internally disorganised conglomerate containing subangular to rounded clasts of exclusively intrabasinal origin. This has been locally termed the 'Duniehinnie member'. The clasts range in size up to 10 m diameter and are usually matrix supported although the nature of the matrix varies from coarse sandstone to mudstone. Coarse greywacke beds up to about 3 m thick are sporadically interbedded with the conglomerate as are very rare units of thinly bedded greywacke and siltstone up to 50 cm thick. However, neither the bases of the coarse conglomerates above these interbeds nor the base of the conglomeratic member show significant erosion into the underlying beds. Overall the assemblage of sedimentary features suggests deposition from debris flow and high-density sheet flows over the flanks of a large debris cone (Kelling et al., 1987) developed in the A1 subfacies of Pickering et al. (1986). Palaeocurrents and lateral sedimentological changes within the member suggest movement of the flows towards the north-east although for the most part deposition probably took place in a series of small ponded basins.

Conformably overlying the 'Duniehinnie member' conglomerates are about 450 m of greywackes and siltstones locally known as the 'Chair member'. Greywacke is the dominant lithology and most commonly forms tabular well-graded beds between 20 and 80 cm thick. Sporadic thicker beds range up to 3 m, probably as a result of amalgamation, and rare intraclast conglomerates 50–150 cm thick and thin interbedded siltstones also occur. A representative section is shown in Figure 14g. The siltstone rarely exceeds 15 m in thickness but one exceptional development exposed near Parker's Point [NX 077 434] is almost 100 m thick. The siltstones are locally associated with red and green shale laminae. The 'Chair member' greywackes, mostly T*ab* or T*abc* turbidite units of the C2 subfacies (Pickering et al., 1986), have been interpreted as a lobe and minor channel association by Kelling et al. (1987). The lobe deposits are parallel sided, moderately well graded and occasionally arranged into thickening- and coarsening-upwards cycles. The minor channel deposits have erosive bases, are commonly amalgamated and have slumped horizons and minor intraclast rudites interbedded with them. The laminated siltstone units were most probably deposited in an inter-channel or lobe fringe environment. At Black Port [NX 0772 4285] Scrutton and McCurry (1987) recorded a floated-in specimen of the Telychian tabulate coral *Propora edwardsi*.

GALA 8 (Port Logan Formation)

The greywackes of the Gala 8 unit overlie Moffat Shale Group lithologies at the northern side of Clanyard Bay [NX 101 380]. The Clanyard Bay Fault Zone is particularly complex, involving a coincidence of back thrusting with the typical Southern Uplands southward-propagating structures. However, the northernmost of the several shale imbricates present follows the conventional pattern, being faulted on its southern margin and conformably merging with greywackes to the north. Graptolite faunas from this northermost shale inlier range from a possible Ashgill assemblage up to at least the Llandovery *sedgwickii* Biozone and possibly to the lowermost

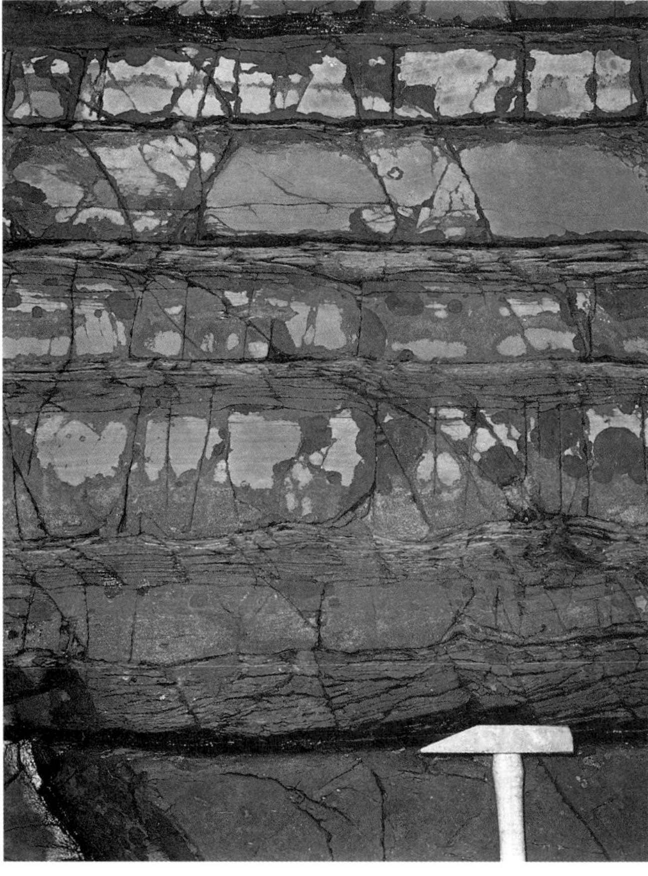

Plate 7 Well-defined turbidite units of the Gala Group (tectonostratigraphical unit 8) near Port Logan [NX 092 402] (D 4059).

turriculatus Biozone (Figure 6). This provides a maximum age for the greywacke sequence but the greater part of the *turriculatus* Biozone is unproven; significantly younger *crispus* Biozone faunas occur in interbedded mudstone horizons within the greywacke sequence at Grennan Quarries [NX 1267 3943 and 1258 3932] and Dunbuck [NX 0955 3850].

The Gala 8 unit is at least 800 m thick and is dominated by greywacke beds 20 cm to 1 m thick (Plate 7), with sporadic thicker beds ranging up to 3 m. A representative measured section is shown in Figure 14h. Greywackes are usually T*ab* or T*abc* turbidite units with some beds showing the full T*a–e* development. Erosive bases to the beds are common and bottom structures are well developed. Units of thinly bedded greywacke, siltstone and shale are widely interbedded with the greywacke and generally range from less than 1 m to about 5 m thick. However, locally the siltstone and shale association exposed on the coastal section exceeds 100 m in thickness and has been given member status (McCurry, 1990). In the vicinity of Slate Heugh [NX 093 396] 120 m of blue-grey mudstone and laminated siltstone interbedded with pale, very thin carbonate laminae and thin (less than 2 cm) greywacke beds forms the 'Slate Heugh member'. Between 50 and 100 m stratigraphically above this member, another very similar unit crops out in the vicinity of Green Saddle [NX 093 393]. This 'Green Saddle member' is about 135 m thick and is marked by beds of dark grey chert up to 10 cm thick within the shale and siltstone. At the stratigraphical top of the Gala 8 unit a third mudstone/shale/siltstone sequence the 'Strones Bay member' crops out around Strones Bay [NX 095 387] and contains the *crispus* Biozone graptolite faunas. This member is principally composed of blue-grey mudstone with thin (<10 cm) interbeds of laminated siltstone. Locally the siltstones are associated with fine-grained greywacke beds which may be as much as 50 cm thick.

In the turbidite classification scheme of Pickering et al. (1986) the greywackes mostly fall within the C2 subfacies, whereas the mudstone/siltstone interbeds fall within either the D2 or E2 subfacies. The assemblage of sedimentary features suggested to Kelling et al. (1987) that deposition took place in a channelised environment, with both channel-fill and channel-levée sequences present, intimately associated with thick units of fan-margin silts. This implies that the succession was formed in a mixed-sediment to mud-rich fan system but the presence of interbedded chert in the 'Green Saddle member' perhaps implies interchannel deposition or more distal, pelagic sedimentation. Palaeocurrent data derived from bottom structures in the channelised greywackes shows fairly consistent turbidity flow towards the south-west (Figure 15f). Paradoxically cross-lamination high in the greywacke beds and the associated ripples exposed on numerous bed tops show a trend perpendicular to this and imply current movement principally towards the south-east. This contradiction has been noted in many other turbidite sequences and has recently been taken by Kneller et al. (1991) as evidence of sedimentation in a laterally confined depositional system.

SIX

Silurian greywacke succession: Hawick Group

Greywacke sequences at the southern end of the Rhins of Galloway, south of the Clanyard Bay Fault Zone, are assigned to the Hawick Group. Two formations are recognised, the Cairnharrow Formation in the north and the Carghidown Formation in the south forming the Mull of Galloway headland (Figure 5). Correlation of the lithologically distinctive Carghidown Formation is relatively secure but the status of the strata assigned to the Cairnharrow Formation is more ambiguous. This latter sequence has previously been regarded as the southernmost unit of the Gala Group (e.g. McCurry, 1990 and in Barnes et al., 1987) and given the title Clanyard Bay Formation. However, one characteristic of the Hawick Group greywackes is a markedly calcareous matrix and this phenomenon has now been noted farther north-east in the Gatehouse of Fleet district (Sheets 4E and 5W) in the greywacke sequence immediately south of the equivalent there of the Clanyard Bay Fault Zone. On that basis the Hawick Group has been extended by White et al. (1992 for 1991) and the Cairnharrow Formation defined. In this account the structural correlation is maintained to the Rhins of Galloway and the strata south of Clanyard Bay accordingly assigned to the Cairnharrow Formation. Three local aspects of the geology of the southern Rhins of Galloway further complicate the correlation of the Cairnharrow Formation.

1. Farther north-east the Hawick Group has three component formations, the Kirkmaiden Formation intervening between the Cairnharrow and the Carghidown formations. This lateral variation has been explained as a facies change between the Kirkmaiden and Carghidown formations which therefore, for at least part of their outcrop, occupy the same structural unit in the imbricate thrust stack (Barnes, 1989, fig. 4).

2. The Cairnharrow Formation has been intruded by the Portencorkrie complex (Chapter Eight) and is extensively hornfelsed. This complicates lithological correlation.

3. The Hawick Group strata on the Rhins of Galloway, south of the Clanyard Bay Fault Zone, occupy an anomalous structural position involving north-directed thrusting in opposition to the south-directed regional pattern (discussed more fully in Chapter Seven). Correlation based on deduced structural position is therefore made more difficult but, since the Cairnharrow and Carghidown formations are both equally affected, the principle is not negated.

CAIRNHARROW FORMATION

The strata south of the Clanyard Bay Fault zone form a mainly south-younging sequence terminated in the south by a major strike fault across which the younger Carghidown Formation is juxtaposed. The sequence has been previously described as the Clanyard Block by Barnes et al. (1987) and the Clanyard Bay Formation (Port Mona member) by McCurry (1990). Its inclusion within the Hawick Group is based on along-strike facies comparisons and the presence of a widely developed calcareous matrix in the greywackes (White et al., 1992). Maximum age control is provided by the underlying Moffat Shale Group which, at the south side of Clanyard Bay [NX 097 377], is exposed as a south-younging assemblage ranging from the *cyphus* to the *convolutus* Biozones. The greywacke/shale contact is tectonised and, by correlation with supposedly comparable strata farther north-east, the greywackes of the Cairnharrow Formation on the Rhins are most likely to be of rather younger, *turriculatus* Biozone or *crispus* Biozone age (Figure 6).

The Cairnharrow Formation, as exposed on the Rhins of Galloway, is about 1000 m thick and is dominantly composed of turbidite greywackes with variable bed thickness. Compositionally the greywackes are fairly felsic; quartz forms about 30 per cent of the clasts (Figure 16), feldspar (principally plagioclase) ranges from about 8 per cent to 15 per cent and fine-grained acid igneous lithic clasts form between 5 and 10 per cent. Most of the greywackes studied in detail also contain a small proportion, usually 1 or 2 per cent each, of basaltic, low-grade metamorphic and sedimentary lithologies. Palaeocurrent flow, deduced from bottom structures, suggests that most depositing currents flowed towards the north or north-west with a minority showing the reverse sense of flow towards the south (Figure 17a).

The greywackes immediately overlying the Moffat Shale Group and forming the base of the Cairnharrow Formation are generally bedded in the range 50 cm to 1 m. Beds are T*ab* or T*abc* turbidite units of the C2 subfacies of Pickering et al. (1986), commonly with the laminated divisions particularly well developed. Interbedded sequences of dark grey interlaminated mudstone and siltstone up to 40 m thick occur locally with sporadic pale-weathering carbonate-rich laminae and black shale horizons up to 50 cm thick. The apparent absence of diagnostic graptolite faunas in these black shales is probably the result of hornfelsing in the contact zone of the Portencorkrie intrusive complex. Higher in the succession (the Port Mona member of McCurry, 1990) bedding becomes more variable, locally very thin or quite massive with an overall range of 5 cm to 2.5 m. The average bedding thickness decreases markedly towards the top of the formation (southern part of the outcrop), where the average bedding thickness is about 25–30 cm and the fine-grained greywackes and laminated siltstones (commonly in T*bcd* units) are interbedded with dark mudstone laminae.

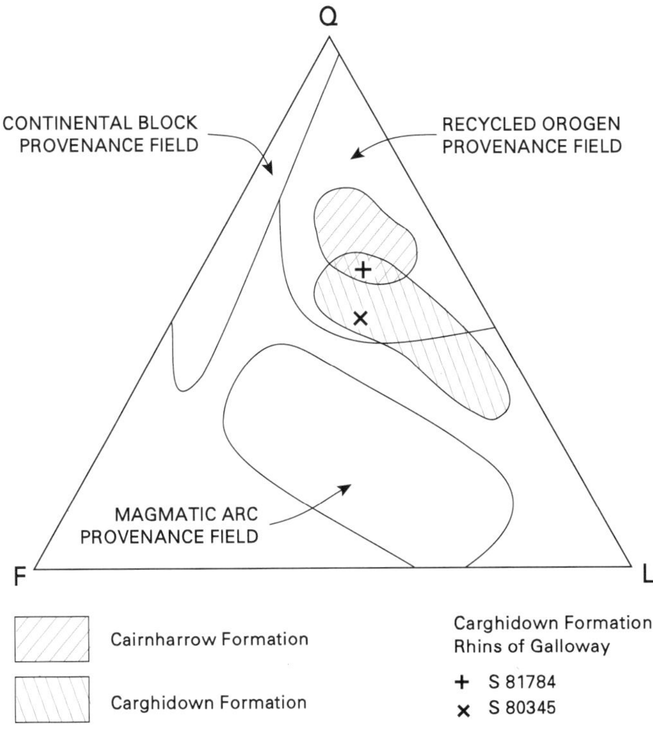

Figure 16 Compositional range of Hawick Group greywackes. Provenance fields from Dickinson and Suczek (1979).

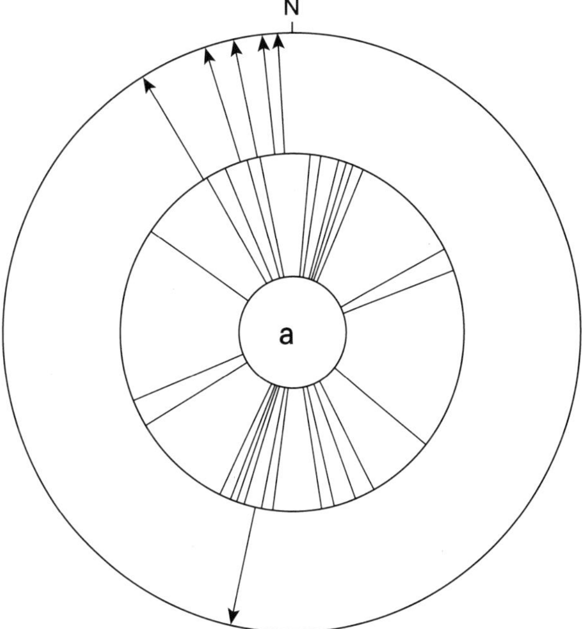

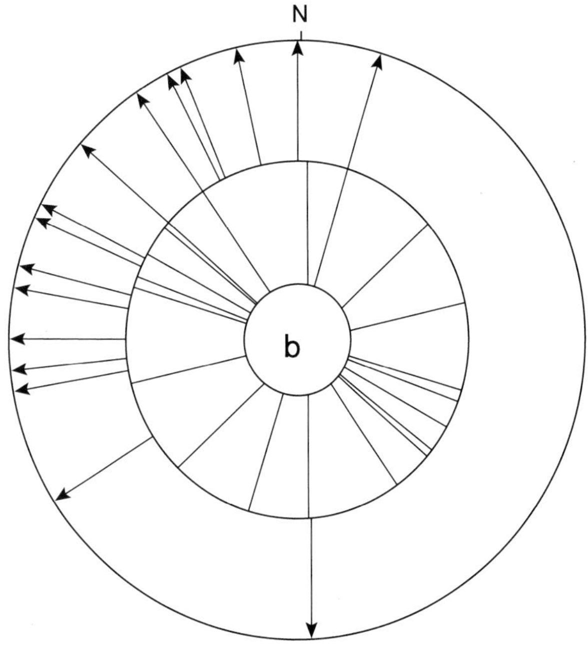

Figure 17 Palaeocurrent data from the Hawick Group (structurally corrected) after McCurry (1990).

CARGHIDOWN FORMATION

In the Rhins of Galloway district the Carghidown Formation is devoid of biostratigraphically diagnostic faunas or floras. The best lithological correlation, based on the presence of a calcareous matrix to the greywackes and interbedded red mudstones, is with a *crenulata* Biozone sequence farther north-east in the Southern Uplands (White et al., 1992). This is the basis for the age assigned in Figure 6. However, the sequence farther north-east lies in a structural zone to the south of that occupied by the Rhins Carghidown Formation and the implication of the facies variation model is that the Rhins Carghidown Formation could be as old as the *griestoniensis* Biozone, the age of the Kirkmaiden Formation on the Whithorn promontary (Barnes, 1989; White et al., 1992 for 1991).

Whatever the age, the Carghidown Formation on the Rhins of Galloway is at least 1250 m thick (McCurry, 1990) and consists principally of thinly bedded greywackes. The most marked compositonal feature of these greywackes is their high matrix-carbonate content but in terms of their clast compositon they are very similar to the greywackes of the Cairnharrow Formation. Quartz, comprising both mono- and polycrystalline grains with some strained quartzites, forms about 30 per cent of the clasts with feldspar, mainly plagioclase, forming about 10 per cent (Figure 16). Lithic clasts are principally fine-grained acid igneous lithologies, variably between 5 and 10 per cent, with a few percent of basic igneous, low-grade metamorphic and sedimentary lithologies usually present. Red haematite-coated biotite grains are a common and distinctive accessory. From the evidence of bottom structures the turbidity currents depositing these greywackes had a provenance broadly east or south-east of the depositonal area (Figure 17b).

The succession is dominated by T*ab*, T*abc* and T*bc* greywacke turbidite units with bed thickness generally in the 10 cm to 40 cm range and only rarely exceeding 70 cm. The lower part of the succession (the north of the outcrop) contains a high proportion of lenticular beds in channelised sequences but generally bedding is regular and parallel sided; it can be related to the C2 subfacies of Pickering et al. (1986). The distinctive red mudstone interbeds are ubiquitous but generally thin, ranging up to about 5 cm. The red mudstone occurs interbedded with grey-green silty mudstone, against which the bed margins are diffuse, mottled and/or interlaminated. The red mudstone beds are internally structureless and laterally very persistent. A primary origin for the red colouration is supported by the occurrence of patches of red mudstone mixed with green mudstone within rare small-scale slump units.

SEVEN

Caledonian structure

At the end of the 19th century Peach and Horne had completed their revision survey of the Southern Uplands and had published their monumental Memoir (Peach and Horne, 1899). Impressed by the generally steep bedding attitude and the widespread minor fold hinges, their structural interpretation envisaged upright, tight to isoclinal folding throughout the region. The work of Lapworth (1878) had shown that in biostratigraphical terms the oldest Southern Uplands strata cropped out in the north-west and the youngest in the south-east; to accommodate this Peach and Horne proposed that the ubiquitous tight folding was disposed in anticlinoria–synclinoria systems. Advances in sedimentological understanding during the middle part of this century showed Peach and Horne's interpretation to be erroneous. Kelling (1961) in the Rhins of Galloway and Walton (1955) in Peeblesshire established compositional differences in the various greywacke sequences which constrained the interpreted fold geometries. Further, extensive tracts of the Southern Uplands proved to have a uniform direction of younging, in steeply inclined beds, and thus an absence of major folding. That younging direction was usually towards the north-west and hence appeared to contradict the biostratigraphical evidence. However, elsewhere in the region extensive folding was confirmed and the overall fold geometry and attitude suggested that there was little variation in exposed stratigraphical level across the folded zones. From this re-interpretation Craig and Walton (1959) conceived the Southern Uplands structure as a series of large NE–SW-trending monoforms, the steeply inclined but unfolded limbs to the north-west of the flat-lying but folded limbs; these in turn were truncated to the south-east by major strike faults downthrowing to the south-east to satisfy the biostratigraphical evidence.

The presence of major strike faults and a refined interpretation of the biostratigraphy, noting the sequential decrease in age from north-west to south-east (Figure 6), were central to the accretionary prism model for the Southern Uplands proposed by Leggett et al. (1979). Subsequent discussion of the terrane in these terms has tended to accentuate the structurally uniform 'steep' belts as accretionary tracts within a prism created as successively younger slices were underthrust at a subduction trench. A rider to this model was a progressive rotational steepening of dip northwards within the prism hinterland; this is not observed and, indeed, the presence of the 'flat' folded zones is a further complication, a problem emphasised by Walton (1983, pp.159–160). Nevertheless, the observed structure is very similar to that seen in some modern accretionary complexes such as the Aleutian–Kodiak terrane (Sample and Moore, 1987).

A structural model for the Ettrick and Moffatdale areas developed by Webb (1983) envisaged the steeply dipping, uniformly younging sequences as a series of horses within a thrust duplex formed by the sequential shearing-out of one fold limb during rotation. An overall imbricate thrust pattern was also deduced by Fyfe and Weir (1976) at Craigmichan Scaur, in Moffatdale. This was fundamental to the thin-skinned, back-arc to foreland-basin thrust model for the Southern Uplands proposed by Stone et al. (1987). All of these thrust-related interpretations envisaged dominantly SE-directed overthrusting but a significant variation on this pattern is seen in south-west Scotland where NW-directed thrusts and SE-younging greywacke units interrupt the regional pattern. The most extensive development of this structural style occurs at the southern end of the Rhins of Galloway where McCurry and Anderson (1989) considered the switch to NW-directed thrusting to result from a change to obduction at the leading edge of an accretionary prism built up by previous underthrusting during subduction.

Detailed structural studies in the south-west part of the Southern Uplands have confirmed the trend towards interpretation of the region's structure in terms of thrust tectonics. Early 'modern' investigations concentrated on the recognition of a number of successive deformation phases (e.g. Rust, 1965) but were complicated by a non-axial planar cleavage and wide areas in which bedding was downward-facing on the cleavage. This problem was partially resolved with the recognition of the fabric as a transecting cleavage developed by rotation of the stress field after folding; Stringer and Treagus (1980) provided a number of examples of this phenomenon in folded sections through the Southern Uplands including sections on the Rhins of Galloway. Rotation of the stress field was linked with an increasing element of sinistral strike-slip in association with thrusting but the progressive nature of the deformation has also been stressed (e.g. Eales, 1979; Knipe et al., 1988) such that the early thrust-related deformation at the thrust front was synchronous with subsequent refolding and adjustment within the thrust hinterland. The strike-slip element involved was superimposed on earlier structures within the hinterland but was contemporaneous with the thrust-related folding at the southern margin of the Southern Uplands from about the late Llandovery (Barnes et al., 1989).

REGIONAL STRUCTURAL PROFILE

A continuous structural cross-section along the Rhins of Galloway is shown on the 1:50 000 Geological Sheet 1 and 3 accompanying this memoir. The section runs from the Llandeilo–Caradoc *N. gracilis* Biozone Corsewall Formation (Leadhills Group) in the north-west, across strike through the Northern and Central belts of the Southern

Uplands, to the uppermost Llandovery *?M. crenulata* Biozone Carghidown Formation (Hawick Group) in the south-east. Structural zonation is marked, with discrete domains having characteristic structural style separated from each other by strike faults. These faults may coincide with lithostratigraphical breaks or may lie entirely within lithostratigraphical formations. Using attitude of bedding, younging direction and fold geometry it is possible to recognise four basic structural patterns. As part of their definition the concept of fold vergence is useful and in this account vergence is defined as follows: a fold pair is said to verge in the direction (perpendicular to the fold hinge) in which a major anticline might be expected. It is an indication of movement sense during deformation (cf. Bell, 1981).

The structural patterns form distinct zones as shown on Figure 18. They are defined below:

Type 1 Uniform, usually steeply inclined or vertical bedding younging consistently northward. The regular pattern of strike and dip is locally interrupted by sporadic south-verging fold pairs.

Type 2 Continuous sequences of south-verging, small- to medium-scale folds separated by minor shears and/or narrow unfolded units of steeply inclined bedding younging northward. Most of the folds are tight or close with axial planes steeply inclined and fold hinges which generally plunge gently; some folds are periclinal.

Type 3 Continuous sequences of close to open folds, ranging considerably in wavelength and amplitude but geometrically neutral; i.e. with no preferred sense of vergence. Axial planes are upright or steeply inclined and fold hinges plunge gently.

Type 4 Continuous sequences of north-verging, small- to medium-scale folds separated by minor shears and/or unfolded units of steeply inclined bedding younging southward. Most of the folds are tight with axial planes steeply inclined and fold hinges which generally plunge gently but which are locally highly variable.

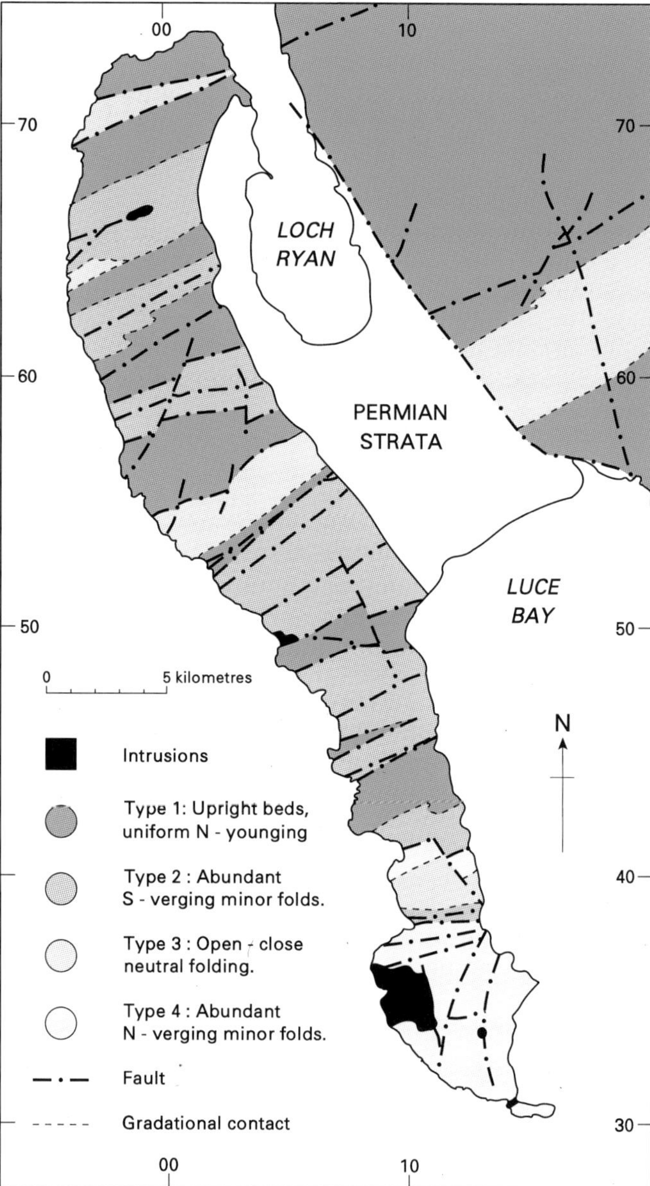

Figure 18 Structural zonation map for the Rhins of Galloway district.

Within that part of the Southern Uplands thrust belt exposed in the Rhins of Galloway area the boundaries between structural zones may either be sharply defined by major faults or they may be more gradational. Thus zones 1 and 2 may merge locally and are clearly related in terms of their origin. Similarly the examples of neutral folding in zone 3 may be regarded as structures formed in the short flat-lying limbs of major south-verging fold pairs in which the major hinges themselves have been faulted out. The greatest structural contrast, therefore, lies between the combined zones 1, 2 and 3, all of which may be related to southward-directed thrusting, and zone 4 which is related to northward-directed thrusting. The northward-directed thrusts are interpreted as back thrusts developing within the thrust hinterland and producing local pop-up structures. The along-strike variation between zones can best be explained in terms of the exposure of varying structural depths within the thrust stack. Neutral zones (3) are likely to be underlain by blind thrusts which, if exposed, would form south-verging zones (2). The south-verging zones (2) contain many small shear zones which probably formed as hanging-wall detachments during thrusting; these may die out downwards as a uniform bedding attitude (1) becomes dominant. The basal décollement of the thrust belt formed initially within the Moffat Shale Group but must have cut up-section during the later stages of thrusting. These deduced relationships are shown diagrammatically in Figure 19. The structural principles follow those discussed by Butler (1982), whilst the concept of blind thrusting and related cover deformation follows Dunne and Ferrill (1988) and Ferrill and Dunne (1989). It should be stressed that structural style

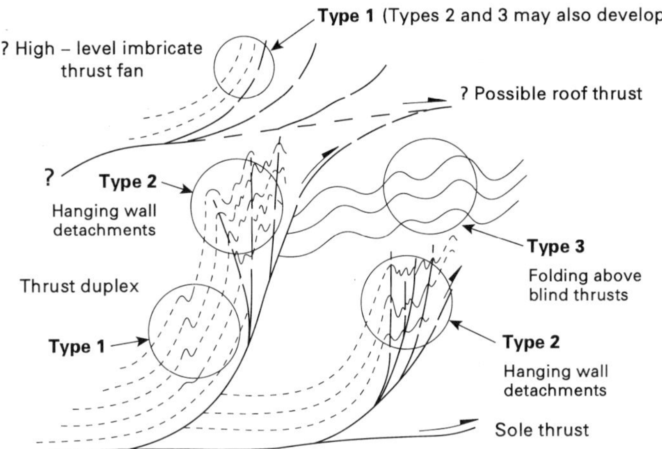

Figure 19 Variation in structural style within a developing thrust stack. Structural style is not linked with absolute depth within the thrust stack but with the overall geometry of the major thrust planes.

is not linked with absolute depth within the thrust stack but with the overall geometry of the major thrust planes. The structural pattern described is consistent with both of the principal developmental models for the Southern Uplands shown in Figures 3 and 4: accretionary prism (Leggett et al., 1979) or back-arc to foreland-basin thrust belt (Stone et al., 1987). The earlier structural cross-section figured by Kelling (1961, Figure 8) is incompatible with a detailed analysis of the minor fold domains.

Additional or syn-thrusting strike-slip effects have also undoubtedly occurred, although their magnitude is difficult to quantify. Anderson and Oliver (1986) identified the Cairngarroch Fault as a locus of such movement and regarded it as the continuation of the Orlock Bridge Fault which, in Northern Ireland, marks a major stratigraphical break. The status of the Cairngarroch Fault as the local Ordovician-Silurian boundary is confirmed but it does not trend parallel to the stratigraphical boundaries in the Silurian (at least) and so the effective stratigraphical break in fact decreases north-east in the Rhins of Galloway area: Shinnel Formation against Gala 3 in the south-west and Shinnel Formation against Gala 1 in the north-east (Figure 5). Thus a larger stratigraphical gap might be expected to the south-west in Ireland across the Orlock Bridge Fault (Anderson and Oliver, 1986) whereas the gap appears to decrease further towards the north-east. There recent work by Floyd and Rushton (1993) has demonstrated that *anceps* biozone Ordovician strata are faulted against *acuminatus* Biozone Silurian strata.

The structural evidence for post-thrusting (and in the northern part of the region post-cleavage) sinistral strike-slip movement is widespread and is not restricted to the vicinity of any particular lineaments. The strike-slip event has been described in recent discussion (e.g. Barnes et al., 1989) and assigned to the earliest Wenlock. Hence the final thrust episodes at the southern margin of the Southern Uplands were contemporaneous with sinistral strike slip, presumably in response to an increasingly oblique stress regime. The minor fold hinges formed at that time in the southern structural zones are thus more variable and curvilinear than those formed earlier in the northern zones. Since it is not possible to quantify relative movements by thrusting or strike slip, the apparent importance of any one strike fault may be the result of either or a combination of the two. This uncertainty applies equally to all of the major strike faults including the Orlock Bridge-Cairngarroch Fault, the status of which as a major terrane boundary is still open to question (cf. discussion by Floyd et al., 1987), particularly since the identification of an *anceps* Biozone fauna in the Shinnel Formation (Floyd and Rushton, 1993) (Figure 6) has significantly reduced the size of the apparent biostratigraphical break reported by Anderson and Oliver (1986).

LOCAL FOLDING PATTERNS

The preceding regional synthesis has concentrated on the first major thrust-related deformation which is the most important throughout the district. This can conveniently be designated the D_1 deformation event, although it would have been diachronous as the thrust front propagated southwards. The subsequent episode of strike-slip movement has also been mentioned but intervening between these in many parts of the Rhins of Galloway were minor folding and crenulation phases which locally produced the dominant structures and fabrics. These are regarded as accommodation structures formed in the thrust hinterland contemporaneously with the development of D_1 structures at the thrust front. They may conveniently be grouped together as products of a D_2 event but, like the D_1 thrusting, they would have been diachronous, with structures in the north of the thrust belt older than those in the south. The strike-slip shear episode is regarded as the D_3 deformation event, although it should be stressed that it was synchronous with the later stages of D_1 development in the south of the thrust belt and is therefore likely to be penecontemporaneous with (and possibly earlier than) some D_2 deformation in the thrust hinterland. These relationships have been partially quantified by Barnes et al. (1989) and are summarised in Figure 20.

The D_{1-3} designation will be used in the following description of the local structure but the relative time connotations in such a diachronous deformation sequence must be remembered. The structure is reviewed sequentially within each of the major thrust-defined tectonostratigraphical units or tracts. The text is intended for use in conjunction with the 1:50 000 Rhins of Galloway Geological Sheet. Generalised structural sections through parts of the Leadhills Group have also been figured and discussed by Needham (1993).

LEADHILLS GROUP

Corsewall Formation

The northern part of this structural unit contains uniform upright bedding with a regular strike of about 060°

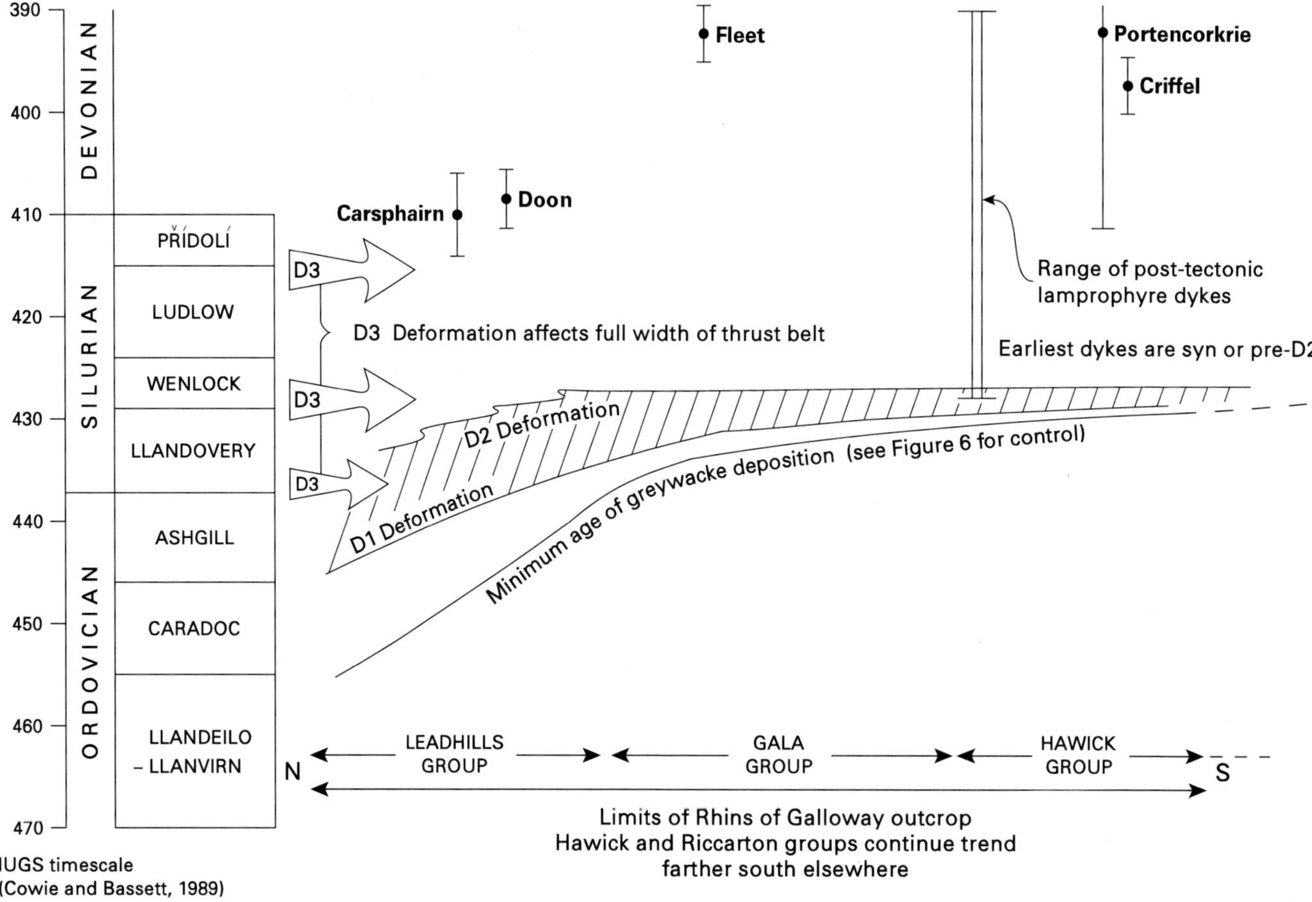

Figure 20 Summary of data controlling the timing of deformation in the Southern Uplands thrust belt (qv Barnes et al., 1989, fig. 1).

Ages of post-tectonic plutons:

Carsphairn	: 410 ± 4, Rb-Sr, Thirlwall (1988)	Criffell	: 397 ± 2, Rb-Sr, Halliday et al. (1980)
Loch Doon	: 408 ± 2, Rb-Sr, Halliday et al. (1980)	Portencorkrie	: this memoir, Chapter Eight
Fleet	: 392 ± 2, Rb-Sr, Halliday at al. (1980)	Dyke ages	: Rb-Sr and K-Ar, Rock et al. (1986)

and a consistent sense of younging towards the north-west. These characteristics are typical of Type 1 structural zones and are believed to have resulted in part from block rotation during D_1 thrust-related deformation. A major strike fault marks the southern margin of this Type 1 zone and separates the upright NW-younging beds from SE-younging moderately inclined south-dipping beds. These SE-younging beds form the north limb of a major, open D_1 syncline on the limbs of which are minor congruous fold structures. Cleavage is not well developed. The large syncline is exposed on the west coast of the Rhins but the convergence of strike faults cuts out all of the south-dipping limb on the east coast, north of Lady Bay [NX 026 718]. There the bedding is consistently steeply inclined and NW-younging. Farther north-east, on the east side of Loch Ryan north of Finnarts Bay [NX 048 728], the bedding is also steeply inclined and predominantly NW-younging but the presence of more minor, south-verging fold pairs suggests a transition to Type 2 structure. Taken in isolation the Corsewall Formation syncline is a neutral, Type 3, structure (Figure 18) but it can also be regarded as part of a large-scale south-verging fold pair, the anticlinal hinge of which has been removed by faulting. On this basis the total poles to bedding for the Corsewall Formation are shown stereographically in Figure 21a and define a fold hinge plunging gently ENE.

The southern margin of the Corsewall Formation is marked by the Glen App Fault, one of the few strike faults to be fairly well exposed and thus amenable to kinematic analysis. The exposed fault zone at Finnarts Bay [NX 052 726] shows minor folding about steeply plunging hinges and vein arrays compatible with both sinistral and dextral movement, the former generally preceding the latter. On the opposite side of Loch Ryan in Lady Bay [NX 026 718] the exposed Glen App Fault Zone shows a sinistral sense of rotational extension between fault splays and the development of a sinistral S-C fabric. Farther south-west in Dounan Bay [NW 967 688] sinistral shear is confirmed by the asymmetry of tight minor folding about vertical hinges and by the geometry of quartz vein arrays. Quartz veins cut by fault zones con-

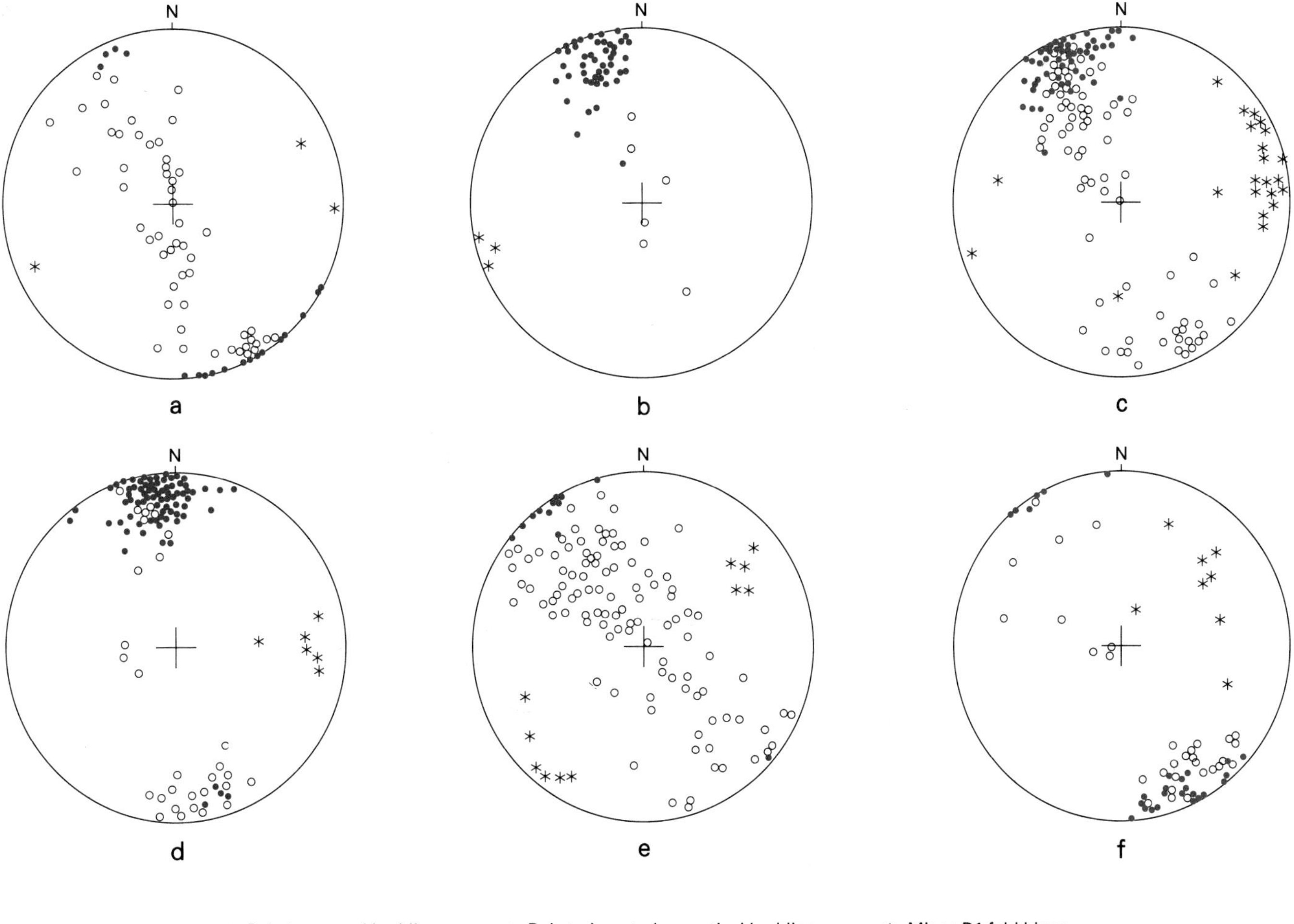

Figure 21 Summary of D_1 structural data for the Leadhills Group.

a. Corsewall Formation.
b. Kirkcolm Formation for about 2 km north from Portobello [NW 961 663].
c. Kirkcolm Formation for about 3 km north from Broadsea Bay [NW 973 600].
d. Portpatrick Formation north of Portpatrick [NW 999 541].
e. Portpatrick Formation south of Portpatrick.
f. Shinnel Formation between Morroch Bay [NX 020 520] and Portayew [NX 038 505].

taining several centimetres of clay gouge are evidence for possible relatively late reactivation of movement. Most of the sinistral shear evident along the Glen App Fault probably occurred during the D_3 deformation episode.

Kirkcolm Formation

The lower Kirkcolm Formation tectonostratigraphical unit (or units) contains an alternation of structural Types 1 and 2. Zones of uniformly steeply inclined and usually slightly overturned NW-younging strata (Frontispiece) are intercalated with zones in which south-verging minor folding dominates, although the overall younging sense is still to the north-west. In some cases the boundary between the two structural types is very abrupt and is probably a zone of minor strike faulting; elsewhere the zones appear to merge, with one style gradational to the other over a distance of some tens of metres. The alternation of types occurs on all scales and the distribution shown in Figure 18 is a generalisation; Type 2 is taken to replace Type 1 when more than about 30 per cent of the cross-strike section is affected by minor south-verging folds. The scale of the minor folding present is also very variable and the D_1 south-verging fold pairs may have amplitude and wavelength ranging from a few centimetres to several tens of metres. This is partly controlled by lithology, with the larger folds tending to be restricted to sequences of more thickly bedded greywacke with only a small shale/siltstone component. All these D_1 structures have an associated weak locally developed axial-planar slaty cleavage. Their geometry is summarised and contrasted with that of Type 1 structures, in the two stereograms in Figure 21 (b and c) illustrating typical sections from the west coast of the Rhins of Galloway: north from Portobello [NW 961 663] for Type 1 and north from Broadsea Bay [NW 973 600] for Type 2. Farther north-east, on the eastern side of Loch Ryan, there is much less minor D_1 folding affecting the Kirkcolm Formation and all of the sequence there is regarded as essentially Type 1 structure (Figure 18). One of the few D_1 fold zones present is responsible for the broadening of the Galdenoch Formation outcrop east of Cairnryan [NX 095 690]. This may mean that a relatively deeper structural level (in terms of D_1) of the Kirkcolm Formation tectonostratigraphical units is exposed there.

Manifestations of D_2 deformation are fairly widespread within the lower Kirkcolm Formation unit as small north-directed back thrusts often associated with local north-verging minor fold pairs. No D_2 cleavage development has been observed. One complex zone south of Portobello [NW 960 662] shows the possible interaction of D_2 and D_3 deformation; there a north-verging fold pair has an extremely curvilinear hinge ranging from gentle to steep plunge towards the north-east in only a few metres. This structure affects thinly bedded greywackes and in general the effects of D_3 are only seen in such lithologies, or in the laminated siltstones commonly interbedded with the greywackes. There, sporadic small-scale tight or isoclinal folds plunge steeply and have a sinistral sense of asymmetry. A much larger scale variably plunging fold causes the arcuate outcrop of the Galdenoch Formation at Port Beg [NW 960 635] where there is also evidence for the folding of a very weakly developed slaty cleavage. However, in this case the folding is south-verging to dextral and its precise assignation to the deformation history remains unknown. At only one locality is a probable late cleavage developed; an apparently D_3 fabric on the east side of Loch Ryan south of Finnarts Bay [NX 052 722]. In this vicinity the greywackes are downward facing on a sporadically developed slaty cleavage with a spaced fabric developed nearby parallel to the axial plane of steeply plunging folds in laminated siltstone. The spaced fabric may be a product of the D_3 deformation episode, particularly since nearby D_1 folds have no associated cleavage, even in their hinge zones which plunge gently to the north-east.

The upper Kirkcolm Formation on the Rhins of Galloway is affected by Type 2 structures and to the east of Loch Ryan is fairly typical of Type 1. The same contrast therefore exists as was apparent with the lower part of the formation. A slaty cleavage is developed in places on the Rhins and appears to be axial planar to the south-verging minor folds. The folds themselves are tight to isoclinal with axes usually plunging gently to the south-west.

The southern margin of the lower Kirkcolm Formation tectonostratigraphical unit (or units) is marked by the imbricate zone of the Glaik Fault which crops out on the west coast of the Rhins south of Broadsea Bay [NW 976 588]. Intense shearing is localised in black shale and metabentonite of the Moffat Shale Group and no definitive kinematic indicators were observed. The southern margin of the upper Kirkcolm Formation is an imbricate zone exposed on the west coast of the Rhins between the Cable House [NW 980 581] and Knock Bay [NW 982 576]. At the former locality the Crailloch Fault is marked by zones of sheared chert and black mudstone, whilst at the north side of Knock Bay a complex zone of refolding affects thinly bedded greywacke. Fold hinges in this zone are variable but usually steeply plunging and the refolding seems associated with east–west dextral shear. The Killantringan Fault which forms the southern margin of this zone and separates the upper Kirkcolm Formation unit from the structurally underlying Portpatrick Formation, is not exposed.

Portpatrick Formation

The Portpatrick Formation tectonostratigraphical unit is divided into two distinct structural zones by a major strike fault exposed on the Rhins of Galloway at Portpatrick harbour [NW 997 542]. To the north the structure is typically Type 1 with vertical or steeply inclined bedding striking regularly ENE and younging northwards. Minor D_1 south-verging fold pairs, although rare, range considerably in size and throughout the section a penetrative slaty cleavage, dipping steeply to the south, is developed congruous with the bedding. The structural style is illustrated in the stereogram (Figure 21d) which summarises data from the west coast of the Rhins of Galloway.

At Portpatrick the southern boundary fault to the Type 1 zone is exposed in the sewer outfall adjacent to the harbour. Intensely sheared and quartz-veined black shale has experienced polyphase deformation with apparently multiple refolding of quartz veins. Fold hinges are mainly steeply plunging and fold asymmetry suggests dominantly sinistral shear movement. To the south of the Portpatrick Fault the structural style changes to Type 3: overall neutral vergence in a close to open, upright fold sequence with wavelengths ranging up to several hundred metres. The lateral persistence of this distinctive fold style is remarkable and similar trends are evident in cross-sections from the Rhins of Galloway and the Water of Luce area (Jackson, 1985), although the cross strike width of the Type 3 zone is greater in the eastern area. The Portpatrick Fault may thus be extrapolated through the vicinity of New Luce [NX 175 645] where it may coincide with the zone of quartz veining and minor steeply plunging late (?D_3) folds, with a weak axial-planar spaced cleavage and sinistral asymmetry, seen east of Cruise Farm [NX 187 628]. Both on the Rhins coast and in the New Luce area this Type 3 zone tends towards Type 2, south-verging structure, towards its southern margin. This tendancy is more marked in the east where fold-hinge plunge in the Water of Luce area is generally of 5–10° towards the north-east with an upright penetrative slaty cleavage striking north-east. Data from the Rhins of Galloway Type 3 zone are summarised in the stereogram (Figure 21e); folding is close to open with hinges gently NE-plunging in the north of the zone and gently SW-plunging in the south. A penetrative slaty cleavage is ubiquitous and, although markedly refracted through the graded greywacke beds (Plate 8), is generally steeply inclined. At one locality on the Rhins peninsula near The Swan [NX 010 527] small-scale, north-verging fold pairs locally affect both bedding and slaty cleavage and are probably the result of D_2 deformation.

The southern margin of the Portpatrick Formation tectonostratigraphical unit is marked by the broad fault zone which is exposed on the west coast of the Rhins between Morroch Bay [NX 018 522] and Port of Spittal Bay [NX 020 320]. The Moffat Shale Group is exposed at the base of the greywacke sequence and has been imbricated during the D_1 thrust deformation episode (see discussion in Chapter Three). Minor folds, invariably tight to isoclinal and often with sheared axial surfaces, have either subhorizontal or steeply inclined hinges. The former probably relate to the D_1 episode and, for the most part, are south-verging. A subhorizontal D_2 crenulation cleavage is very locally developed in the south of the zone. The steeply plunging folds are usually asymmetric in a sinistral sense and may relate to the D_3 episode, although no examples of fold interference were observed. The bulk of the deformation at all stages has probably been taken up along very thin and intensely sheared zones within the black shale and hyaloclastite sequence. These have an anastomosing habit with a geometry which locally suggests formation under a sinistral shear couple. The lowermost unit in the basal imbricate section of the Portpatrick Formation paradoxically has typical Type 1 structure; these steeply inclined beds between Morroch Bay and Port of Spittal Bay young consistently northwards and strike north-east.

Shinnel Formation

Two tectonostratigraphical units contain Shinnel Formation strata and in each the structural style is similar; Type 1 and Type 2 alternate on a local scale, with Type 2 dominant overall. This variation is partly controlled by lithology, with the more thinly bedded parts of the sequence showing the most minor folding. Fold hinges show a variable plunge towards the north-east. D_1 structural data is summarised in Figure 21f. Some of the D_1 structures are quite large, with wavelengths of several hundred metres, and in their limbs congruous minor folds are developed such that the overall younging and minor fold vergence appears to alternate across strike. All this is the result of D_1 deformation and should be differentiated from the small but fairly widespread, incongruously north-verging folds which also affect cleavage and are, therefore, probably a D_2 phenomenon. Two styles of D_2 minor folding are present, both apparently north-verging for the most part; fairly upright structures are most common in the northern unit, north of the Portayew Fault, whereas north-verging recumbent structures are most common in the southern unit, south of Portayew. In both cases it is unusual for either the amplitude or the wavelength of the folds to exceed 2 m. A penetrative slaty cleavage is developed in association with the D_1 folds; this is locally slightly transecting to be apparently axial planar in cross-section but rotated several degrees clockwise of the fold hinge line in plan view.

The Portayew Fault is the dividing line between the two tectonostratigraphical units of the Shinnel Formation. It is exposed on the west coast of the Rhins at Portayew [NX 039 504] as a zone of imbricated Moffat Shale Group strata containing numerous steeply inclined anas-

Plate 8 Marked cleavage refraction across graded turbidite units within the Portpatrick Formation near Tandoo Point [NX 005 530] (D 3747).

tomosing shear planes and variable small-scale tight folds. Intense but irregular brittle deformation is ubiquitous. The southern margin of the fault zone is in fact a south-directed thrust (cf. Kelling, 1961, fig. 8) which probably postdates the D_1 episode, and is most likely to be a later D_2 accommodation structure. Farther south, the southern tectonostratigraphical unit of the Shinnel Formation has the Cairngarroch Fault at its base. This fault has been described in detail by Anderson and Oliver (1986) as the continuation of the Orlock Bridge Fault from Northern Ireland; it is effectively the Ordovician–Silurian boundary and its regional significance has been discussed earlier in this chapter. Anderson and Oliver (1986) describe intense shearing, minor folding and S–C fabrics indicative of sinistral shear. On the west coast of the Rhins of Galloway the southern part of the tectonostratigraphical Shinnel Formation unit is intruded by the Cairngarroch igneous complex (Chapter Eight). The thermal aureole of this intrusion overprints the fault zone fabrics which are exposed immediately south of the intrusion near Calves Hole [NX 046 491]. Since the Cairngarroch igneous complex resembles other intrusions in the area which have been dated at approximately 400 Ma, this relationship provides a minimum age for the sinistral shear episode in this area (?D_3, Figure 20). A similar effect can be observed in the east of the Rhins, near Sandhead [NX 098 504], where the thermal aureole of a concealed intrusion overprints the Orlock Bridge Fault (Kimbell and Stone, 1992).

GALA GROUP

Units 1 and 2

The two most northerly tectonostratigraphical units of the Gala Group are not exposed on the west coast of the Rhins (Figure 5) and their exposure farther north-east within the Rhins of Galloway district is extremely limited. As far as can be judged from the limited evidence available they contain a mixture of Type 1 and Type 2 structure with the latter probably dominant. A slaty cleavage is widely developed and seems to be clockwise transecting relative to fold hinges although the evidence for this within the Rhins of Galloway district is very sparse and somewhat ambiguous.

Unit 3

This tectonostratigraphical unit has a relatively small outcrop in the vicinity of Money Head [NX 045 483] in the west of the Rhins of Galloway (Figure 5). Within it the structure is uniformly of Type 1 with steeply inclined beds consistently younging north and, for the most part, dipping north (Figure 22a). A slaty cleavage developed in the finer-grained lithologies is congruous with the bedding attitude and refracts markedly into the coarser parts of the graded greywacke beds. The rare D_1 folds present are tight to isoclinal, south-verging fold pairs with subhorizontal hinges. Open folding of bedding and slaty cleavage, with subhorizontal axial planes and wavelengths of 1 to 10 m, is probably a D_2 effect; no associated cleavage is developed.

The base of the unit is exposed both at Strandfoot [NX 052 482] and in the Cairnweil Burn [NX 088 494] as an imbricated zone of Moffat Shale Group strata with complex minor-folding relationships and localised shearing.

Unit 4

The structures within this unit are mainly of the Type 2 style, with steeply inclined bedding, generally younging north, folded by numerous south-verging D_1 fold pairs. In the north of the unit a much larger than average D_1 fold pair has congruous minor folding on its limbs and so locally the D_1 folds are north-verging. The D_1 fold hinge orientation is quite variable and some fold hinges are perpendicular and even downward facing. This may be the result of interaction between the D_1 and D_3 fold regimes. Structural data for the unit are summarised in Figure 22b. A slaty cleavage is widely developed in association with the D_1 folds and varies from axial planar to slightly clockwise transecting. The effects of D_2 deformation seem to be limited to minor localised north-directed thrusting.

At the base of the Gala 4 tectonstratigraphical unit the Gillespie Burn Fault crops out on the west coast of the Rhins of Galloway, just to the north of Back Drug [NX 070 463], as a complex zone of brecciation, quartz veining and shearing within the greywacke sequence. The most intense deformation is seen in interbedded laminated siltstones where the overall sense of asymmetry in steeply plunging folds is sinistral.

Unit 5

This tectonostratigraphical unit is divided into two zones of contrasting structural style by a strike fault concealed in the vicinity of Ardwell Bay [NX 071 451] on the west coast. To the north the structure is of Type 2 with abundant minor D_1 fold pairs affecting an overall steeply inclined, north-younging greywacke sequence; fold hinges are variable but most are moderately to gently plunging towards either north-east or south-west (Figure 22c). The fold style becomes more neutral locally at the northern end of Ardwell Bay and a series of open to close anticlines and synclines have hinges plunging gently to the south-west with upright slaty cleavage axial-planar or a few degrees clockwise transecting (Plate 9a). Southward of this neutral fold zone the bedding is steeply inclined and south-younging making the zone anticlinal overall. This interpretation contrasts with the north-verging fold complex in a south-younging sequence illustrated by Stringer and Treagus (1981, Figure 4c).

To the south of the putative Ardwell Bay fault the structural style is essentially Type 1, although the degree of overturning is greater than is normally the case and here the dip is gently south (Figure 22d). Minor open to close folds in this zone are downward facing but the associated, apparently axial-planar, slaty cleavage is incongruous such that bedding and folds are downward facing on cleavage. Local north-directed thrusts are probably the

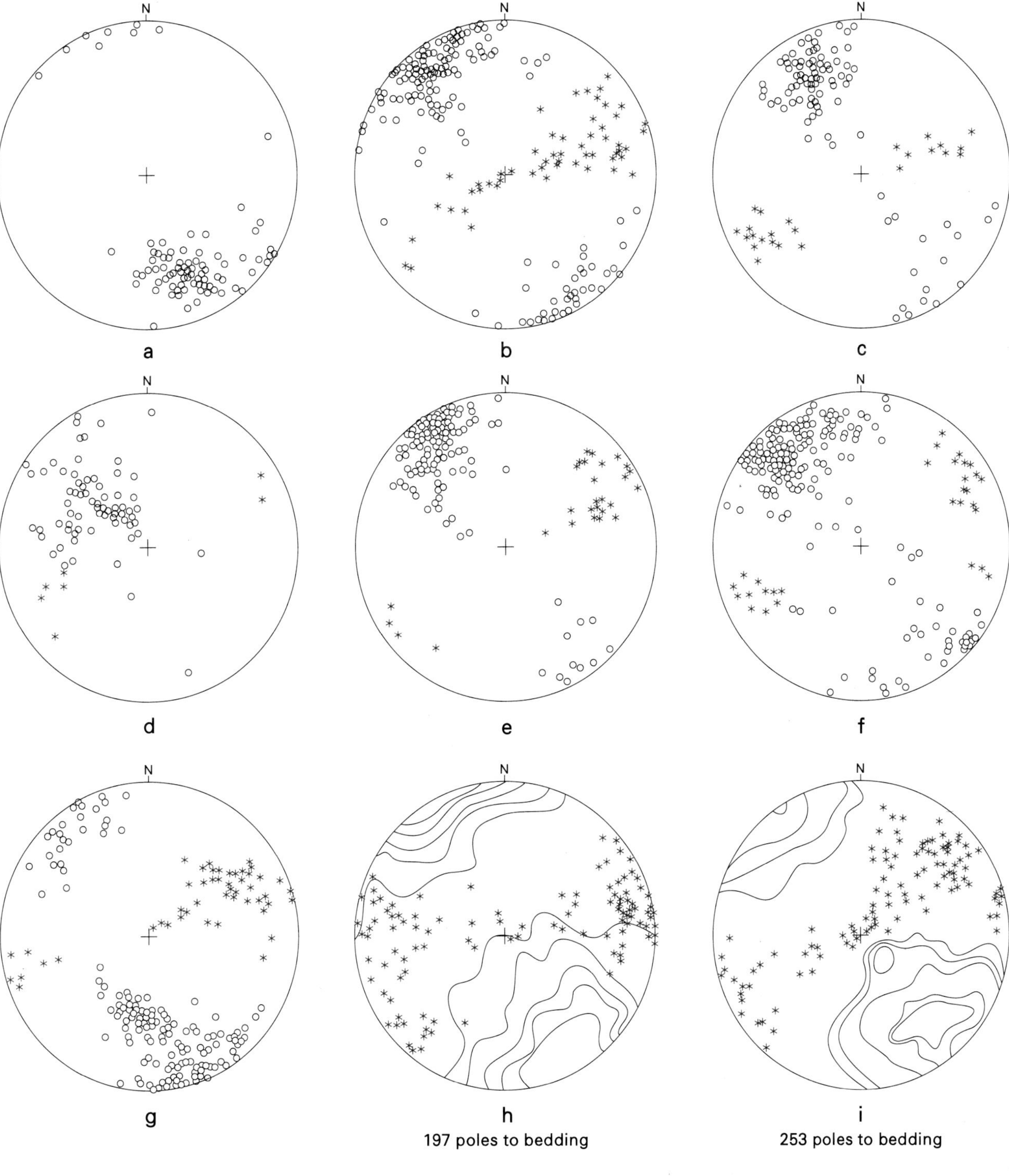

Figure 22 Summary of structural data from the Gala and Hawick groups.

a. Gala 3.
b. Gala 4.
c. Gala 5 north of Ardwell Bay [NX 070 450].
d. Gala 5 south of Ardwell Bay.
e. Gala 6.
f. Gala 7.
g. Gala 8.
h. Cairnharrow Formation (Hawick Group).
i. Carghidown Formation (Hawick Group).

In stereograms a to f the dominant sedimentary younging direction is to the north.
In stereograms g to i it is to the south.

a

b

Plate 9 Fold structures affecting the Gala Group greywackes (tectonostratigraphical unit 5) near Ardwell Bay.

a. An open D_1 hinge plunging gently towards the SW [NX 072 453] (D 4202).

b. A tight, steeply plunging D_3 hinge [NX 068 448] (D 4211).

result of D_2 accommodation deformation. The southern margin of this anomalous Type 1 zone is complicated by imbrication adjacent to The Hooies Fault. Within the fault zone perpendicular fold hinges have a sinistral sense of asymmetry and fold both south-younging bedding and a subparallel slaty cleavage (Plate 9b). They are amongst the best developed D_3 structures in the Rhins of Galloway district.

Unit 6

Typical Type 2 structures characterise this tectonostratigraphical unit. Bedding is steeply inclined and youngs northward overall with numerous small south-verging fold pairs present. Where these D_1 fold structures are larger the south-younging limbs may be locally affected by small-scale north-verging D_1 folds. A penetrative slaty cleavage is developed locally and is axial-planar to the D_1 folds. Bedding strike is consistently NE–SW, the beds generally slightly overturned, and fold hinges plunge gently, mainly to the north-east (Figure 22e). Possible D_2 structures, open folds with subhorizontal axial planes, are sporadically developed, particularly in the north of the unit.

Close to the southern margin, in the Drumbreddan Bay Fault Zone, the structure becomes locally complex with north-verging downward-facing folds having an axial-planar slaty cleavage. The Moffat Shale Group strata at the base of the greywacke sequence has localised and anastomosing planes of intense shearing and complex zones of minor folding.

Unit 7

The northern part of this tectonostratigraphical unit is typically Type 1 in structural style; north-younging bedding is steeply inclined, usually slightly overturned, and strikes approximately NE–SW. Rare D_1 south-verging fold pairs have axial-planar slaty cleavage and gentle hinge plunge towards either the north-east or south-west. Farther south, around the Mull of Logan [NX 075 420], the folding becomes much more intense and can be resolved into three major D_1 south-verging anticline–syncline pairs. Congruous minor D_1 structures verge north or south as appropriate on the limbs of these structures, with gentle hinge plunge to north-east or south-west. The overall style is of Type 2 and the D_1 structural data is summarised in Figure 22f. Axial-planar D_1 slaty cleavage is locally developed. Small-scale open to close folds, with sporadic gently inclined SE-dipping axial-planar crenulation cleavage, are widely developed as D_2 structures. The transition from Type 1 to Type 2 is gradational and there is no evidence of fault control. Towards the southern margin of the unit, on the north side of Port Logan [NX 095 413], the geometry of both D_1 and D_2 structures becomes much more variable with some steeply plunging hinges; this may be a D_3 influence. The southern boundary fault, the Laurieston Fault, is not exposed on the Rhins of Galloway and is most likely cut out by a major back thrust presumed to underlie Port Logan.

Unit 8

On the Rhins of Galloway this tectonostratigraphical unit occupies a structural pop-up (as defined in Butler, 1982) between opposing D_1 thrusts. The deformation style therefore varies from Type 4 (south-younging north-verging D_1) in the north, through Type 3 (neutral) in the centre, to Type 2 (north-younging south-verging D_1) in the south. Throughout the unit the D_1 folds are generally close and plunge variably to the north-east. Bedding attitude is also variable as would be expected of the dominant Type 3 structure. D_1 fold data is summarised in Figure 22g; a slaty cleavage is sporadically developed and varies from axial-planar to slightly clockwise transecting of D_1 folds. All of the D_1 structures in the Gala 8 unit pop-up are regarded as penecontemporaneous, the north-directed thrust developing as a back thrust synchronously with continued southward propagation at the main thrust front. The amount of back-thrust movement is likely to be small, since the biostratigraphical 'step' between the Gala 7 and Gala 8 tectonostratigraphical units does not disrupt the regional pattern dictated by the overall southward-directed thrust geometry (Figure 6).

All of the D_1 structural styles are equally affected by minor, open to close D_2 folds with gently dipping axial planes and, locally, an axial-planar crenulation cleavage. More rarely, upright D_2 folds occur which are coaxial with D_1 and have a steeply inclined axial-planar crenulation cleavage. In the southern part of the unit, on the northern side of Clanyard Bay [NX 101 381], tight steeply plunging folds deform bedding and both the slaty and crenulation cleavages. These D_3 structures have variable asymmetry but a sinistral sense of movement is dominant overall. A steeply inclined axial-planar NE–SW crenulation cleavage is locally developed in association with these D_3 folds.

The southern margin of the Gala 8 tectonostratigraphical unit is the complex Clanyard Bay Fault Zone, made more complex on the Rhins of Galloway by the juxtaposition of outcropping north- and south-directed thrusts. Intense shearing and brecciation is widespread with abundant, usually tight, folds varying considerably in style and orientation. The northern part of the fault zone is probably dominated by Type 2 structures in the foot wall of a major south-directed thrust; in contrast, the southern part can be structurally related to Type 4 fold style in the imbricated hanging wall of a north-directed back thrust. An alternative structural interpretation by McCurry (1990) envisaged all of the deformation being related to north-directed thrusts.

HAWICK GROUP

Cairnharrow Formation

This tectonostratigraphical unit forms part of a regionally anomalous, generally south-younging sequence affected by north-verging D_1 folds characteristic of Type 4 structure. The north-verging structures are tight to close anticline-syncline pairs with wavelengths of several hundred metres. The hinge zones of these folds are commonly disrupted by faulting but their positions can be deduced by the opposing vergence of the minor congruous folds in their limbs. The longer, south-younging limbs have abundant north-verging minor folds whereas the short north-younging limbs carry south-verging minor folds. A penetrative slaty cleavage is widely developed and varies from axial-planar to a few degrees clockwise transecting of the minor fold hinges. The D_1 hinges have a variable plunge to either ENE or WSW and locally hinges are curvilinear. D_1 structural data is summarised in Figure 22h. In general, the geometry of the D_1 structures in the Cairnharrow Formation tectonostratigraphical unit is compatible with development above a north-directed back-thrust generated penecontemporaneously with south-directed propagation of the sole thrust. However, the age difference between this unit and the one to the north is very small (Figure 6), suggesting that only limited thrust movement has occurred. This structural configuration and models for its generation will be discussed more fully following the account of deformation in the Carghidown Formation (below).

The D_1 cleavage is refolded and/or crenulated locally by minor NE–SW-trending folds which may have either gently or steeply plunging hinges. The former are open, small-scale folds, with gently inclined axial planes, which may verge either to north-west or south-east; they were probably produced by D_2 deformation. The steeply plunging folds are generally tight and have an overall sinistral sense of asymmetry, although a dextral sense may be dominant locally; they may relate to either D_2 or D_3 deformation. Few of the post-D_1 structures have wavelengths exceeding 1 m and any associated crenulation cleavage is usually restricted to the hinge zones.

The southern boundary structure of the Cairnharrow Formation tectonostratigraphical unit is not exposed. Later north–south fault structures locally separate this unit from its successor to the south. The position of the tract boundary may be deduced from the first appearance of the distinctive interbedded red mudstone lithology in the Carghidown Formation to the south.

Carghidown Formation

This tectonostratigraphical unit, like its neighbour to the north, contains characteristic Type 4 structure, with dominantly south-younging strata and north-verging fold pairs. The major structures are D_1 fold pairs with wavelengths of several hundred metres; long limbs young south, short limbs young north and the axial planes of the folds are steeply inclined, trending approximately NE–SW. Hinge zones are commonly faulted out such that areas of opposing younging and minor fold vergence are separated by faults. The minor folds themselves are congruous with the larger D_1 structures such that northerly vergence is dominant. However, whereas the axial-plane orientation is fairly consistent, striking NE–SW and steeply inclined, fold hinge plunge within that plane is extremely variable with individual hinges curvilinear or sheath-like. This structural pattern is illustrated in Figure 22i. A clockwise-transecting and penetrative slaty cleavage is widely developed. It would appear that the D_1 back thrusting was accompanied by NE–SW shear which, from the asymmetry of the sheath folds and the cleavage relationships, was sinistral.

The D_1 folds and fabric are commonly refolded and crenulated by small-scale D_2 structures. North-verging close to open minor folds (D_2) are fairly widespread with NE–SW hinge trend and gently inclined axial planes. Steeply plunging folds refold D_1 folds, and the associated slaty cleavage locally, and are particularly well developed north of West Tarbet [NX 140 310]. However, where these structures interfere with steeply plunging D_1 minor folds it is often difficult to tell them apart. In the West Tarbet area further complexity is caused by the apparent reversal, at some localities, of the D_2 and D_3 episodes, with steeply plunging sinistral minor folds which fold the D_1 cleavage, cut across by a 'D_2' gently inclined crenulation cleavage. These relationships suggest that the deformation sequence is of coincidental thrust-related (D_1) and transpressive (D_3) deformation followed by continuing compressive accommodation (D_2) in the thrust hinterland (Figure 20).

DISCUSSION OF NORTH-VERGING FOLD GENERATION

North-directed D_1 thrusting is anomalous within the Southern Uplands structural sequence and does not appear to continue far along strike from the Rhins of Galloway district (Barnes et al., 1987; Barnes, 1989). The implication of any back-thrusting model invoked to explain this geometry, is that strata deposited ahead of the thrust front, instead of being incorporated at the base of the thrust stack, are carried for some distance across the thrust hinterland. This should be recorded by a disruption of the steady southerly reduction in age of the tectonostratigraphical units now seen (Figure 6). The larger the back thrust in terms of distance carried, then the larger should be the jump in the stratigraphy as more of the thrust hinterland is covered. On this basis the only candidate for significant movement is the thrust separating the Cairnharrow and Carghidown formations (Figure 5) where representative strata of the *griestoniensis* Biozone may be absent. However, the poor faunal control makes even this deduction uncertain. In terms of visible fault fabrics one structure within the Carghidown Formation may be significant; at Portankill [NX 141 325] a thin zone of black mudstone is intensely sheared and quartz veined, possibly marking the outcrop of another plane of imbrication within the back-thrust unit.

Arguing within an overall accretionary prism interpretation for the Southern Uplands, McCurry and Anderson (1989) account for the major structural contrast (styles 1–3 versus style 4) by a switch from subduction to obduction. However, this would most likely have been a large-scale regional phenomenon and seems to be incompatible with the biostratigraphical relationships seen in Figure 6 where two of the back-thrust units are apparently of the same age and overlap in age with the most southerly of the southward thrust units. There is no evidence for a 'missing' portion of the thrust hinterland. Farther south-west along strike, on the Ards Peninsula of Northern Ireland, Barnes et al. (1987, figs. 2, 6) have correlated the Rhins of Galloway Type 4 structural zone with the south-younging northern limb of the Castle Hill-Portavogie Syncline, a major structure contained between a pair of opposing thrusts. This is in effect a structural pop-up (see discussion in Butler, 1982) and a similar interpretation of the Rhins structure is preferred. However, since the back thrusts in the Rhins of Galloway example are regarded as antithetic to the frontal thrust, the mechanism responsible may be associated either with frontal ramp climb or with layer-parallel shortening at a tip in front of a propagating thrust. The former is perhaps the more likely since the angular difference between the developing thrusts could be smaller and their subsequent rotation to a parallel attitude thus facilitated. This argument is equally applicable to the structural development of the Gala 8 unit.

Overall therefore the north-directed thrusting responsible for development of structural style 4 might best be interpreted as back thrusting within the hinterland, penecontemporaneous with the continuing southward propagation of the main thrust front. This phase of back thrusting may be regarded as part of the D_1 structural event preceding the widespread minor back thrusts which formed during subsequent (D_2) readjustments within the thrust hinterland. This interpretation contradicts the subduction–obduction model of McCurry and Anderson (1989) but is inconclusive in respect of the wider controversy surrounding the development of the Southern Uplands thrust belt. This controversy is unlikely to be resolved from structural argument alone.

FAULTING

Faults are very common throughout the Rhins of Galloway district and their throws are very variable. At one extreme are observable movements on a mm scale, whereas Anderson and Oliver (1986) have argued for more than 400 km of strike slip movement on the Orlock Bridge Fault. In general suggestions of large throws on any of the faults in the district remain speculative. Five principal groups of faults are recognised:

1. Early faults related to D_1 folding and thrusting.
2. Gently to moderately dipping thrust faults.
3. Steeply inclined or vertical faults trending approximately NNE–SSW and with a sinistral horizontal offset.
4. Steeply inclined or vertical faults trending approximately NW–SE and with a dextral horizontal offset.
5. Strike-parallel (NE–SW) steeply inclined faults with a sinistral offset.

Group 1

Changes in the direction of younging commonly occur at bedding-parallel or subparallel faults which have presumably disrupted fold hinges. Many of these faults probably originated as hanging-wall detachments during D_1 thrust generation and it is thus no coincidence that they are particularly associated with structural styles 2 and 4. The throw on these faults is often difficult to assess but both northerly and southerly, normal and reverse downthrows are certainly present. The major faults of this group are the principal imbricate structures within the thrust system (Figure 6) which now appear at outcrop as large reverse faults downthrowing south.

Group 2

The D_1 fold structures and associated slaty cleavage are cut and deformed locally by sporadic minor thrust faults which strike between NE–SW and E–W and have both northerly and southerly dips of between 5° and 45°. The fault planes themselves are commonly arcuate and observed throws are rarely in excess of 2 m. It seems most likely that these reverse faults formed as part of the D_2 deformation episode in response to compression within the thrust hinterland.

Groups 3 and 4

These two fault trends form a conjugate pair and the structures are widely distributed throughout the Rhins of Galloway district. Their geometry is summarised in Figure 23. Subhorizontal slickensides are a feature of a number of the faults and confirm a horizontal wrench movement. All of these faults are vertical or very steeply inclined. Those displaying a sinistral sense of horizontal offset trend mainly between 350° and 030° whereas the dextral wrench faults trend mainly between 110° and 150°. The local dominance of one or the other member of the conjugate pair exercises a controlling influence on the morphology of the west coast of the Rhins of Galloway. This effect is particularly marked where there has been fault reactivation during the Permian; the major Permian basin boundary faults of the district (the Loch Ryan Fault and the North Channel Fault) both have trends within the range of the Caledonian dextral wrenches. Some of the conjugate fault planes contain or are cross-cut by uncleaved members of a Caledonian dyke swarm, other planes contain variably foliated dykes, whereas still other fault planes cut and displace dykes. The dykes and the wrench faults thus appear to be, at least in part, penecontemporaneous. A suite of undeformed lamprophyres from the same Caledonian swarm in Kirkcudbrightshire have given radiometric ages in the range 398 to 418 Ma (Rock et al., 1986) to provide a minimum age for the wrench fault movement. Similar wrench fault geometries have been observed along strike

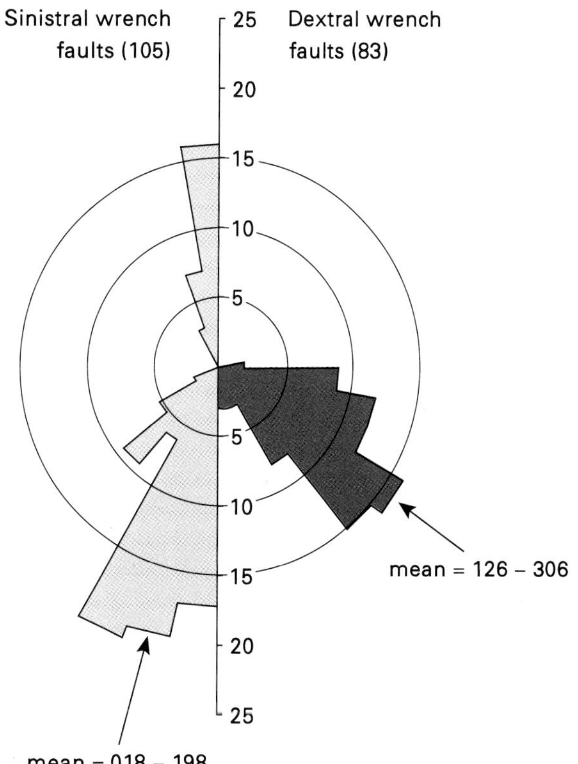

Figure 23 Summary of conjugate wrench fault geometry.

to the north-east (Barnes, 1989) and to the south-west (Anderson, 1987).

Group 5

The major tectonostratigraphical tract boundary faults have mostly been reactivated by late sinistral shear. However, it is possible that some, probably those not associated with Moffat Shale Group inliers, may not have been initiated during D_1 thrusting but, instead, have developed purely as major strike-parallel sinistral wrench faults. A primary candidate in this category is the Cairngarroch Fault in which the main fabric-generating movement postdates the S_1 thrust-related cleavage but predates the c.400 Ma minor intrusions (Anderson and Oliver, 1986). Farther north-east Lintern et al. (1992) have noted that the Orlock Bridge Fault forms the northern margin to a high strain zone up to 5 km wide (the Moniaive Shear Zone) with evidence for two tectonic events: widespread mid-Wenlock sinistral shear succeeded by Lower Devonian sinistral shear localised along the Orlock Bridge Fault.

The reactivation history of this group of faults clearly overlaps that of the conjugate wrench fault system. The NE–SW strike-parallel system has been utilised locally by transfer faulting at both the east and west margin of the Loch Ryan Permian basin and appears to afford a major controlling influence on the southern margin of the basin beneath Luce Bay. This will be discussed in greater detail in Chapter Eleven in the light of geophysical modelling. The more northerly faults, particularly the Glen App lineament, were reactivated as essentially normal fault structures during the Devono-Carboniferous development of the Midland Valley graben to the north. These movements may have influenced the local depth of exposure within the Southern Uplands thrust belt and hence affect the observed pattern of low grade metamorphism. This problem will be discussed further in Chapter Nine.

EIGHT

Intrusive rocks

A variety of igneous rocks are intruded in the Rhins of Galloway district. Most are late Caledonian in age and range from the substantial Portencorkrie diorite–granodiorite compound stock to narrow dykes of felsite, microdiorite or lamprophyre. A much younger suite of larger basalt dykes is assigned to the Tertiary.

PORTENCORKRIE COMPLEX

The Portencorkrie plutonic complex crops out some 25 km south of Stranraer (Figure 5) and is one of the smallest of the Galloway Caledonian granitoid bodies. It is compositionally zoned from dioritic margins to a granodioritic core and was emplaced into steeply dipping and folded Silurian (Hawick Group) greywackes and shales. Its outcrop shape is roughly rectangular: approximately 2.5 km from north to south and extending inland from the coast for about 2.2 km to a probably faulted (or at least fault-controlled) eastern boundary. Exposure inland is very poor but there is almost total coastal exposure from the northern margin at Laggantalluch Head [NX 084 363] to the southern margin just south of Crammag Head [NX 089 340].

Teall (in Peach and Horne, 1899) gave the first brief petrographic description of this complex in his study of the Galloway granites. A detailed petrographic study by Holgate (1943) concluded that an outer earlier diorite, composed of pyroxene-mica-diorite and hornblende-mica-diorite, was intruded by a central 'granite' causing extensive hybridisation of the adjacent diorite. Holgate further argued that the diorite body had undergone 'in situ crystallisation differentiation' so that it passed from a relatively basic outer margin to more acidic varieties towards the contact with the central 'granite'.

Petrography

The following account is based principally on specimens collected from the coastal exposures which allow a complete transect of the intrusive complex (Figures 24 and 25).

A QAP plot of the modal minerals (Le Maitre, 1989) indicates that the marginal rocks range from quartz-diorite to quartz-monzodiorite and the central zone rocks vary from quartz-monzodiorite to granodiorite (Figure 26a). For convenience the marginal zone rocks will be referred to as diorite and the central zone rocks as granodiorite. A selection of representative geochemical analyses is given in Appendix 4.

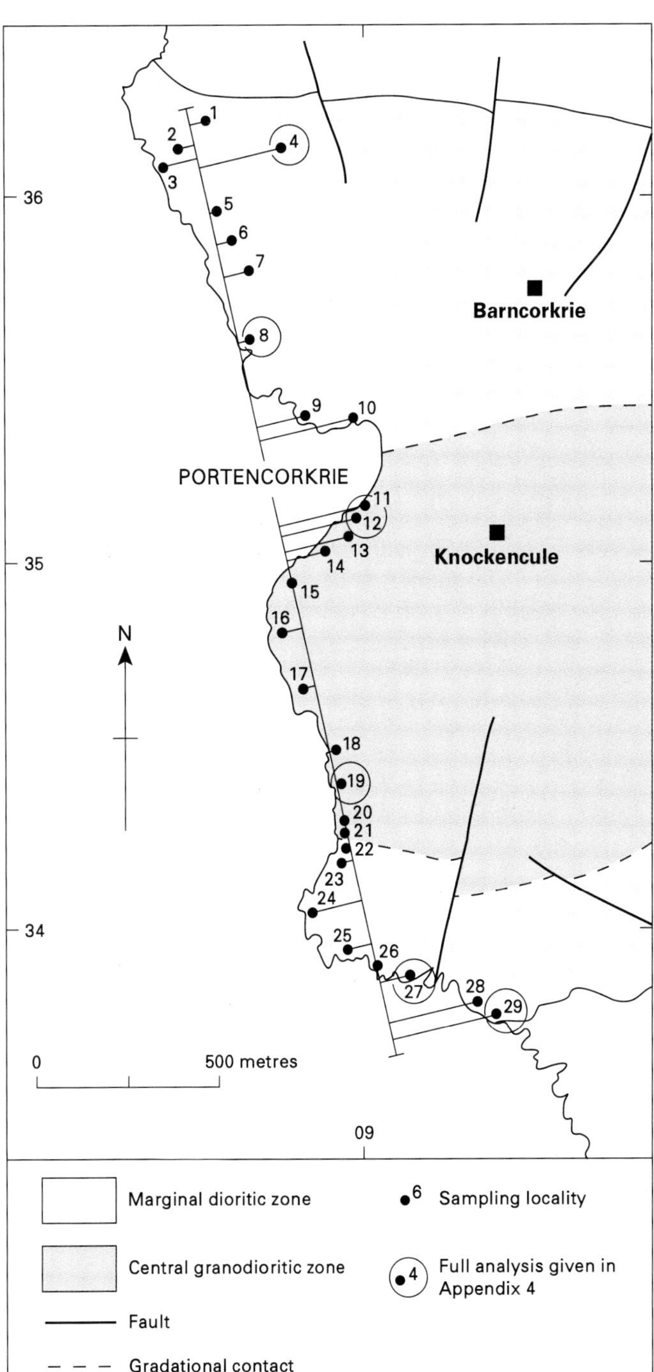

Figure 24 The coastal outcrop of the Portencorkrie Complex showing location of specimens in the geochemical traverse (Figure 25) and analytical table (Appendix 4).

PYROXENE-MICA-DIORITE

This rock-type forms most of the northern side of the intrusion. The diorite is fine to medium grained with up to

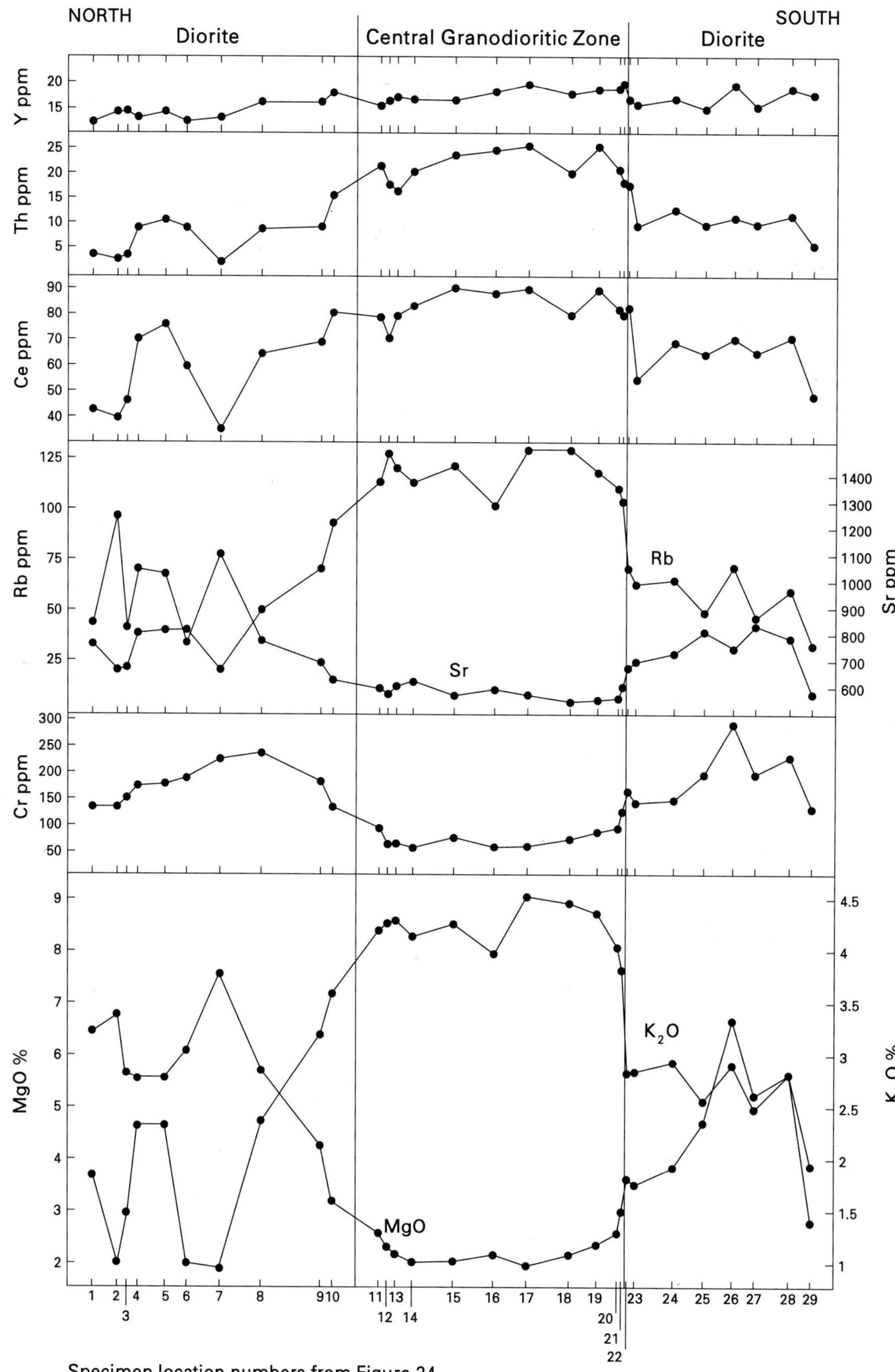

Figure 25 A geochemical traverse across the Portencorkrie Complex.

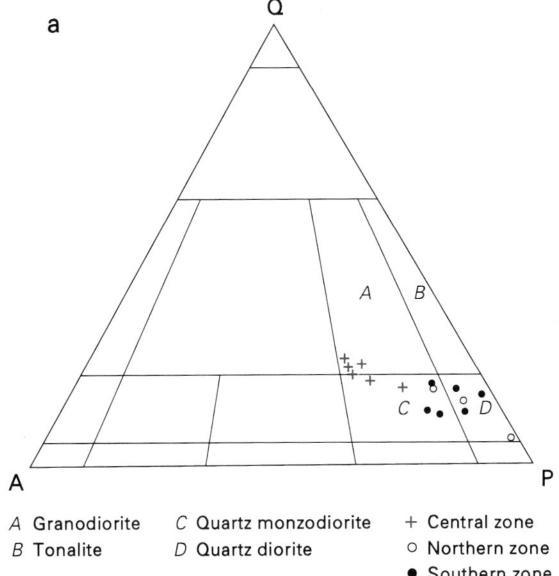

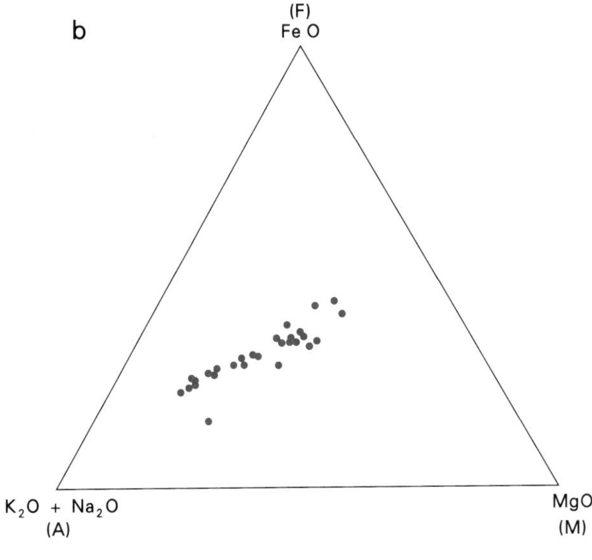

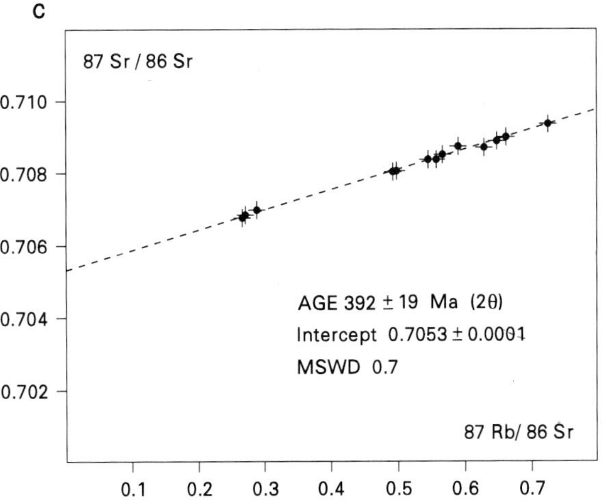

Figure 26 The Portencorkrie Complex.

a. QAP plot of modal minerals, fields after Le Maitre (1989).
b. AFM plot for specimens located on Figure 24.
c. Rb-Sr isochron for granodiorite from the centre of the complex.

65% zoned andesine, up to 25% clinopyroxene and up to 10% biotite as the main mineral constituents. Minor K-feldspar is common in proportions up to 10% in some specimens. Quartz and hypersthene are present in accessory to minor quantities with apatite and opaque iron oxides as the main accessories. The clinopyroxenes are anhedral and slightly porphyritic (up to 2 mm) with a fine sieve texture and the plagioclase laths are commonly aligned in a fluxion texture (Plate 10a). Biotite occurs in skeletal crystals and the hypersthene is pink, pleochroic and granular (Plate 10b and c). Mafic concentrations of coarse anhedral (up to 3 mm) brown zoned amphiboles and clinopyroxenes occur in some specimens and both minerals show replacement by a pale green amphibole. One specimen contains brown amphibole replacing the clinopyroxene, although the rest of the rock appears very fresh.

Hornblende-mica-diorite

This rock type occurs on the northern and southern margins of the intrusion; it is dominant in the southern part but contacts with the other dioritic rocks are not seen. It differs from the pyroxene-mica-diorite in that the clinopyroxene is largely replaced by pale green amphibole which may develop a subhedral crystal shape (Plate 10d and e). Compared with the pyroxene-diorite, orthopyroxene is less common or absent and quartz and K-feldspar become increasingly common towards the central granodiorite. A brown biotite content of up to 10% is similar to that of the other diorite but the plagioclase (zoned) is generally more sodic (oligoclase rather than andesine) and shows more alteration. The texture is an anhedral mosaic with plagioclase and biotite crystals generally up to 3 mm across, whilst in places the former are porphyritic (up to 5 mm). K-feldspar commonly occurs as poikilitic plates up to 5 mm across (Plate 10f) and in some specimens there is a fluxion texture of aligned plagioclases. Mineral proportions vary: commonly 20–30% K-feldspar, 40–50% plagioclase, 5–10% quartz, up to 10% biotite and between 5% and 25% amphibole. Generally the proportions of K-feldspar and quartz increase, and the hornblende and biotite decrease, towards the central granodioritic zone.

Central granodioritic zone

This zone is dominated by a medium-grained, locally K-feldsparphyric granodiorite with hornblende and biotite as the main mafic constituents. The rock has an anhedral mosaic texture with varying degrees of alteration of the plagioclase. Contacts between the granodiorite and the surrounding dioritic types are all gradational. At the southern margin of the central zone, hornblende-mica-diorite gradually changes northwards (cf. 'zones of hy-

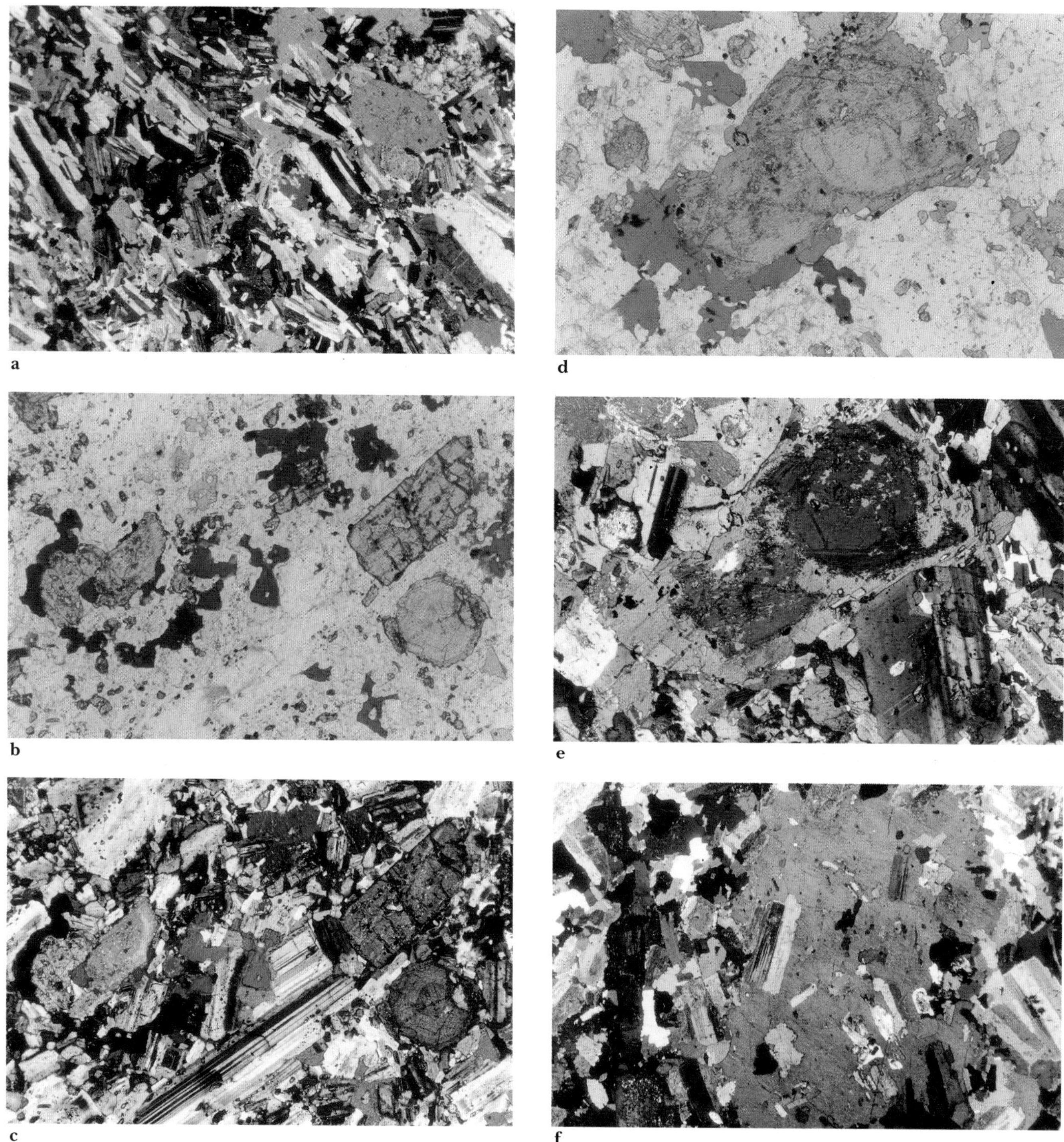

Plate 10 Representative photomicrographs illustrating the compositon and texture of the Portencorkrie Complex.

a. Fluxion texture in pyroxene-mica-diorite. Crossed polarisers ×10 GN012.

b. and c. Skeletal biotite and granular hypersthene in pyroxene-mica diorite. b, plane polarised light; c, crossed polarisers ×25 GN013 and GN014.

d. and e. Clinopyroxene replaced by pale-green amphibole in hornblende-mica diorite. d, plane polarised light; e, crossed polarisers ×25 GN015 and GN016.

f. Poikilitic plates of K-feldspar in hornblende-mica-diorite. Crossed polarisers ×10 GN017.

Photomicrographs by Dr J W Gaskarth, University of Birmingham.

brids', Holgate, 1943) to a rock with more quartz and K-feldspar, less amphibole and biotite and more-sodic plagioclase. No clinopyroxene is seen in the cores of the amphiboles from the central zone. The northern contact is sharper with the change from pyroxene-mica-diorite to granodiorite occurring over a relatively short distance. There is no particular evidence of hybridisation, the changes being largely in mineral proportions from the hornblende-mica-diorite to the granodiorite and including total replacement of clinopyroxene by amphibole. At one locality in the north of the complex, pyroxene-mica-diorite is cut by a thin vein of coarse granitic material similar to that forming the central granitic zone.

Geochemistry

Samples from the coastal transect (Figure 24) were analysed for major elements and a selected suite of trace elements, using XRF techniques at the University of Aston. Representative analyses for the main rock types are given in Appendix 4. The spatial variation in chemistry, illustrated in Figure 25, shows a general increase in K_2O, Rb, Th, Ce and Y towards the centre of the body and a corresponding decrease in MgO, Cr and Sr. Some of the variation in the dioritic parts may be the result of magma contamination and observed mafic concentrations within the rock are probably the remains of xenoliths. There is a marked change in concentrations at the margins of the central granodiorite, which was mapped in the field between specimen locations 10 and 11 on the north side and between 21 and 22 on the southern side.

Harker diagram plots (Figure 27) show continuous variation between the diorites with around 52% SiO_2 through to the granodiorite with values up to 69%. The plots show well-defined regular trends and as such are compatible with fractional crystallisation and, perhaps to a lesser extent, hybridisation. The plots for alkalis and CaO, together with an AFM plot (Figure 26b), show these rocks to be calc-alkaline and thus similar to the other plutonic bodies of the Southern Uplands.

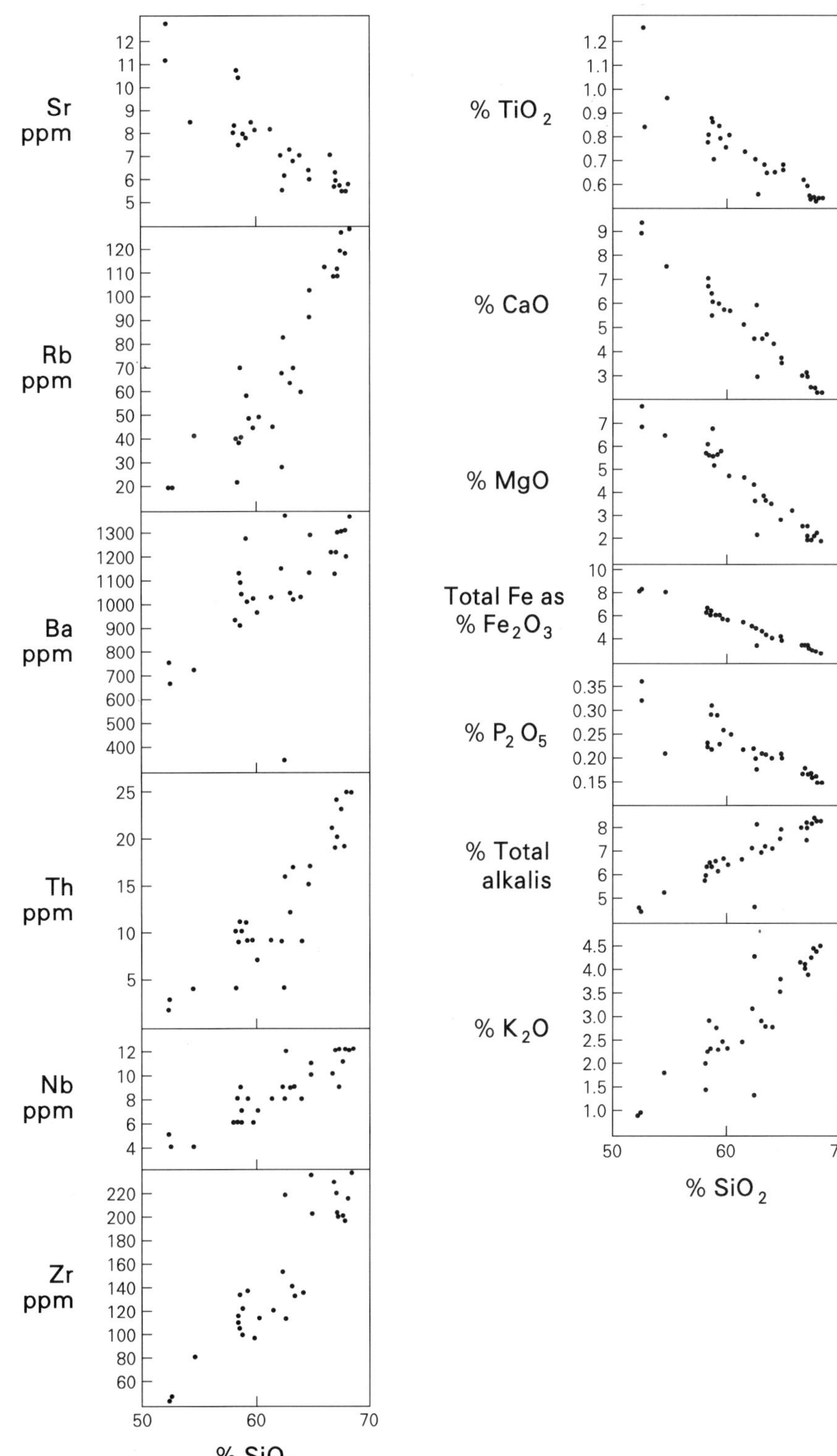

Figure 27 Harker diagrams to show variation of selected elements and major oxides with silica in the Portencorkrie Complex.

Petrogenesis

Recent models for the zoned granitic plutons of the Southern Uplands based on mineralogical and geochemical studies (Halliday et al., 1980; Tindle and Pearce, 1981; Stephens and Halliday, 1984; Tindle et al., 1988; Shand, 1989) suggest petrogenesis via fractional crystallisation of basic/intermediate magmas, with some degree of assimilation of metasedimentary crustal material. Multiple intrusion of magma fractionating at depth was used to explain the apparent abrupt changes from dioritic to granitic rocks for the Cairnsmore of Carsphairn pluton (Tindle et al., 1988) and a similar mechanism could apply for Portencorkrie. In common with the other Southern Uplands plutons, the Portencorkrie complex occupies an anomalous position for a subduction-related granite. By the time of its intrusion the Iapetus Ocean had effectively closed, whichever geotectonic model for the Southern Uplands is preferred. It is perhaps more likely that genesis of the Portencorkrie magmas occurred during deep-seated strike-slip movements (Watson, 1984).

Geochronology

The central granodioritic lithology of the Portencorkrie plutonic complex has been dated by Dr Jane Evans of the NERC Isotope Geosciences Laboratory. A Rb-Sr isochron age of 392 + 19 Ma was obtained (initial ratio 0.7053 + 0.0001, MSWD 0.7) (Figure 26c). Full analytical details are given in Appendix 5

CAIRNGARROCH COMPLEX

The polyphase granodioritic-dioritic Cairngarroch complex crops out over several hundred square metres on the west coast of the Rhins peninsula south and west of West Cairngarroch Farm [NX 052 493]. The igneous rocks were intruded into deformed Ordovician strata of the Shinnel Formation and the southern margin of the complex is formed by the Cairngarroch Fault (Figure 5). Intrusion postdates movement on the fault but it seems probable that the Cairngarroch Fault was a major controlling influence on the site and shape of the subsequent intrusive body. Possible roof pendants of metagreywacke seen in the sea cliffs in the north-west of the complex suggest that the highest part of an intrusive body is there exposed. The petrography, geochemistry and mineralisation of the Cairngarroch complex have been discussed in detail by Allen et al. (1981) from which work the following account is largely drawn.

Petrography

The north-western part of the intrusive assemblage (the Bay Complex of Allen et al., 1981) contains two main lithological components: a dark grey biotite-hornblende-microtonalite and a pinkish porphyritic biotite-hornblende-granodiorite. The oldest part of the composite intrusion is believed to be the microtonalite (S67007, S68049) exposed in the extreme north-west. It is uniformly fine-grained and consists essentially of zoned, randomly orientated oligoclase-andesine phenocrysts, up to 0.6 mm long, clear interstitial quartz, fresh or partly chloritised brown biotite and, in approximately the same proportion as biotite, calcite/chlorite pseudomorphs after green amphibole. The feldspar is usually partly altered to calcite and sericite. The south-east part of the coastal section consists of porphyritic granodiorite which has a sharp intrusive contact with the older microtonalite. The latter is also cut by dykes, up to 3 m thick, continuous with, and lithologically similar to, the granodiorite. There is some textural variation within the granodiorite but the dominant lithology (S68055) consists of closely spaced, subhedral and euhedral crystals of andesine, up to 3 mm long, showing both normal and oscillatory zoning and with small exsolved blebs of K-feldspar. The plagioclase is set in a groundmass mosaic of quartz, K-feldspar and plagioclase. Brown biotite, in places partly chloritised, slightly exceeds green hornblende in proportion. The latter is commonly represented by pseudomorphs of calcite and chlorite.

The southern extremity of the coastal section is particularly complicated and the presence of numerous metagreywacke screens prevents clear observation of the relationships between this part of the Cairngarroch complex and that to the north. This southern marginal zone and the inland exposures around West Cairngarroch Farm (the Glen Complex of Allen et al., 1981) comprise, in their probable order of emplacement, quartz-porphyry, porphyritic quartz-microdiorite and quartz-microdiorite. Quartz-porphyry, the earliest intrusive phase, occurs as small brecciated and altered xenoliths and enclaves, up to 8 m wide, enclosed within the porphyritic quartz-microdiorite. The latter typically contains (S67002, S67003, S67010) plagioclase phenocrysts up to 2.5 mm long and muscovite/calcite pseudomorphs after biotite in an equigranular or recrystallised matrix of feldspar and quartz. Locally this lithology may be affected by brecciation, sericitisation and/or pervasive veining and replacement by calcite. Aphyric quartz-microdiorite forms most of the inland exposures of the Cairngarroch complex. The typical lithology is composed principally of subhedral, partly intergrown, zoned andesine crystals, ranging in size from 0.15–2.5 mm, patchily developed interstitial quartz, brown biotite and pseudomorphs of yellow ?serpentine and calcite after amphibole. There is much local variation in grain size and quartz content. Alteration in feldspar varies from minor replacement by calcite to intense sericitisation. Biotite, though usually fresh, is totally chloritised in some rocks.

Geochemistry

The pervasive hydrothermal alteration and widespread Fe-As-Cu-Mo mineralisation reported by Allen et al. (1981) and discussed in more detail in Chapter Thirteen of this memoir, precludes identification of the primary geochemical characteristics of the Cairngarroch complex. Selected analytical results are shown in Appendix 4 but these have considerable ranges and are of doubtful value in petrogenetic terms. However, Allen et al. argued that K:Rb ratios suggested an order of evolving intrusive lithologies whereby the microdiorite was intruded first, followed by the microtonalite and with the granodiorite as the final intrusive phase. This supports and extends the order of intrusion deduced from field relationships.

CALEDONIAN DYKE SWARM

Dykes exposed in the Rhins of Galloway district form part of the Southern Uplands regional swarm and are concentrated in the southern half of the peninsula. They are a common feature of the coastal sections throughout the district and it is likely that their absence from the 1:50 000 solid geology map over much of the inland part of the district simply reflects the relatively poor exposure there. Many more dykes are present than it has been possible to show on that map. The dykes range in composition from dark-coloured mica-bearing and hornblende-bearing lamprophyres to feldspar-porphyries and fine-grained felsites. The mica-lamprophyres are largely confined to the area south of the Portencorkrie plutonic complex and are a continuation of the narrow NE-trending regional zone which extends across the whole of the Southern Uplands (Rock et al., 1986). The dykes are generally thin (up to 2 m) and in the field appear to vary from fresh to completely altered. Hornblende-lamprophyres are also present in this zone but, in addition, have a wide distribution to the north of the Portencorkrie complex. The hornblende-lamprophyres are also generally thin (1–2 m) but may rarely reach 10 m in thickness. The porphyrites and felsites are generally lighter in colour and are commonly pervasively altered. They are present throughout the Rhins of Galloway district but are dominant in the northern part and most abundant in the central areas of the peninsula. Dykes are commonly intruded parallel to the bedding and so have a broadly NE–SW general trend consistent with the regional strike. However, the late Caledonian fault planes have also been utilised for dyke intrusion and so NNE or NW trends are locally dominant (Figure 23).

Petrography

Alteration to varying degrees is very common in all the dykes and consists largely of replacement of feldspars by sericite and carbonate and of pyroxenes by chlorite. This makes the identification of feldspar types impossible in many specimens and in others even the rock-type identification is made very difficult. However, enough relatively fresh dykes exist to allow the identification and description of the major varieties.

Mica-lamprophyres

These dykes are distinguished by the presence of brown biotite phenocrysts as the main mafic constituent; they have plagioclase as the most common feldspar and are therefore classed as kersantites. They exhibit a wide range of features on which they are divided into three types:

i. The first type has a fine-grained groundmass consisting largely of pale brown altered feldspar (probably plagioclase) some parts of which have a spherulitic (devitrification) texture. Biotite phenocrysts (up to 5 mm across) comprise around 10% of the rock and commonly have carbonate along cleavages. Pseudomorphs after a few pyroxene phenocrysts (up to 3 mm) are also present. Variation within this type is seen largely through changes in the quantity and sizes of the biotites. A fine-grained variant has up to 30% of modal biotite, commonly flow-aligned, set in a very fine, dark-coloured matrix and containing a number of chloritic pseudomorphs (up to 10%) probably after pyroxene. Another variant has both more abundant large (5 mm) zoned biotites (up to 20%) and large (up to 4 mm) euhedral pseudomorphs after pyroxene. Ocelli are common and contain carbonate with intergrown feldspars on their margins. Tiny scattered anhedral opaque grains are ubiquitous in accessory to minor quantities.

ii. The second type has a pale brown feldspathic matrix which is somewhat coarser than that seen in type i. The feldspathic matrix poikilitically encloses granular and lath-like clinopyroxenes (up to 1 mm across) and brown biotites which form 20% and 10% respectively of the mode (Plate 11a and b). The feldspar is somewhat altered and is either untwinned or simply twinned. The pyroxenes occur in groups and exhibit varying degrees of replacement by chlorite in some specimens and by quartz and carbonate in others. One specimen contains a large xenolith (>5 cm) consisting of a mosaic of intergrown coarse quartz. The xenolith is surrounded by a plagioclase-rich zone in which there is intergrown carbonate; tiny granular pyroxenes are abundant close to the xenolith.

iii. The third type only crops out adjacent to the northern margin of the Portencorkrie complex and is a brown amphibole-bearing variety. Large (up to 20 mm) brown zoned amphiboles (20%) and large (up to 10 mm) biotites (15%) are the main phenocryst phases (Plate 11c and d). Clinopyroxene phenocrysts (up to 8 mm) with some chloritic alteration, are more sparsely distributed (up to 5%). The groundmass is of plagioclase (andesine) with accessory to minor quantities of interstitial quartz. Carbonate ocelli (up to 3 mm) are present with both biotite and feldspar intergrown with the carbonate on their margins. Variation in this type extends to a lithology with more clinopyroxene phenocrysts (up to 5 mm and 10%), skeletal biotites (up to 3 mm and 10%) with only a few large (6 mm) brown zoned amphiboles; the groundmass in this case is of altered granular clinopyroxene and plagioclase. Xenoliths of quartz are present in several of the dykes of this type and have sharp contacts with the host lamprophyre.

Hornblende-lamprophyres

These dykes are characterised by amphibole as their main phenocryst phase with no accompanying biotite phenocrysts. The typical hornblende-lamprophyre has elongate brown amphiboles (30–45%) as phenocrysts (up to 5 mm) set in a groundmass of subhedral zoned plagioclases which have been sericitised to varying degrees (Plate 11e). This composition identifies the dykes as spessartites. The groundmass feldspar dimensions vary

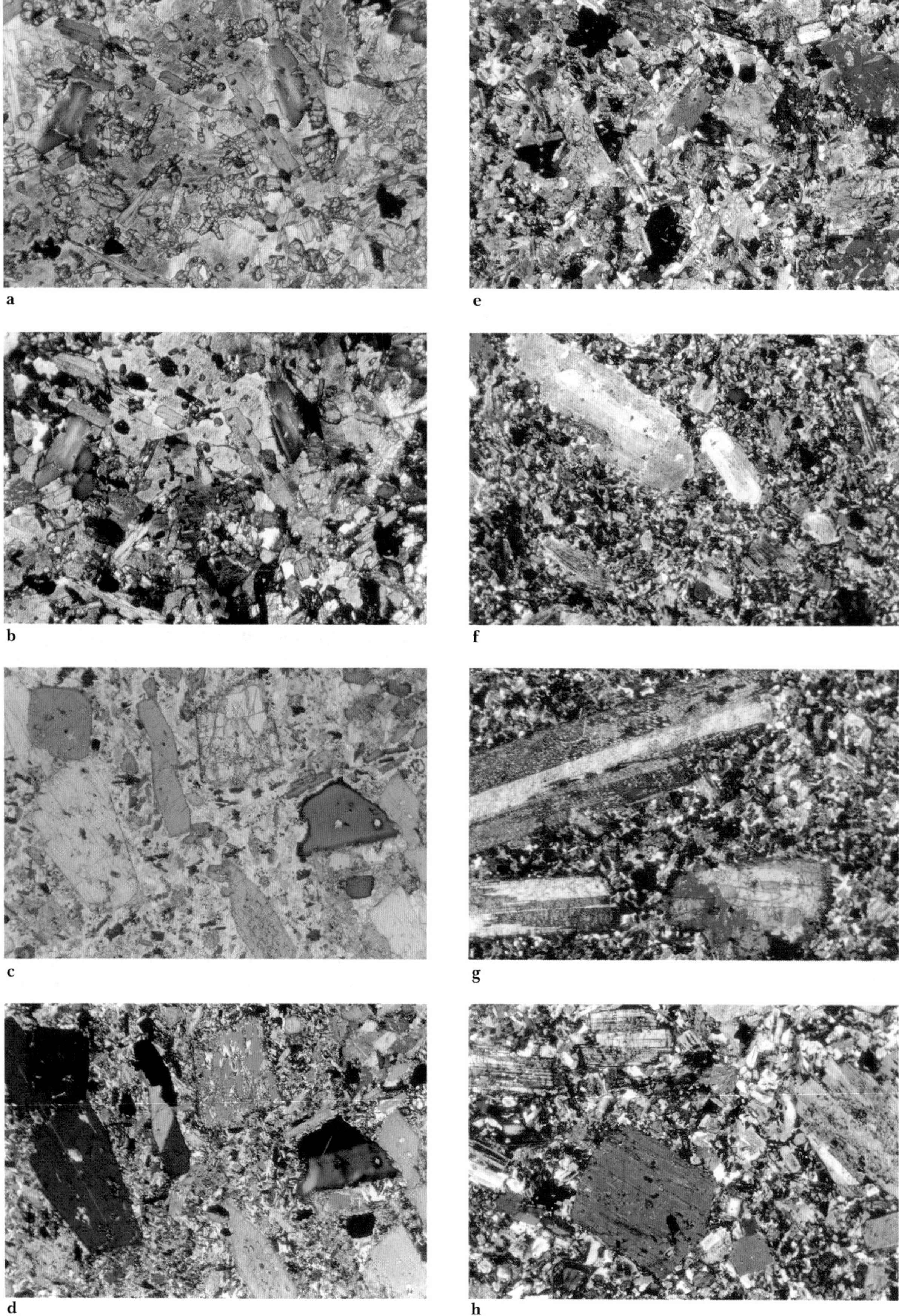
a
e
b
f
c
g
d
h

Plate 11 Representative photomicrographs illustrating the composition and texture of dykes from the Rhins of Galloway district.

a. and b. Pyroxene and biotite poikilitically enclosed in feldspathic matrix from a mica lamprophyre. a, plane polarised light; b, crossed polarisers ×25 GN018 and GN019.

c. and d. Amphibole and biotite phenocrysts in a mica lamprophyre. c, plane polarised light; d, crossed polarisers ×10 GN020.

e. Typical hornblende lamprophyre with amphibole phenocrysts in a sericitised plagioclase groundmass. Crossed polarisers ×10 GN021.

f. Porphyrite with large plagioclase and smaller biotite phenocrysts. Crossed polarisers ×10 GN022.

g. Porphyrite with plagioclase and clinopyroxene phenocrysts. Crossed polarisers ×10 GN023.

h. Porphyrite with plagioclase and amphibole phenocrysts. Crossed polarisers ×10 GN024.

Photomicrographs by Dr J W Gaskarth, University of Birmingham.

from 2 mm to less than 0.25 mm, hence different specimens have differing porphyritic textures. In some varieties needle-like amphiboles occur in a fine matrix, in others the phenocrysts and groundmass plagioclase laths are aligned, producing trachytic flow textures, and yet in others the brown amphiboles are zoned and associated with large (5 mm) subhedral clinopyroxene phenocrysts (10–15%). The clinopyroxene shows varying amounts of replacement by chlorite and may be associated with coarse epidote. In the coarser rocks apatite needles, up to 1 mm long, are common accessories. Less-common features of the hornblende-lamprophyres include:

i. Carbonate-filled ocelli (up to 5 mm) with some feldspar intergrown at the margins.

ii. A round xenolith (15 mm) consisting of a concentration of fine green amphibole (up to 0.25 mm) within which are larger (1 mm) brown amphiboles apparently being replaced by the green form.

iii. A very fine-grained feldspathic groundmass in which there are skeletal irregular brown amphiboles (20% and up to 4 mm).

iv. Veins of amphibole-poor fine-grained feldspathic material, with accessory quartz, which cut the normal rock and appear to be segregations.

PORPHYRITES AND FELSITES

These lithologies are grouped together because of their common high content of plagioclase and a general absence of large quantities of mafic minerals. Subdivision is based on the presence or absence of phenocrysts and their mineralogy. The non-porphyritic variety, felsite, consists of small (0.25 mm) plagioclases (90%) intergrown with small (0.5 mm) needle-like altered amphiboles (5%). Rare examples are even more finely grained and are composed of a mass of spherulitic feldspars with a few small patches of quartz and carbonate. Porphyritic lithologies are more abundant. A common variety, feldspar porphyrite, has a groundmass of small subhedral plagioclases, with minor chlorite, surrounding subhedral plagioclase phenocrysts ranging up to 5 mm in size and from 40% down to 10% in abundance. Minor amphibole and/or biotite are also present. These rocks are all pervasively sericitised and generally altered. Three less-common porphyritic 'felsic' dyke lithologies have also been observed:

i. A plagioclase- and biotite-phyric variety has up to 40% plagioclase phenocrysts and 5% biotites set in a generally fine-grained groundmass (Plate 11f). The groundmass shows a variety of chill/quench features including small (0.25 mm) plagioclases mixed with numerous small (0.5 mm) spherulites and myrmekitic quartz–feldspar intergrowths occurring both on large phenocrysts and as round spherulitic bodies. The plagioclase phenocrysts are variably sericitised and the biotites are commonly replaced by chlorite with many tiny needles of rutile. Apatite (up to 0.5 mm) and sphene are common accessories along with small granular opaques. One specimen, from the southern part of the peninsula, contains a small (10 mm) round xenolith of fine-grained mica-lamprophyre, and in other dykes a few small (up to 3 mm) round quartz xenocrysts with reaction rims are also present.

ii. A plagioclase- and clinopyroxene-phyric variety has large (up to 10 mm) zoned elongate plagioclase laths (20%) with similarly sized euhedral clinopyroxenes (15%) showing various degrees of chloritic replacement (Plate 11g). The groundmass consists of small (up to 0.5 mm) altered plagioclases with minor (up to 5%) biotite, interstitial quartz and granular opaques.

iii. A plagioclase and amphibole-phyric variety has large (up to 5 mm) phenocrysts of subhedral green amphibole (10–15%), zoned plagioclases (10–15%) and a few smaller (up to 2 mm) biotites in a fine-grained plagioclase-rich groundmass (Plate 11h).

VOLCANIC VENT AGGLOMERATE

A small volcanic vent exposed on the shore of Maryport Bay [NX 144 340] has been identified by McCurry (1990). The majority of the clasts forming the vent breccia, which has an outcrop diameter of about 50 m, are pervasively carbonatised greywackes but clasts of micromonzonite and feldspar-phyric porphyrite are also present. The presence within the vent of these characteristic Caledonian dyke lithologies suggests that vent formation was coeval with intrusion of the Caledonian dyke swarm. There is, however, no definite evidence for the age of the vent.

Geochemistry

Many of the dykes show pervasive alteration in thin section and this is emphasised by their variable loss on ignition (LOI) values, although some H_2O and CO_2 may be primary. For purposes of this discussion, analyses of only the least-altered lithologies are used and, to facilitate intersample comparisons in various discriminant diagrams, the major element analytical data used are recalculated to 100% volatile free. The analytical data for major and trace elements and the rare earth elements (REE), for both representative mica- and hornblende-bearing lamprophyres and for representative porphyrites, is summarised in Appendix 4. The SiO_2 values in both groups of lamprophyres are variable with the hornblende-lamprophyres generally having higher contents (54–62% as against 51–55%); the hornblende-lamprophyres (spessartites) are generally also higher in Al_2O_3. Conversely, the mica-lamprophyres (kersantites) are generally richer in K_2O, P_2O_5 and Fe_2O_3. Harker diagram plots (Figure 28) show discrimination between the two lamprophyre types, with the mica variety having higher K_2O and lower SiO_2 for the same MgO content. The porphyrites overlap with the hornblende-lamprophyres, with generally lower MgO and higher SiO_2 and K_2O. Plots of Cr v. MgO and total alkalis v. MgO do not discriminate between the groups but the former shows a strong correlation between the two 'elements'. Plots of K_2O v. SiO_2 and total alkalis v. SiO_2 show the mica-lamprophyres to lie in the fields typical of shoshonitic rocks, whereas the hornblende variety and the porphyrites are in the fields of high-K and medium-K andesites (Figure 29).

Compared with mid-ocean ridge basalt (MORB) the trace element abundance patterns (Figure 30) are virtually identical for both mica- and hornblende-lamprophyre, although the former appears a little more enriched, particularly in P and Th. They are both strongly enriched in the low field-strength elements (Sr, K, Rb, Ba, Th) and to a lesser degree in some high field-strength elements (Nb, Ce, P) and appear to be a little depleted in Ti, Y and Yb (normalising values are those of Pearce, 1982; 1983). The porphyrites have a similar pattern of enrichment of low field-strength elements and perhaps a little lower content of the other elements except Zr and Y. Determination of REE show both groups of lamprophyres to be LREE enriched relative to chondritic values with Ce_N in the range 42 to 125 and Yb_N at about 10.

A comparison of the dykes with other members of the regional swarm described elsewhere in the Southern Uplands (Barnes et al., 1986; Rock et al., 1986, cf. Macdonald et al., 1985) shows very marked similarities in overall chemistry and chemical patterns. The rocks in the Rhins of Galloway district probably therefore have a similar petrogenesis and include components from the deep mantle, the crust and deep-derived volatiles.

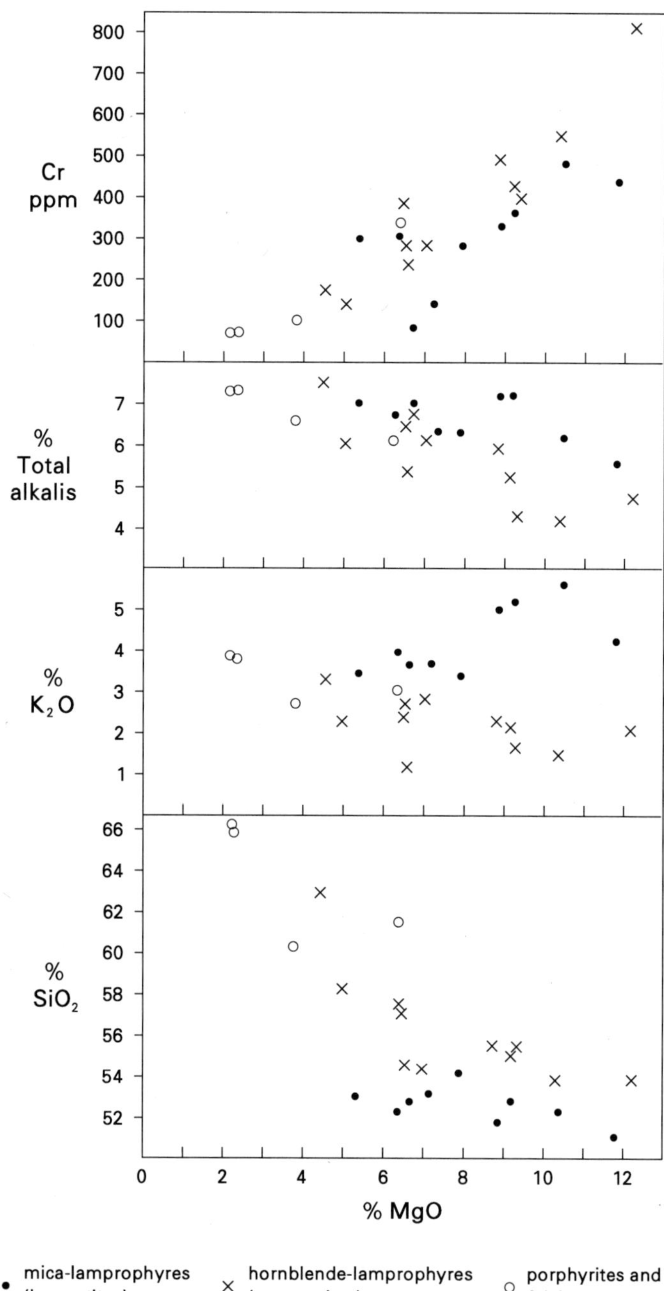

Figure 28 Variation diagrams with selected elements and major oxides against MgO (using data recalculated to 100% volatile-free) to show discrimination between mica- and hornblende-lamprophyres.

Timing of intrusion

Radiometric age determinations in the range 395–418 Ma (Rb-Sr and K-Ar) have been obtained for lamprophyre dykes in the Kirkcudbright area (Rock et al., 1986), north-eastwards along strike from the Rhins of Galloway district. No such absolute ages are available from the Rhins district but a few porphyrite dykes cut and therefore postdate the Portencorkrie plutonic complex which has been dated at 392 ± 19 Ma (Rb-Sr) (Figure 26c). The Portencorkrie complex is a post-tectonic intrusion and in the Rhins of Galloway district all of the dykes postdate the regional D_1 thrust-related deformation; dykes cross-cut slaty cleavage and fold hinges at numerous localities. However, McCurry (1990) reports that at least some dykes in the southern part of the Rhins peninsula were intruded prior to at least some of the localised D_2 deformation and the development of the associated crenulation cleavage. Furthermore, Barnes (1989) has described and figured lamprophyre dykes (kersantites), deformed by and intruded synchronously with the D_2 deformational event, from the Whithorn promontory on the opposite side of Luce Bay from the southern Rhins promontory. The lithologies concerned are identical to those on the Rhins from which they are only 25 km north-east along the regional strike. Dykes are also both cut by and intruded along the conjugate late Caledonian fault planes.

Within the Rhins of Galloway district an instructive sequence of strike-parallel, 1–3 m-thick porphyrite dykes is exposed on the coast at the south side of Finnarts Bay [NX 051 725]. The Glen App Fault is only a short distance to the north and, although the surrounding turbidite strata are deformed by D_3 strike-slip shearing, the northernmost dyke (closest to the fault) is entirely unaffected; it is a post-tectonic intrusion. In striking contrast, the next dyke, some 25 m farther south, is pervasively foliated with an irregular and anastomosing spaced fabric, steeply inclined and trending NE–SW parallel to the planar fabric in the enclosing sedimentary rocks. This dyke seems most likely to have been intruded prior to or during the D_3 deformation. Continuing southwards, the next porphyrite dyke shows only marginal foliation but has been boudinaged, with a partially brittle response, by horizontal extension. Either this dyke was intruded prior to deformation and was sufficiently robust to withstand it, or it was intruded during the closing stages of the D_3 event. The next dyke southward is entirely unfoliated and post-tectonic. A clear sequence emerges of porphyrite dyke intrusion spanning the D_3 deformational episode which is believed to have been mainly Wenlock and later in age (Barnes et al., 1989; cf. Barnes, 1989, table 3). A similar pattern emerges for the lamprophyres; both on the Rhins of Galloway and the Whithorn promontory their intrusion both preceded and followed D_2 deformation, whilst at The Hooies [NX 068 446], on the west coast of the Rhins, a lamprophyre dyke cuts across a large D_3 fold hinge.

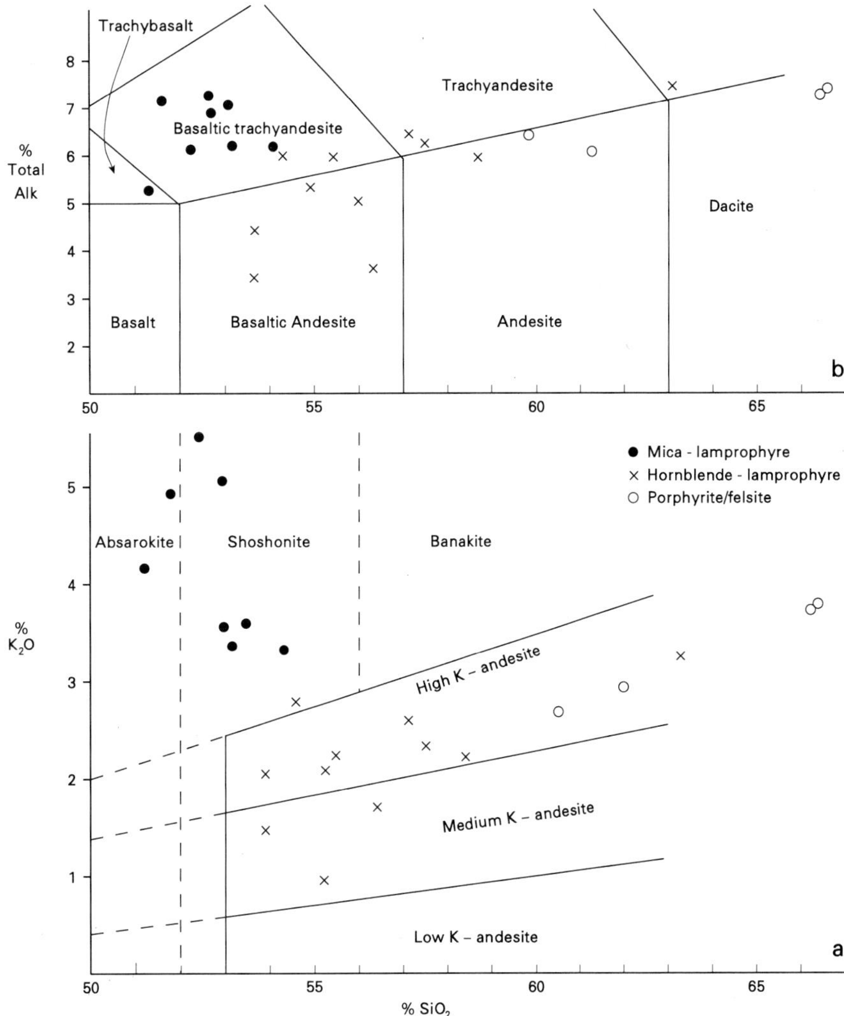

Figure 29 Compositional fields for lamprophyres and porphyrites from the Rhins of Galloway district. All analyses recalculated to 100% volatile-free, with total Fe as Fe_2O_3.

a. Comparison with conventional K-Si classification of calc-alkaline rocks with subdivisions shown after Peccerillo and Taylor (1976) and Gill (1981).
b. Comparison with total alkali-silica classification for all volcanic rocks with subdivisions after Le Maitre (1989).

A synthesis of all the regional evidence for the relationship of dyke intrusion to the deformation sequence reveals that dykes were intruded over a considerable time interval, from the late (or possibly mid-) Silurian to the early Devonian, and from pre-D_2 to post-tectonic (Figure 20). There was overlap in the emplacement of the different dyke types but the earliest may well have been the mica-lamprophyres, whereas the last dykes emplaced were probably porphyrites, examples of which cut the Portencorkrie complex. Elsewhere porphyrite dykes cut lamprophyre dykes and at least one porphyrite dyke contains probable lamprophyre xenoliths. The D_2 deformation was related to structural accommodation in the thrust hinterland (discussed further in Chapter Seven) whilst D_1 deformation was still active at the thrust front. The earliest lamprophyre intrusion (at least) was therefore taking place whilst thrust deformation was still active. The implication of these relationships for the geological development of the Southern Uplands thrust belt are considered at greater length by Barnes et al. (1986), Rock et al. (1986) and Stone et al. (1987).

TERTIARY DYKE SWARM

Throughout the Rhins of Galloway district sporadic dykes crop out which have a doleritic compositon, have been relatively little altered and have a broadly north to

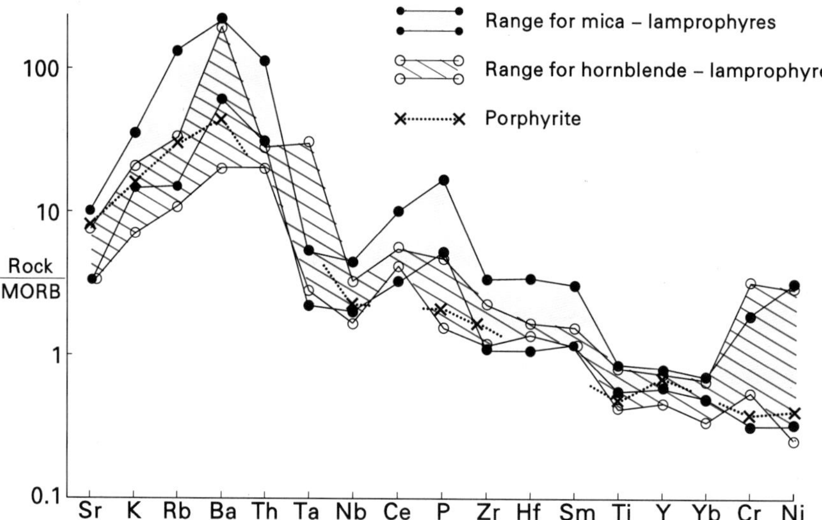

Figure 30 Ranges of MORB-normalised plots for mica- and hornblende-lamprophyres to show overlap and similarity of patterns. A representative porphyrite is shown for comparison.

Normalising values, after Pearce (1982; 1983), in ppm except where stated: Sr 120; K_2O 0.15%; Rb 2; Ba 20; Th 0.2; Ta 0.18; Nb 3.5; Ce 10; P_2O_5 12%; Zr 90; Hf 2.4; Sm 3.3; TiO_2 1.5%; Y 30; Yb 3.4; Cr 250; Ni 120.

north-west trend. Thickness of these dykes ranges from less than 10 cm up to about 4 m; the thinner dykes are extremely meandering and utilise bedding, cleavage, joint and fault planes to step sideways. By contrast, the thicker dykes maintain a very regular trend and outcrops can be tentatively linked over several hundred metres or more. Dyke margins are strongly chilled, basaltic and usually cut by closely spaced cooling joints which facilitate weathering such that exposed marginal faces of the dykes often have a honeycombed appearance. The central, coarser-grained portions of the dykes are doleritic with ophitic to subophitic texture developed between plagioclase (labradorite to bytownite; generally less than 2 mm in length) and augite. Olivine is usually present, but in very variable quantities, and typically is partially or wholly pseudomorphed by bowlingite, chlorite or serpentine. Accessory minerals include opaque spinels and rare analcime. The approximate proportions of the essential components are plagioclase 40–60%, augite 20–45%, olivine (including pseudomorphs) up to 20%. Amygdales are present in most specimens, particularly the finer-grained marginal lithologies, and may be filled with devitrified glassy residuum, carbonate, chlorite or zeolite.

In all respects the dykes are similar to the Tertiary dykes described by Harrison et al. (1987) from Ailsa Craig, 25 km north of the northernmost point of the Rhins peninsula. There the dykes cut the Ailsa Craig microgranite which has given a Rb/Sr isochron age of 61.5 ± 0.5 Ma (Harrison et al., 1987); this provides a likely maximum age for the dykes on the Rhins of Galloway. They seem most likely to be members of the Arran and/or Mull swarms.

NINE

Low-grade metamorphism of the Lower Palaeozoic sequence

Studies of low-grade metamorphism in the Lower Palaeozoic rocks of the Southern Uplands of Scotland by Oliver and Leggett (1980) have shown that the prehnite-pumpellyite facies is widely developed in volcaniclastic turbidites and associated metabasites. White mica (illite) crystallinity, mica b_o parameters and graptolite reflectance data recorded by Oliver et al. (1984) and Kemp et al. (1985), indicate that anchizonal and late diagenetic grades are commonly developed in mudrock lithologies. These studies employed a series of low density north–south sampling traverses across the Southern Uplands, including a 32-sample traverse of the Rhins of Galloway (Oliver et al., 1984). Based on the improved tectonostratigraphical scheme described in this memoir (Figure 6), a collaborative study with Birkbeck College, London University, examined white mica crystallinity in the Rhins of Galloway district using a sampling density of approximately 1 mudrock per 2.5 km^2 (Merriman and Roberts, 1993). Results were used to generate a contoured metamorphic map (Figure 31).

The white mica crystallinity survey sampled typical fine-grained mudrock lithologies which together constitute up to about 5 per cent of the stratigraphical succession seen in each greywacke formation or tectonostratigraphical unit. Mudrocks form interbeds of variable thickness within all of the greywacke-dominated sequences and form the major part of the underlying Moffat Shale Group. With advancing deformation and metapelitic grade, the mudstone and shale transform to slate, which commonly has cleavage developed subparallel with bedding lamination. The slate has occasionally been worked for local roofing use, as at Grennan quarries [NX 127 394], but is generally of poor commercial quality.

Detailed optical, scanning electron microscope (SEM) and transmission electron microscope (TEM) textural studies of representative mudrock samples confirm that diagenetic-zone mudstones, with white mica crystallinity (Kubler) indices $\Delta°2\theta$ >0.42, typically contain silt-size grains of quartz, albite, K-feldspar, biotite flakes, magnetite and rare chromite, in a phyllosilicate matrix which may lack an obvious fabric. Weakly cleaved shale and slate of the anchizone (0.24–0.42 $\Delta°2\theta$) has a bedding-parallel fabric of abundant albite and detrital mafic phyllosilicates, minor quartz, anatase and apatite in a matrix of anastomosing phyllosilicate intergrowths. As cleavage development strengthens, slate of epizonal grade ($\Delta°2\theta$ <0.24) shows coarser intergrowths of orientated phyllosilicates enclosing grains of quartz, albite and detrital phyllosilicate.

Textures and the crystallite size of phyllosilicates forming the matrix of representative mudrock samples were studied by TEM (Merriman et al., in press). Phyllosilicate textures include nanometric-scale folds, annealed fold-hinge fractures and numerous crystal dislocations, recording a complex history of brittle and ductile deformation. Accommodation in the core of folds resulted in kinking and intracrystalline dislocation parallel to the (001) planes of the intergrown chlorite and phengite crystallites. Hinge-line fractures at high angles to the (001) planes have also developed and have been annealed by subsequent growth of phyllosilicates along the (001) planes, resulting in a meshwork of intergrown chlorite and phengite crystallites. The thickness of white mica and chlorite crystallites, measured normal to (001), shows size distributions positively skewed towards thicker crystallites. Both the mode and the mean of the crystallite populations increase with advancing grade, but white mica appears to grow more rapidly than chlorite.

The less-than 2 μm mineralogy of 200 mudrock samples was analysed by X-ray diffraction (XRD) techniques at Birkbeck College, London University. Diagenetic-zone mudstone and shale both consist of chlorite with subordinate illite and corrensite and minor amounts of kaolinite, mixed-layer illite/smectite, albite, quartz and hematite. Illites show broad, generally symmetrical 10Å peaks with Kubler indices in the range 0.42–0.66 $\Delta°2.\theta$. Considerably broader, asymmetrical 10Å peaks are found in metabentonites in the Moffat Shale Group, due to the abundance of mixed-layer illite-smectite (Merriman and Roberts, 1990). The metabentonite results were not included in the white mica crystallinity database since their correlation with the mudstone results is uncertain. Shale and slate of anchizonal grade are typically composed of chlorite and phengitic $2M_1$ K-mica, with minor albite and quartz; neither corrensite nor paragonite are detectable in the <2 μm fractions. Epizonal slates contain $2M_1$ K-mica and chlorite, with minor albite, quartz and rutile.

Analytical electron microscope (AEM) analyses of chlorites indicate that, with advancing grade, the contents of silica and alkalis are reduced, reflecting the progressive elimination of interlayered corrensite. As grade advances, phengite crystallites become progressively less siliceous and more aluminous, with a slight increase in magnesium content (Merriman et al., in prep.).

Kubler indices from the 200 mudrock samples were used to generate the contoured white mica crystallinity map (Figure 31); the techniques used to obtain crystallinity data and the basis for selecting the isocryst intervals used are detailed elsewhere (Roberts et al., 1991). The map shows that, over much of the district, isocrysts commonly trend subparallel to the traces of the strike-parallel faults. Contour intervals, such as the diagenetic/anchizone and anchizone/epizone boundaries, are commonly faulted discontinuities and grade may change abruptly across many of the tectonostratigraphical tract boundary faults. These features suggest a close relation-

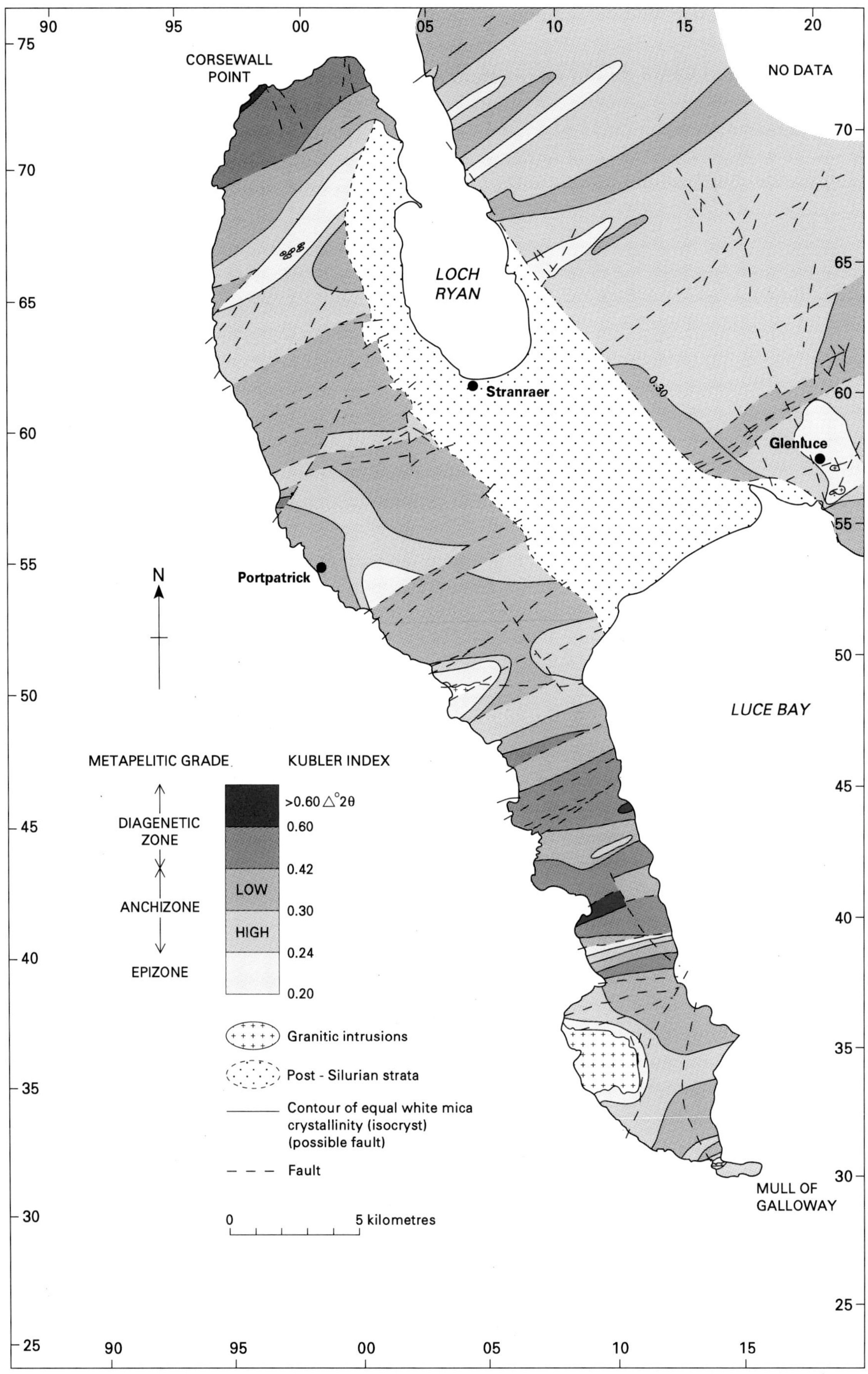

Figure 31 Contoured metamorphic map of white mica crystallinity (Kubler) indices for the Rhins of Galloway district.

ship between the imbrication of the succession and regional metamorphism. Although no systematic variation in grade in relation to the younging direction of strata is found within fault-bounded tracts, the distribution of crystallinity data in relation to the tectonostratigraphy shows metamorphic grade rising southward through the Leadhills Group. Thereafter it decreases farther south through sequentially younger tracts of Gala Group strata but then increases abruptly southward into the Hawick Group. This is illustrated by the ranges and mean values of Kubler indices for the major tectonostratigraphical units which are shown in Figure 32 plotted on a biostratigraphical chart simplified from Figure 6. The oldest strata, forming the Corsewall Formation, are predominantly of late diagenetic grade. South-east of the Glen App Fault, the metamorphic grade, as indicated by ranges and mean Kubler indices, increases abruptly into younger strata so that most samples from the Kirkcolm, Portpatrick and Shinnel formations possess Kubler indices characteristic of the mid- or high-anchizone. Due to limited exposure, data is very sparse for Gala Group tracts 1, 2 and 3 cropping out south of the Orlock Bridge Fault. However, white mica crystallinity data from the Kirkcowan district (Sheet 4W) indicates that grade initially falls on crossing the Orlock Bridge Fault into Gala 1, but again increases into Gala tracts 2 and 4. In the Rhins of Galloway district grade generally falls across the sequentially younger Gala tracts 4, 6,and 7, with the result that late diagenetic mudstones are widely distributed in the southern part of the Gala Group between the Mull of Logan and Port Logan (Figure 31). The wide range of Kubler indices found in the Gala 8 unit is due to a belt of high-anchizonal to epizonal, laminated silty slates forming a strike-parallel belt passing through Grennan Plantation [NX 125 397] and possibly faulted against late diagenetic grade mudstones. Across the Clanyard Bay Fault Zone, grade increases abruptly in the Hawick Group. This may be partly as a result of contact effects from the Portencorkrie granodiorite but, well outside the likely area of contact metamorphism, regional grade increases from the Cairnharrow into the younger Carghidown Formation, where both slates and interbedded sandstones have a penetrative cleavage.

Isocrysts which trend at high angles to the tract-bounding faults in Figure 31, mostly reflect contact overprinting of the pattern of regional metamorphism by late Silurian/early Devonian granitoid intrusions and dyke complexes (see Chapter Eight). Contact metamorphism typically reaches high-anchizone or epizonal grades and develops a pattern of isocrysts broadly concentric with an igneous outcrop, as seen around the Portencorkrie and Cairngarroch intrusions; this effect is generally wider than the aureole delineated by recognisable hornfelsing. Similar patterns are seen around the geophysically delin-

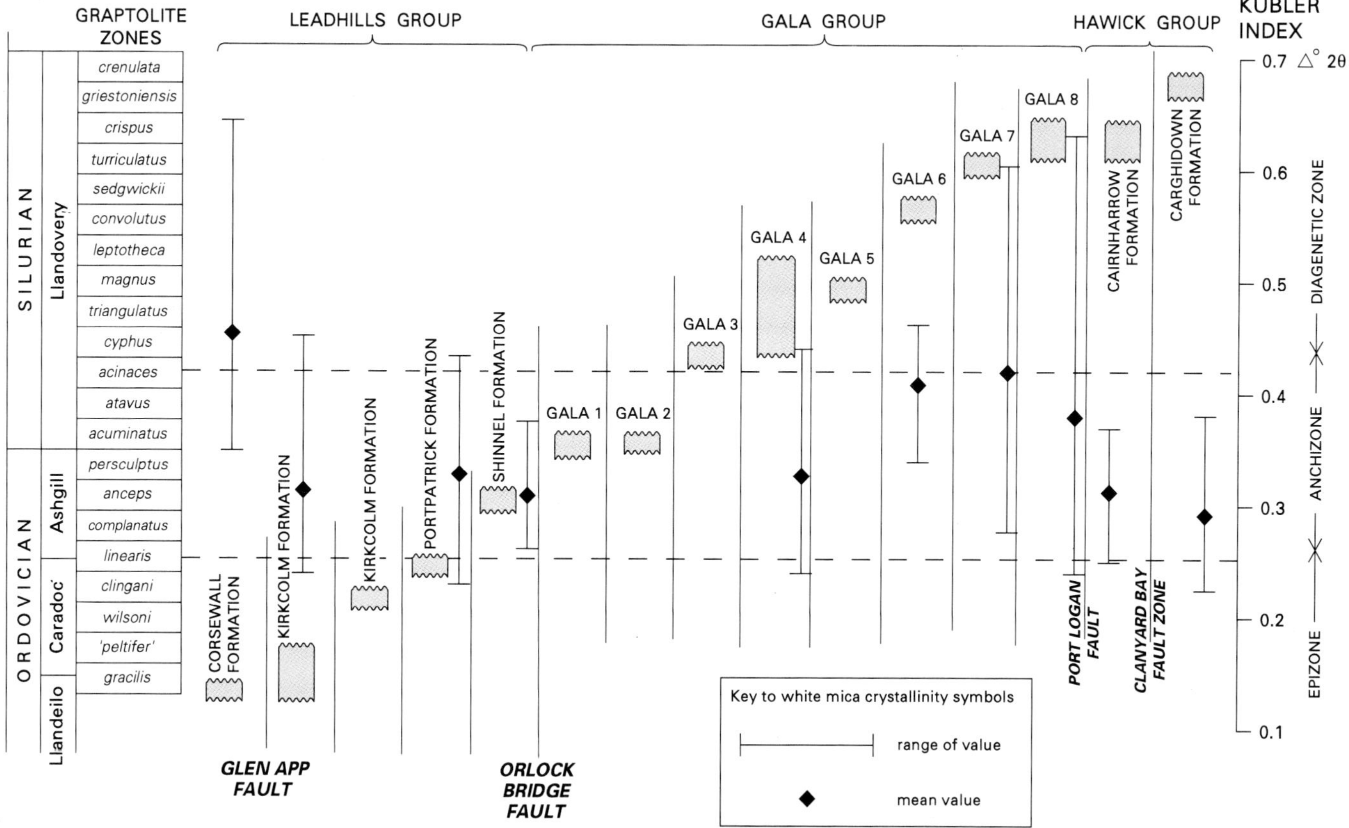

Figure 32 White mica crystallinity ranges for each of the Lower Palaeozoic tectonostratigraphical units.

eated but concealed intrusion at Sandhead (Kimbell and Stone, 1992), and in the Portpatrick Formation north-west of the Morroch Bay Fault where the epizone isocrysts have a semicircular trace. However, in this latter example there is no corresponding geophysical expression. The concentric patterns developed around the Cairngarroch and Sandhead intrusions extend across the Cairngarroch Fault, indicating that igneous emplacement occurred after the sinistral strike-slip fault movement proposed by Anderson and Oliver (1986).

Normal faulting associated with the development of the Loch Ryan–Luce Bay Permo-Carboniferous basin has exposed different levels of burial in metamorphosed and imbricated Lower Palaeozoic strata. Both the isocryst map (Figure 31) and statistical analysis of the white mica crystallinity dataset indicate that grade is consistently lower in the steeply dipping Ordovician rocks on the downthrown western side of the Loch Ryan Fault compared with the equivalent similarly steeply inclined strata to the east. These relationships imply that a depth-related pattern of metamorphism was acquired by burial of already steeply inclined strata. If the succession had initially acquired a pattern of normal burial metamorphism whereby grade increases into older strata, and had been subsequently imbricated and rotated, older strata would still be expected to show higher grades than younger strata. Across the Northern Belt and parts of the Central Belt, the regional pattern is in fact one of inverted burial metamorphism, with grade increasing into sequentially younger tracts of strata. Such a pattern of regional metamorphism is consistent with its development during thrust imbrication whereby younger strata were buried beneath older strata. Within the Northern Belt the crystallinity data therefore supports a deformation sequence whereby tracts comprising the NW-younging Kirkcolm, Portpatrick and Shinnel formations were sequentially underthrust and buried beneath the older Corsewall Formation. The diagenetic state of the Corsewall Formation confirms that it formed the upper unit of the thrust stack but the broadly comparable metamorphic grade of the younger units suggests that they each experienced a similar history of underthrusting. They must therefore each have been accreted into the leading edge of the thrust system within a duplex developed beneath an upper thrust stack which contained the Corsewall Formation.

Since there is no evidence for the imposition of burial metamorphism through increasing thickness of sedimentary overburden, a significant rider to this model is the possibility that thrusting commenced soon after deposition of the Kirkcolm Formation if not earlier, that is in the late Ordovician. This is compatible with the accretionary prism model of Leggett et al. (1979) shown in Figure 3 but would require earlier closure in the back-arc model of Stone et al. (1987) than has been previously suggested (Figure 4). The underthrust tracts acquired a depth-related pattern of metamorphism as they were imbricated and steepened; they are possible *tectonic* analogues of the underplated slate belts within the Kodiak accretionary complex (Sample and Moore, 1987). Underthrusting appears to have continued into the early Llandovery, but the depth of burial probably declined within the *convolutus* Biozone, and underthrusting may have ceased within the *turriculatus* Biozone. Back thrusting of the SE-younging strata of the Gala 8 unit, now cropping out south of the Port Logan Fault (McCurry and Anderson, 1989; see discussion in Chapter Seven) as part of the top of the thrust stack, is consistent with its widespread mudstones and shales late diagenetic grade. However, the Clanyard Bay Fault Zone appears to represent a significant metamorphic discontinuity, with grade and hence probable depth of burial increasing abruptly into the Hawick Group. Burial of the Hawick Group is not consistent with underthrusting since, in this case, strata young towards the south-east. The increased complexity and deformation within the Hawick Group may in itself be enough to explain this metamorphic contrast but an alternative possible explanation is that late, out of sequence thrusting on the Clanyard Bay Fault Zone carried the Gala Group, forming the top of the thrust stack, south-eastwards over the Hawick Group. Another possible explanation for the abrupt changes seen across the major strike faults on the Rhins of Galloway, hinges on their late reactivation as normal faults. Thus different levels of the thrust stack could be juxtaposed; a good example of this effect (Figure 33) is the separation of the diagenetic grade Corsewall Formation from the upper anchizonal Kirkcolm Formation by the Glen App Fault.

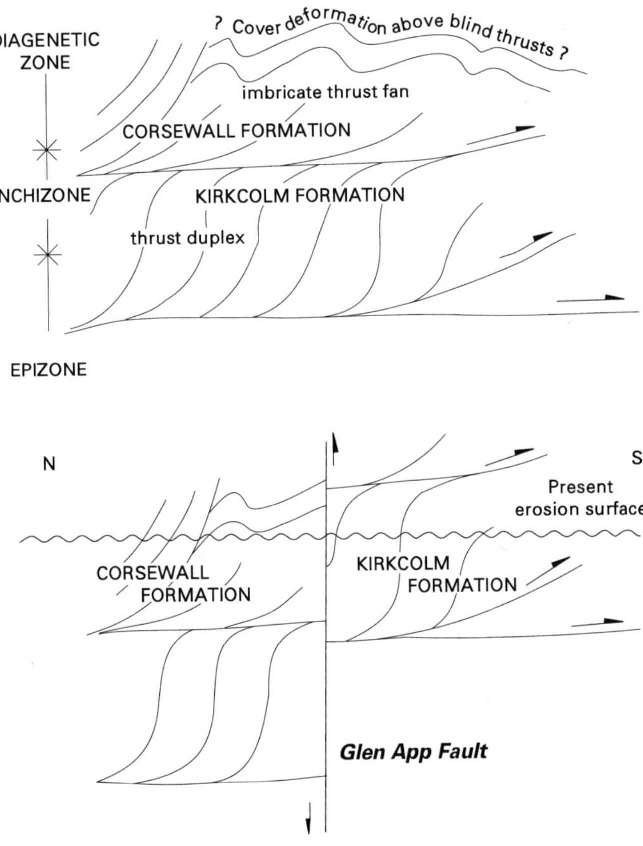

Figure 33 Development of burial metamorphism within an imbricate thrust stack. Subsequent faulting juxtaposes different grades.

TEN
Carboniferous and Permian strata of the Stranraer Basin

The occurrence of Upper Palaeozoic strata containing plant fragments on the western side of Loch Ryan was first reported by Moore (1842), although he comments that they had '...long been known to exist and have led to several fruitless researches for coal...' Although exposure is very sporadic, an unconformable relationship with the underlying Lower Palaeozoic greywackes is apparent. Further, the early surveyors correctly surmised that the Stranraer isthmus, Loch Ryan and Luce Bay were underlain by Upper Palaeozoic rocks, principally Permian breccias, which terminated eastwards against the Loch Ryan Fault, marked by a pronounced break of slope. The depth of the basin and confirmation of its overall shape were established by geophysical surveys (Mansfield and Kennett, 1963; Bott, 1964). These showed an asymmetric basin with its axis close to the Loch Ryan Fault; approximately 1.5 to 2 km of strata are preserved in the deepest part. Independent confirmation of these dimensions was provided by a comparison of stratigraphical and structural patterns on either side of the basin (Kelling and Welsh, 1970), although subsequent geological revision may have devalued the results of their analysis. Nevertheless, the morphology of the Stranraer basin is not in dispute: a thick sequence against the eastern boundary fault thins westward to overlie unconformably Lower Palaeozoic greywackes (Figure 34). This is a typical half-graben structure, one of several which trend approximately NW–SE and sequentially transect the Southern Uplands terrane from Northern Ireland to Moffat. The Stranraer basin apparently narrows and closes in the north whereas the broader southern end is abruptly terminated at the Cairnholy Fault (Figure 34), an early Caledonian structure presumably utilised as a transfer fault and partially reactivated during Permian extension. A similar, but much smaller, transfer effect is seen in the vicinity of the Orlock Bridge Fault, whilst the unconformity of the Permian over the Lower Palaeozoic strata shows signs of syndepositional faulting adjacent to several of the Caledonian strike faults. The geophysical evidence for the shape of the Stranraer basin is discussed more fully in Chapter Eleven. One significant result of the likely pivotal opening of the Stranraer basin would have been the clockwise rotation, by a few degrees, of Caledonian structural strike trends on the Rhins of Galloway peninsula relative to their orientation on the eastern side of the Loch Ryan Fault.

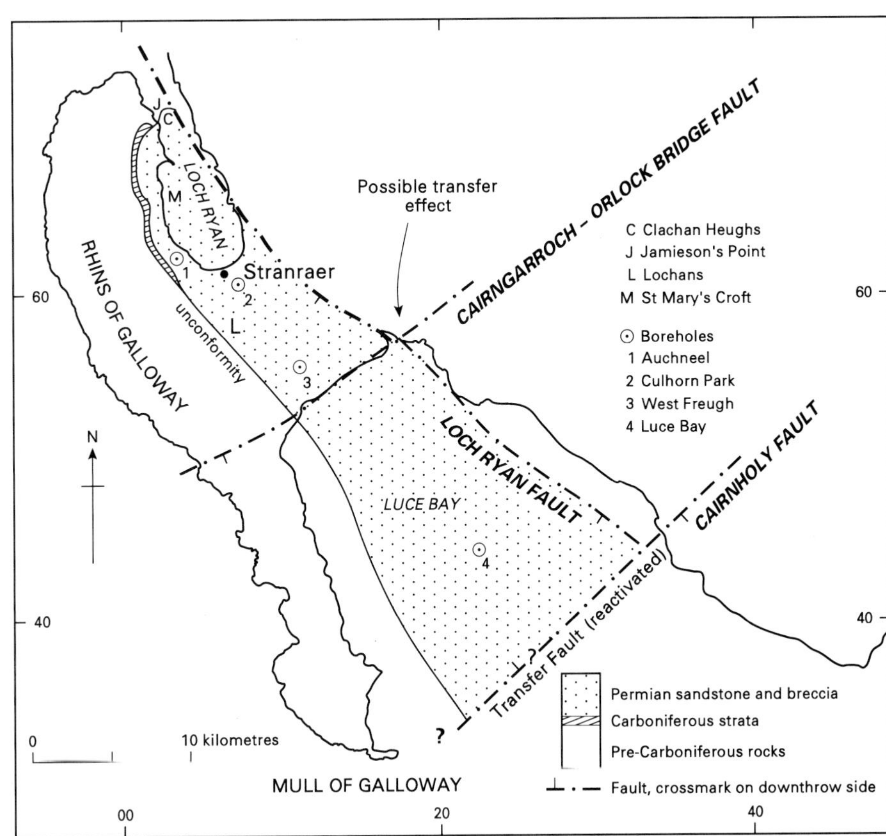

Figure 34 Summary map for the Stranraer Permian basin.

CARBONIFEROUS

Leswalt Formation

On the eastern side of the northern Rhins peninsula the basal strata of the Stranraer basin sequence are approximately 30 m of grey, red and mottled yellow-brown sandstones interbedded with purplish grey shales and rare seatclays. These beds have a variable but generally gentle easterly dip and lie unconformably on the steeply inclined Lower Palaeozoic greywackes. They crop out as a narrow north–south strip between Jamieson's Point [NX 032 711] and Lochans [NX 060 572]. In general terms the sequence becomes more arenaceous upwards (Fuller, 1958) with the micaceous sandstones containing sporadic poorly preserved plant remains. A slightly better-preserved flora from thin interbedded siltstones was collected by Macconochie in 1871 (reported in Geikie and Irvine, 1873) and by Manson in 1919. It has been re-examined by P J Brand who has identified the following:

Alethopteris cf. *lonchitica*
Asterophyllites cf. *equisetiformis*
A. aff. *longifolius*
Calamites sp.
Stigmaria ficoides
S. minuta
S. sp.
Lepidodendroid shoot indet.

On the basis of the distribution of flora given by Chaloner and Collinson (1986) this assemblage seems most likely to be of Westphalian age. The Carboniferous strata thus belonging to either the Lower or Middle Coal Measures.

A single basalt sheet, probably a lava flow, occurs within the Carboniferous sequence. It is pervasively weathered olivine-basalt with the olivine phenocrysts set in a groundmass of augite and labradorite. Similar lavas which occur farther north, in association with apparent Permian breccia at Ballantrae (Stone 1988) and in the much more extensive uppermost Carboniferous sequence of Ayrshire, have ages ranging from late in the Namurian to early in the Westphalian (Mykura, 1965). From Ayrshire Mykura has also described probable Carboniferous plants in sedimentary rocks between basalts at the base of the Mauchline 'Permian' succession. These possible associates are all compatible with the Westphalian age deduced at Stranraer and illustrate the problems involved in correctly identifying the Carboniferous–Permian boundary.

PERMIAN

Loch Ryan Formation

Although the general attitude of the red sandstone and breccia beds assigned to the Permian is similar to that of the underlying Westphalian strata, the Upper Coal Measures are apparently missing and an unconformable relationship has been deduced by Hinxman and Macgregor (1920) and by Fuller (1958). The Permian rocks exposed are breccias of greywacke clasts (up to 25 cm diameter) in a red sandstone matrix (Plate 12; Loch Ryan Breccia Formation of Brookfield, 1978) with thin interbeds of red sandstone locally. The breccias are dominant and form sea cliffs on the western shore of Loch Ryan at Clachan Heughs [NX 036 702] (Figure 34) where bedding dips a few degrees generally towards the north-west or south-east. The proportion of sandstone interbeds is higher in the intertidal exposures about 5 km farther south near Glenside and St Mary's Croft [NX 035 663] where bedding has a variable but always shallow dip. However, still farther south at Auchneel [NX 037 620] a water bore proved 90 m of breccia identical to that exposed at Clachan Heughs with no significant sandstone interbeds (Ball and Robins, 1985). Breccia was also reported from a borehole on the south-east side of Stranraer near Culhorn Park [NX 069 599] (Ball and Robins, 1985). On the south side of the Stranraer isthmus 134 m of breccia have been proved in another borehole at

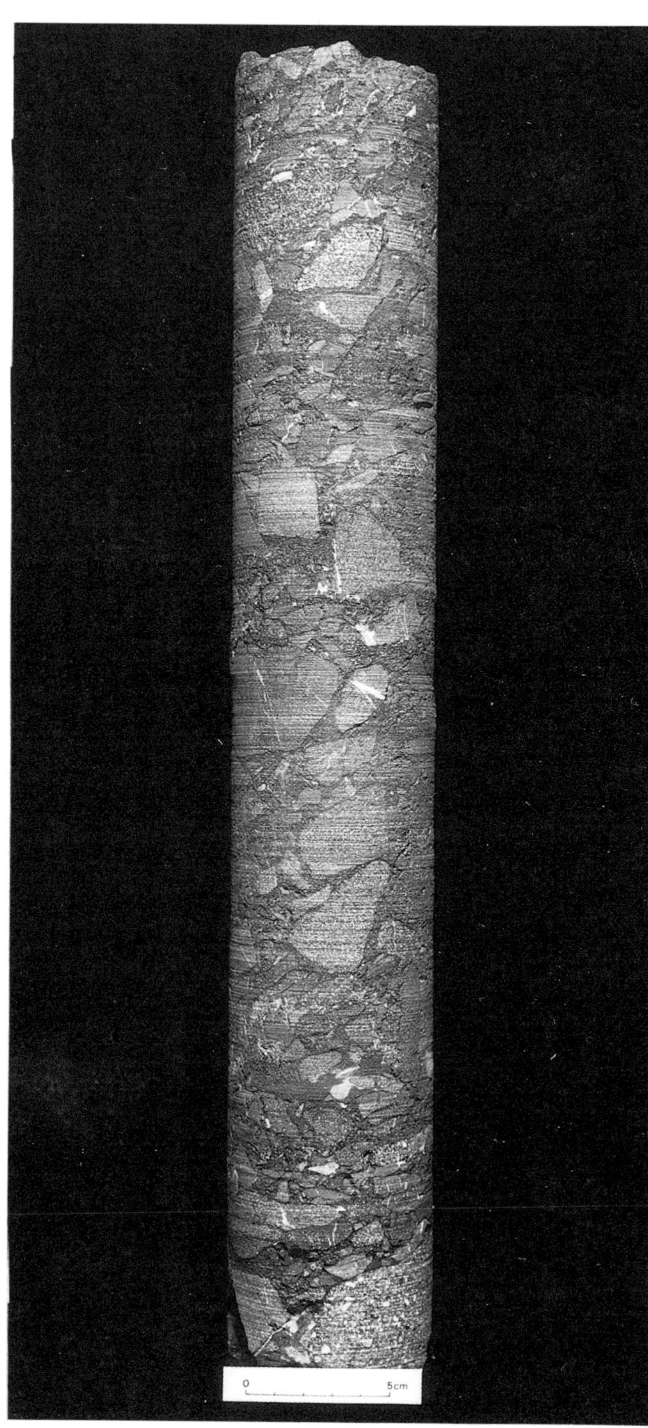

Plate 12 Permian greywacke breccia of the Loch Ryan Formation sampled in a borehole at Auchneel [NX 038 619] (MNS 5150).

West Freugh [NX 108 544], overlying at least 24 m of sandstone (Gauss, 1969). Still farther south, in the central part of Luce Bay an offshore borehole has proved red-brown sandstone (Institute of Geological Sciences, 1982). It is difficult to determine stratigraphical trends within this dataset but an irregular southwards decrease in the breccia:sandstone ratio seems likely. This could imply a northerly source for the breccias and, although pebble imbrication within them is highly variable, Brookfield (1978, fig. 18) was able to demonstrate derivation from the northerly quadrant at Clachan Heughs. The greywackes all have a very local provenance in the Lower Palaeozoic strata but Fuller (1958) considered that distinctive detrital heavy minerals in the breccia matrix were derived from the local Carboniferous succession. Regional correlation of the Permian succession has been discussed by Brookfield (1978) and Stone (1988). An early Permian age seems most likely but cannot be firmly established in the absence of any fossil control.

Hydrogeological tests on the Permian breccias by Robins and Buckley (1988) showed low permeability and minimal yield from test bores; groundwater potential is therefore small.

ELEVEN
Regional geophysical interpretations

Regional Bouguer gravity and magnetic data (Figure 35a and b respectively) provide valuable insights into aspects of the concealed geology of the Rhins of Galloway district. For example pronounced negative gravity effects are observed over the accumulations of relatively low-density sedimentary rocks in the Stranraer and Portpatrick basins, while the aeromagnetic survey of the district delineates magnetic igneous intrusions as well as providing some indications of deeper structure. No seismic reflection data are available for the onshore area, but an offshore survey by the British Institutions Reflection Profiling Syndicate (WINCH line, Figure 36) has imaged structures in the lower crust interpreted as relating to the Iapetus suture zone (Brewer et al., 1983; Hall et al., 1984; Beamish and Smythe, 1986). Further details of the geophysical interpretations relating to the Rhins of Galloway district, together with a review of available rock physical property data, are given by Kimbell (1991).

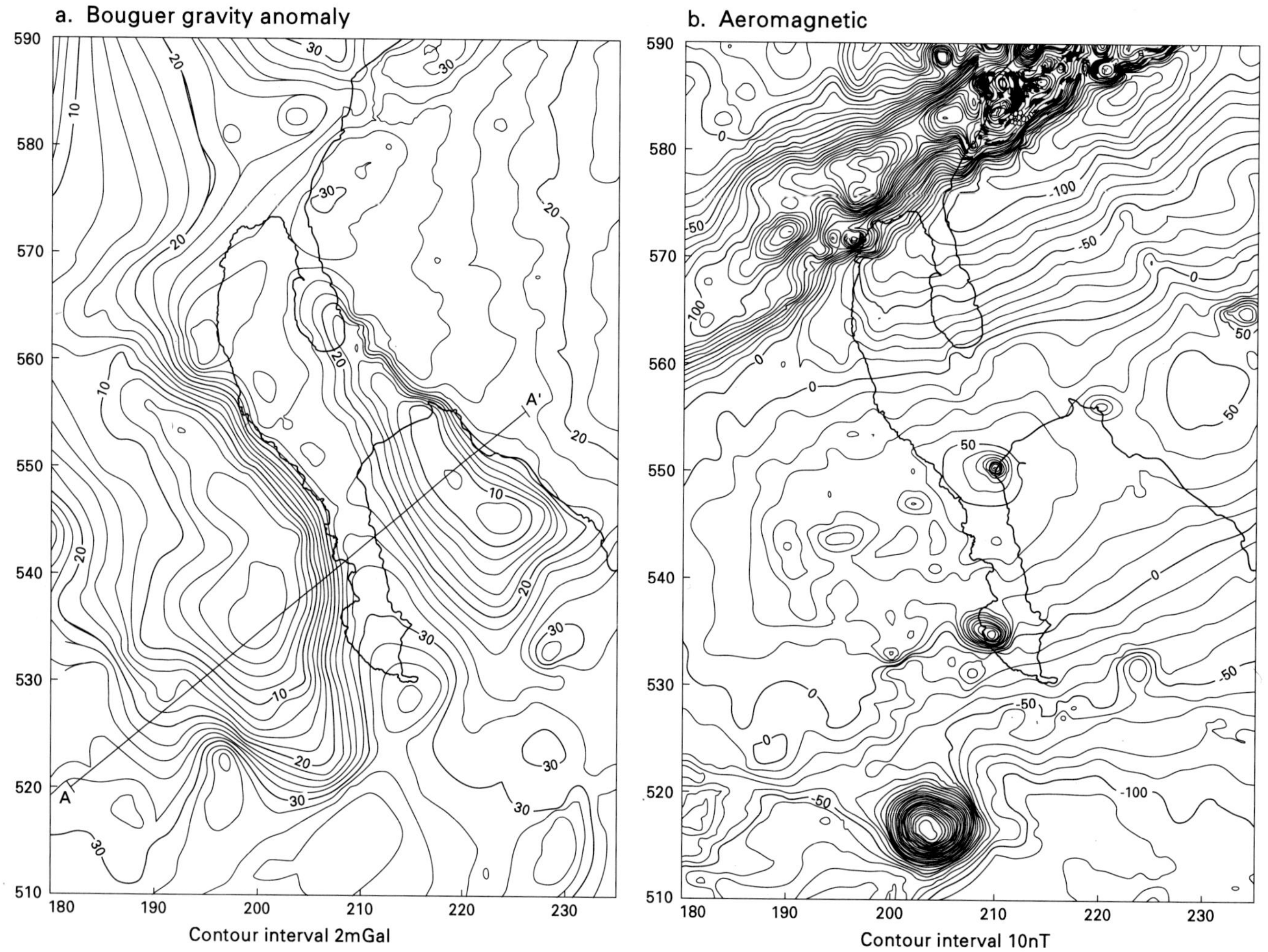

Figure 35 Geophysical data for the Rhins of Galloway district and surrounding area.

a. Bouguer gravity anomaly map. Anomalies calculated against the Geodetic Reference System 1967 and referred to the National Gravity Reference Net 1973. Reduction density = 2.72 Mg/m^3. Contour interval = 2 mGal.

b. Reduced to the pole aeromagnetic map. Contour interval = 10 nT.

GRAVITY SURVEYS

The Bouguer gravity anomaly map for the Rhins of Galloway district (Figure 35a) is based on data from several sources. The land stations are from surveys by Durham University (Mansfield and Kennett, 1963) and by BGS. Most of the marine data were acquired by BGS using a ship-borne gravity meter (Tully, 1969; Day and Sunderland, 1970; Wright et al., 1971) but there are also some sea-bottom gravity observations in the Firth of Clyde (McLean and Deegan, 1978) and in, and to the south of, Luce Bay (Bott, 1964).

The most prominent features on the Bouguer anomaly map (Figure 35a) are the pronounced lows elongated in a NW–SE direction associated with the Stranraer Basin to the east of the Rhins of Galloway peninsula and the Portpatrick Basin to the west. Their approximate extents, as defined by the gravity data, are indicated in the geophysical summary map (Figure 36) which includes two Bouguer anomaly contours (5 and 10 mGal) to show where the greatest thicknesses of low-density sedimentary rocks occur.

The available rock density data (Kimbell, 1991) indicate that the mean density contrast between Permian sedimentary rocks and Lower Palaeozoic basement could be as great as -0.4 Mg/m^3 but is more likely to lie in the range -0.25 to -0.3 Mg/m^3. A smaller density contrast is possible if either of the basins contains significant thicknesses of Carboniferous rocks. The form of the onshore part of the Stranraer Basin has been modelled by Mansfield and Kennett (1963) assuming density contrasts of -0.3, -0.4 and -0.5 Mg/m^3, while Bott (1964) modelled a section of the basin across Luce Bay assuming a density contrast of -0.4 Mg/m^3 (which he considered the maximum likely).

Figure 37 shows a simple 2.5-dimensional model (i.e. constant cross-section with finite strike length) of the basins beneath line A–A' (location shown in Figure 35a). This line crosses both Bouguer anomaly minima and is positioned over Lower Palaeozoic greywacke outcrop at its north-eastern end and where it crosses the Rhins of Galloway; similar rocks have been proved at its south-west end by sea-floor sampling (BGS, 1982). A regional field has been removed which is level at 28 mGal between 0 and 35 km north-east, then reduces to 23 mGal at the north-east end of the line. Densities of 2.45 Mg/m^3 and 2.72 Mg/m^3 have been adopted for the basin-fill and basement respectively; this assumes that Permo-Triassic sedimentary rock predominates in the basins (Kimbell, 1991).

Both basins are asymmetrical, with steeper north-east margins. This asymmetry becomes more marked to the north of this profile in the Stranraer Basin (Mansfield and Kennett, 1963), and is somewhat underestimated in the case of the Portpatrick Basin because the profile is not orthogonal to the basin margin. In addition, the station distribution, particularly nearshore, is such that the gravity gradients are not properly sampled and their steepness may be underestimated; this is the probable reason for apparent mismatches between 'observed' and calculated profiles close to the margins of the Stranraer Basin (Figure 37). The Upper Palaeozoic (and younger) sedimentary rocks in the Portpatrick and Stranraer basins reach interpreted maximum thicknesses of approximately 3 km and 2 km respectively. Independent evidence of thickness is provided by the WINCH seismic reflection profile (Hall et al., 1984) which crosses the east side of the Portpatrick Basin (Figure 36). The seismically estimated depth to basement of 2.1 km is in good agreement with the depth at the profile intersection predicted by the gravity model.

The geometry of the Portpatrick and Stranraer basins suggests half grabens with thickening of the sedimentary infill towards syndepositional faults on their eastern margins (see discussion in Chapter Ten). A number of such basins developed in a belt along the west side of Great Britain (the 'Clyde Belt' of McLean, 1978) in a Permo-Triassic extensional stress field orientated broadly east-west. The bounding faults are likely to be reactivated earlier structures. For example, the Loch Ryan Fault, which forms the eastern margin of the Stranraer Basin, is probably a reactivated Caledonian dextral wrench fault (Kelling and Welsh, 1970). The steepest portions of the rifted basin margins appear to be formed by a single syndepositional fault.

There is evidence in the Bouguer anomaly map of other influences on the form of the Portpatrick and Stranraer basins. Both basins are truncated in the south-east against a linear NE–SW trending feature, as is shown schematically in Figure 36. To the south-east of this line, post-Silurian sedimentary cover is thin or absent, so that Silurian rocks crop out on the Scares [NX 260 340] (Barnes et al., 1988) where a minor Bouguer anomaly high is centred. On the east side of Luce Bay this line appears to coincide with the Cairnholy Fault, a major strike fault within the Hawick Group. The form of both basins also appears to have been influenced by transfer fault reactivation along parts of the Orlock Bridge Fault (Figure 34); southward broadening of the basin across this line is apparent on the east side of the Stranraer Basin and on the west side of the Portpatrick Basin.

A Bouguer anomaly high centred beyond the northern margin of the Rhins of Galloway district [NX 180 890] is caused by the dense igneous components of the Ballantrae Complex. Thence further Bouguer anomaly highs extend south-west to form a belt cutting diagonally across the north of the Rhins peninsula. To the east of Loch Ryan the axis of this belt lies parallel and just to the north of the Glen App Fault, whereas, on the Rhins of Galloway, the limited data available suggest that the axis crosses to the south of and diverges from this fault. It is unlikely that this feature is due to concealed ophiolitic rocks as there is no magnetic evidence of their presence. Moreover, the divergence of the anomaly axis from the regional strike of the Ordovician greywackes precludes a simple association with a relatively dense sedimentary unit. A possible explanation is that the geophysical feature is due to shallow, relatively dense crystalline basement.

AEROMAGNETIC SURVEY

The UK national aeromagnetic survey included the Rhins of Galloway district, which was flown in 1959.

Figure 36
Summary map identifying the main geophysical features of the Rhins of Galloway district and surrounding areas.

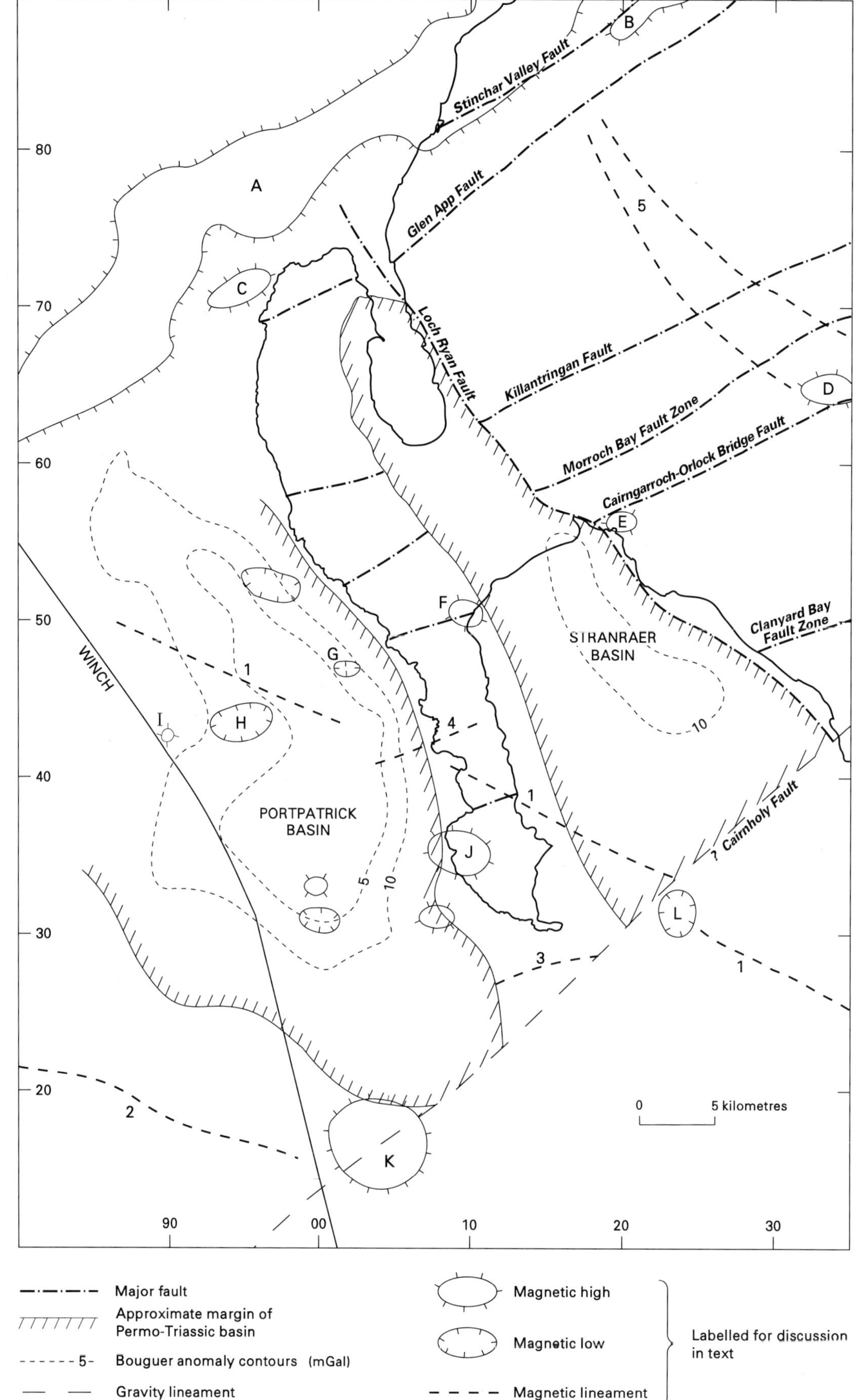

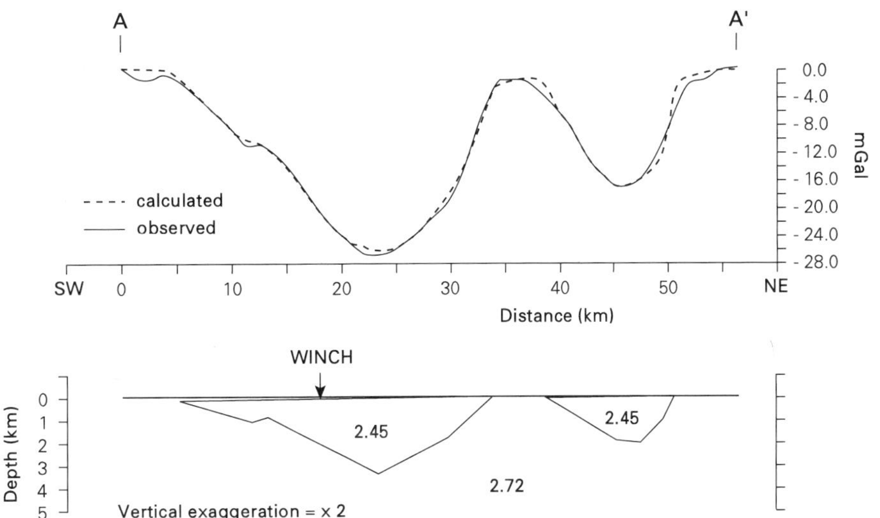

Figure 37 2.5-D gravity model across the Stranraer and Portpatrick Permian basins: profile A–A′ (Figure 35a). Assumed rock densities in Mg/m^3 are indicated. Half strike-length of basins is 15 km.

Flight and tie lines were nominally at 2 km and 10 km intervals respectively and the flying height was 1000 ft (305 m) above terrain. The total magnetic field values were referred to a UK standard reference field. The data have been gridded on a 0.5 km mesh and reduced to the pole to produce the field contoured in Figure 35b. Anomalies should be centred over their source structures in a reduced to the pole map, if the magnetisation of the source rocks is in the direction of the Earth's present field. The limited evidence available suggests that this is a reasonable working hypothesis for most of the magnetic features in the Rhins of Galloway district (Kimbell, 1991) with the exception of some Tertiary features discussed later.

Long wavelength anomaly

The north-west corner of the magnetic map (Figure 35b) is dominated by a magnetic anomaly primarily caused by igneous rocks within the Ballantrae Complex. To the south, a number of disturbances due to relatively shallow sources are superimposed on a long-wavelength magnetic anomaly. The latter increases southwards to a maximum which trends NE–SW, crossing the Rhins of Galloway just to the south of the northern shore of Luce Bay, then decreases towards a low with a similar NE–SW trend and an axis which passes just north of the Isle of Man and along the Solway Firth. The central magnetic high extends north-eastward for at least 100 km across the Southern Uplands, while in the south-west it is truncated just short of the Northern Ireland coast. Its overall form is slightly arcuate and concave towards the north-west.

One possible explanation for the long wavelength magnetic anomaly is that it is due to variations in the depth and/or magnetisation of a magnetic basement within the upper crust. However, Powell (1970) noted that it is difficult to explain the observed magnetic field over the Cairnsmore of Fleet Granite in terms of a model with relatively shallow magnetic basement because, although the granite is largely non-magnetic, it does not cause the magnetic low that would be expected if it were to have punctured such a basement. It is thus inferred that the broad magnetic high which crosses the Rhins of Galloway is due to magnetisation contrasts in the mid to lower crust. Possible explanations are: (i) that a slice of relatively magnetic crust has been sandwiched between the North American (Laurentian) and European (Avalonian) plates in the Iapetus suture zone, or (ii) that there is a major magnetic intrusive body which underlies (and is possibly related to) the less magnetic upper crustal granites.

Short wavelength anomalies

Magnetic features due to near-surface sources are identified on the summary map (Figure 36) and are labelled (alphabetically for highs and lows and numerically for lineaments) for reference in the following discussion. Derived images of the magnetic data, such as shaded relief maps, were used to identify lineaments which are not easily discerned in conventional contour maps.

The NE–SW-trending magnetic high A lies just to the north of the Rhins of Galloway and extends onshore in the Ballantrae area. The onshore feature can be correlated with magnetic igneous rocks within the Ballantrae Complex and, to the south of the Stinchar Valley Fault, with lavas of the younger Downan Point Lava Formation. Anomaly B is due to magnetite-rich greywackes preserved in a separate thrust slice between the Stinchar Valley and Dove Cove faults (Stone and Smellie, 1988). These rocks contain a variety of igneous rock fragments including serpentinites and have relatively high magnetic susceptibility (Powell, 1970; cf. Floyd and Trench, 1989). They are correlatives of the Corsewall Formation exposed at the northern end of the Rhins of Galloway. The source of anomaly C, just off Corsewall Point, is not known but, from its location, appears most likely to be caused by units within the Corsewall Formation or perhaps by an extension of the Downan Point lavas. Anomaly A extends across the North Channel to Northern Ireland, where it is inferred to indicate the presence of ophiolitic rocks at depth beneath the Carrickfergus area (Bennett, 1982).

There are apparent sinistral displacements of the magnetic belt across the north-westward projection of the eastern boundary fault of the Portpatrick Basin, and perhaps also across the Loch Ryan Fault. This sense is the opposite of the likely Caledonian wrench movement on structures with this orientation (cf. Figure 23) but could be due to later Permian reactivation involving normal faulting of a northward dipping magnetic body. This direction of dip is indeed suggested by the magnetic model of Carruthers (1980, fig. 12) for the Ballantrae area. Alternatively the offsets of the magnetic belt could relate to changes in the relative contributions from different sources; possibly the ophiolitic rocks only extend about 20 km offshore, with the apparent continuation of the anomaly being caused by younger lavas or magnetic sedimentary rocks.

Local anomalous magnetic highs D and E coincide with small, late-Caledonian dioritic intrusions at Culvennan Fell, near Kirkowan, and Glenluce respectively. Both D and E lie close to the line of the Orlock Bridge Fault and, on the Rhins of Galloway farther to the south-west along this line, another local magnetic high (F) occurs at Sandhead [NX 100 500] in the north-west corner of Luce Bay. Magnetic dioritic rocks are not exposed in the Sandhead area but detailed geophysical surveys and metamorphic evidence (Kimbell and Stone, 1992) suggest the presence of a late Caledonian dioritic minor intrusive body within 50 m of the surface. Two culminations are apparent but both remain concealed beneath a cover of hornfelsed greywackes. Overall the modelled igneous body has a diameter of about 1.5 km. At Cairngarroch, on the west coast of the Rhins of Galloway, another late Caledonian granodioritic intrusive complex seen adjacent to the Orlock Bridge Fault is the source of low-amplitude disturbances on ground level magnetic traverses (Allen et al., 1981) (compare Figure 39). There is, however, little indication of disturbance in the aeromagnetic displays, probably due to the combination of relatively low magnetic susceptibility and unfavourable position with respect to the flight lines.

Further aeromagnetic anomalies occur along the Orlock Bridge Fault line offshore to the west of the Rhins of Galloway. Anomalies G and H have reversed polarity and are due to sources at relatively shallow depth within the Permian sedimentary sequence of the Portpatrick Basin; Tertiary intrusives appear the most likely source. Farther west, magnetic high I is probably due to a normally magnetised Tertiary intrusion and the relatively high-frequency low-amplitude magnetic disturbances over much of the Portpatrick Basin are also probably indicative of widespread minor Tertiary igneous activity in this area.

A pronounced positive magnetic anomaly (J) occurs over the late Caledonian Portencorkrie Complex described in Chapter Eight as a zoned diorite-granodiorite body. There is no evidence of a magnetisation contrast between the dioritic and granodiorite components of the complex on the airborne profiles. Resolution is limited by the flight line distribution and observation height but modelling indicates that, if a large and significantly less magnetic central core was present, its effect should be discernible. The inference is that either the granodiorite has a similar susceptibility to the neighbouring diorite or it is of limited vertical extent.

A major, approximately circular magnetic high (K) is centred 18 km south-west of the Mull of Galloway, on the line identified from gravity data as marking the truncation of the Stranraer and Portpatrick basins. Comparison of the amplitude of the anomaly measured at sea level with that observed from the air led Wright et al. (1971) to infer that the source is deep seated; they proposed a cylindrical model 3 km in diameter and 3.5 km thick, with a top surface 3.5 km below the sea bed. However, recent modelling suggests that the anomaly can be satisfactorily reproduced by a body with a top surface 0.5–0.6 km below sea level (about 0.4 km below the sea bed) which has a magnetic susceptibility of 16×10^{-3} SI units; the base of the body would be at about 5 km, although this is not well constrained (Kimbell, 1991). The geometry suggests an intrusive source which must be of similar density to the (probably Lower Palaeozoic) host rock as it has no distinct gravity signature; intrusion has taken place on the probable line of crustal weakness defined by the gravity lineament. The most likely source is a late Caledonian dioritic body; a magnetic Tertiary intrusion of this size would typically be associated with a pronounced positive gravity effect and so is considered less likely.

Several magnetic lineaments have been indicated and numbered in Figure 36; some of these are only apparent on the shaded relief plots described above. Lineaments 1 and 2 are NW–SE-trending negative features which are inferred to be due to reversely magnetised basic Tertiary dykes. Where 1 intersects the southern margin of the Stranraer Basin there is an apparent offset and also a local negative closure (L) probably indicating a Tertiary plug at the intersection of lines of weakness. This configuration suggests that the dyke was deflected along a pre-existing fault at the time of intrusion. Where lineament 1 crosses the west coast of the Rhins of Galloway it coincides with the outcrop of Tertiary dykes near Port Logan [NX 093 404]. The probable north-westward continuation of this feature can be traced for about 20 km offshore.

Lineaments 3 and 4 are both short ENE–WSW-trending features but have different polarities. Reversed magnetisation characterises 3 which most probably has a Tertiary intrusive source. Conversely, 4 is normally magnetised and could be either Tertiary or Caledonian; it is a concealed body and the depth to source increases slightly westward across the margin of the Portpatrick Basin, although apparently not as rapidly as might have been expected if its intrusion predated faulting. However, a correlation between this feature and locally elevated metamorphic grade in the Silurian strata to the north of Port Logan [NX 100 430] (Figure 31) tends to support an explanation in terms of a Caledonian igneous source since the thermal effect of Tertiary intrusions is typically very limited.

A pair of positive NW–SE-trending magnetic features (5) have been investigated by Carruthers (1980) and inferred to be due to normally magnetised basic dykes. A Tertiary age seems likely, as does an association with the Arran Tertiary igneous centre.

TWELVE
Quaternary deposits

The distribution of Quaternary deposits preserved in the Rhins of Galloway district are shown on two separate 1:50 000 Drift Geology Sheets: Sheet 1 (Kirkmaiden) and Sheet 3 (Stranraer).

GLACIATION HISTORY

The glacial deposits formed during and after the Devensian glaciation which reached its maximum development about 18 000 years BP (Sissons, 1983; Boulton et al., 1991). At that time the ice sheets extended well beyond the confines of south-west Scotland. Several previous phases of glaciation occurred, although evidence for this is sparse in the Rhins of Galloway district. The presence of marine shells, radiocarbon dated at less than 36 900 years BP, from glacial deposits near Stranraer (Sissons, 1974) indicates a previously unglaciated marine area scoured by a more recent ice sheet. In the vicinity of Ardwell Point [NX 068 446] glacial till is apparently deposited on a wave-cut rock platform about 10–12 m above present sea level which must therefore relate to a preglacial (or interglacial) high sea level.

Glacial striae and landforms such as roches moutonnées and drumlins indicate two opposing ice-flow directions (Figure 38). At some times the Rhins of Galloway district was covered by ice flowing south-west from the higher parts of the Southern Uplands and at other times by part of the main Highland ice sheet flowing towards the south-east. The earlier trend was probably produced by the Southern Uplands ice sheet during the glacial maximum and the common glacial erratics of granite from the Loch Doon and Cairnsmore of Fleet plutons were introduced at this stage. As the Southern Uplands ice sheet waned the Highland ice sheet was able to encroach onto the Rhins of Galloway and ice flowing south-eastwards was channelised particularly into the Loch Ryan–Luce Bay zone of softer Permian rocks which were preferentially eroded. At this stage the higher parts of the Rhins peninsula may have stood above the ice as nunataks. The Highland ice scoured the seabed of the Firth of Clyde before crossing the Rhins and so introduced the till containing marine shells mentioned earlier. Several localities are known for this till (Figure 38) and faunal lists are given by Geikie and Irvine (1873). The Highland ice also introduced into the area glacial erratics of the distinctive Ailsa Craig riebeckite-microgranite (Harrison et al., 1987).

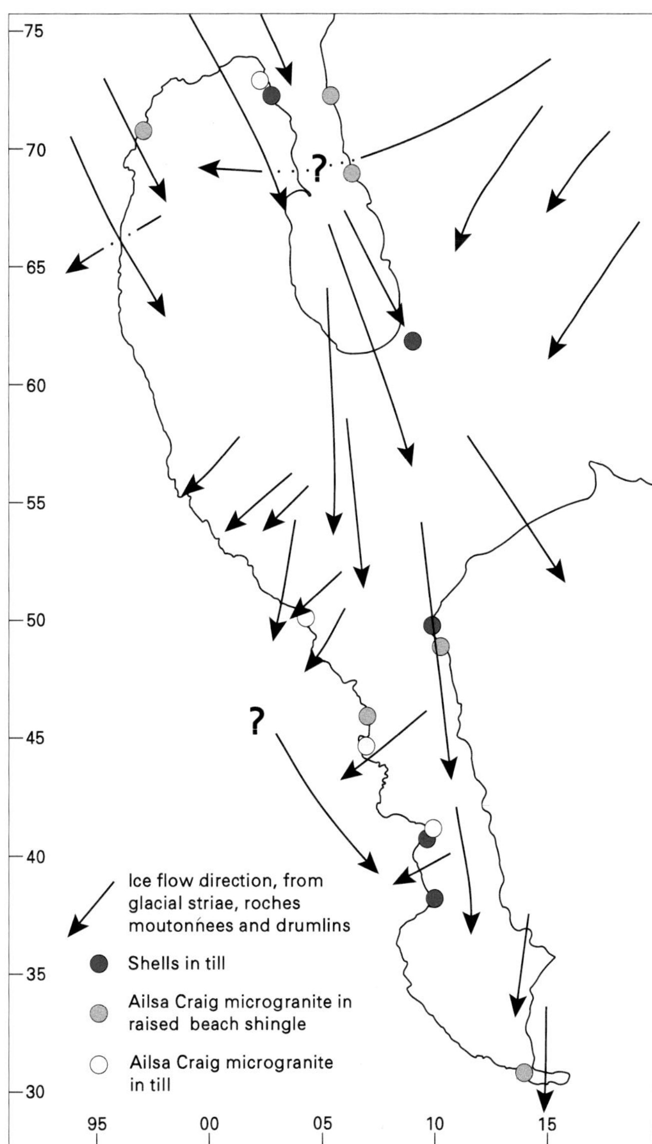

Figure 38 Map of glacial flow-directional data from the Rhins of Galloway district (cf. Boulton et al., 1991, fig. 15.10).

An hiatus in retreat or possibly a slight readvance of the Highland ice is marked by the extensive spread of glacial sand and gravel forming the Stranraer isthmus. This accumulated ahead of a fairly static ice front at the snout of a glacier occupying Loch Ryan and probably linked back to the main Highland ice mass farther north. Climatic amelioration continued and deglaciation was complete by about 13 000 years BP, the Late-glacial (or Windermere) Interstadial (Bishop and Coope, 1977; Sissons, 1983; Boulton et al., 1991). At this time south-west Scotland enjoyed a fairly mild climate but, with poorly developed soils, the vegetation was of pioneer-type park tundra; from insect remains in peat, Bishop and Coope

(1977) estimated a mean July temperature of about 15°C. A return to cold conditions followed and between about 11 000 and 10 000 years BP the climate of south-west Scotland was similar to that of modern polar deserts. This was the time of the Loch Lomond Readvance (or Stade) when an ice cap again built up in the western Highlands and small cirque glaciers developed in the higher parts of the Southern Uplands. Periglacial processes were undoubtedly active throughout the Rhins district and fossil frost wedges have been reported from the glacial sands east of Stranraer (Sissons, 1974, fig. 2).

South-west Scotland was free of ice and experiencing a climate at least as warm as that of the present by about 9500 years BP. Final deglaciation was accompanied by the release of vast quantities of water to the oceans and sea level accordingly rose sharply (the Holocene or Flandrian transgression). Beaches which formed in response to this relatively high sea level, were then uplifted by isostatic recovery of the landmass and now form raised beaches skirting the coastline in many sheltered areas. The period of relatively high sea level also saw the first settlement by Man of the Rhins of Galloway district; several Mesolithic sites have been reported from the western shores of Luce Bay and the north of the Stranraer isthmus (e.g. Jardine and Morrison, 1976).

DRIFT DEPOSITS

Till

Till (or boulder clay) fills hollows and forms gently undulating spreads throughout the district but is topographically most distinctive when forming whale-backed drumlins. These are widely distributed on the Rhins peninsula where most have a NW–SE or north–south trend, suggesting association with the Highland ice sheet (Figure 38). The exception is the central part of the peninsula, towards the west coast, where drumlins and roches moutonnées trend NE-SW as a continuation of the dominant drumlin trend seen to the north-east around Glenluce. This NE–SW trend is associated with Southern Uplands ice emanating from the high ground around Merrick [NX 428 855], the highest point in south-west Scotland at 843 m OD. Till texture varies from a very stiff clay containing relatively few lithoclasts to a sandy clay packed with subangular pebbles and cobbles. The colour also varies; dark charcoal grey, blue grey, brown, and reddish tills are all widely distributed, the last being particularly common on the Rhins peninsula where the till was deposited from SW-flowing ice which had previously eroded the Permian red sandstone of the Stranraer Basin. In places the till can be divided into two stratigraphical layers: a friable sandy clay containing a high proportion of local greywacke clasts resting on a stiff blue-grey clay which may contain a fragmentary fauna of marine lamellibranchs, forams and crustacea (Figure 38). Etheridge provided faunal lists in Irvine (1872) and Geikie and Irvine (1873) for collections of marine material from Lady Bay [NX 027 717], Innermessan [NX 085 633], Sandhead [NX 098 493], Clanyard Bay [NX 102 380] and Port Logan [NX 098 405]. It was probably carried onshore by ice which had previously scoured the sea bed in the Firth of Clyde. Erratics of Ailsa Craig riebeckite-microgranite were introduced from the same direction, although most records are of Ailsa Craig material which has been reworked into raised beach shingle (Figure 38). In general terms the lower boulder clay can be described as a lodgement till, deposited and compressed beneath an advancing ice sheet. By contrast, the upper and poorly consolidated layer probably formed as an ablation till deposited as the ice melted in situ. The latter is the commoner in the Rhins of Galloway district. Till thickness is very variable as the till tended to drape over bedrock irregularities and infill hollows. Till thicknesses of up to 2–3 m are fairly common and 10 m sections are sporadically seen; Irvine (1872) reported about 30 m of till in the Clanyard Bay area.

Glacial sand and gravel

The glacial sand and gravel spread of the Stranraer isthmus is one of the most extensive of such features in south-west Scotland. The deposits are thought to have accumulated at the snout of a stationary and wasting glacier occupying Loch Ryan and, in this environment, several depositional processes were active and are reflected in the surviving landforms. Stratified sand and gravel mounds, often with disturbed layering, are particularly common in the central and northern parts of the isthmus. These are kame mounds, deposited beneath and between stagnant ice masses; when the ice finally melted the stratified sand and gravel bodies were left as positive features although the removal of their support inevitably caused slumping along their margins. Around and beyond these mounds, farther from the glacier snout, an outwash plain was built up by a system of braided meltwater streams. Deposition may have been submarine as well as fluviatile since, at Clashmahew [NX 062 594] just south of Stranraer, Geikie and Irvine (1873) reported shelly marine clay overlying sand and gravel which may have been deposited in prograding delta foresets. On a smaller scale the same process probably operated within ice-dammed meltwater lakes in the vicinity of the glacier snout. By these processes terrace gravels and sands built up at various heights around the kame mounds and were then partially eroded by further meltwater flow. Small lochans and peaty hollows scattered throughout the area may have originated as kettle holes formed by subsidence when blocks of ice buried in the outwash sands finally melted. Borehole records show up to 43 m of sand and gravel (Gauss, 1969) which places rockhead well below sea level.

The scattered irregular deposits of sand and gravel elsewhere on the Rhins peninsula are probably the eroded remains of once more extensive outwash fans and terraces deposited during deglaciation of the district; many of the sandy terraces have a thin peaty cover. Moundy kames are associated with the flatter spreads and all are dominantly composed of well-stratified fine reddish yellow sand with only a small proportion of interbedded fine gravel. Extensive spreads of such glacial sand and gravel occur around Corsewall Point [NW 980 720] and Galdenoch [NW 970 620]. Farther south, spreads of glacial sand and gravel on the eastern side of the peninsula between Chapel Rossan [NX 110 450] and Cailliness Point [NX 150 355] preserve a variety of terrace heights ranging up to a widespread occurrence at 25–30 m above sea level. In the valley of the Water of Luce moundy kame terraces are the remains of a once much more extensive spread which originally choked the pre-existing valley.

Raised beaches and blown sand

Sea level fluctuated in response to eustatic–isostatic imbalance during deglaciation. The remains of shingle terraces containing a marine fauna at heights up to about 20 m above sea level indicate beach formation in response to relatively high Late-Glacial sea levels. Examples of such terraces are preserved at Finnarts Bay [NX 052 725], Glenluce [NX 197 565] and Kilstay Bay [NX 128 385].

Raised beaches ranging from about 5 m to about 8 m above sea level are commonly preserved on the more sheltered stretches of coastline; the shores of Loch Ryan and the west coast of Luce Bay have many good examples. These beaches relate to a relatively high Postglacial sea level.

On the west coast of the Rhins peninsula the only extensive raised beaches are about 5 m above sea level and are preserved in the sheltered areas fringing Clanyard Bay [NX 102 378], intermittently in the north-west between Corsewall Point and Dally Bay [NW 965 690], at Salt Pans Bay [NW 965 615], at Broadsea Bay [NW 973 598] and at Knock Bay [NW 982 578]. A raised beach terrace at Morroch Bay [NX 015 525] has only a veneer of sand above a platform cut in till.

At many localities the raised beaches are continued seaward by a wave-cut rock platform at about 5 m above sea level. Similar rock platforms are developed without the raised beach association on many stretches of the western Rhins coast although their height above sea level is very variable within a range from 2 to 10 m. The highest of these may be related to pre-, late- or interglacial sea levels; at the Hooies [NX 068 447] one such coastal rock platform is covered by till.

Blown sand covers a wide area at the head of Luce Bay and encroaches northward on to raised beach deposits, peat and alluvium. Smaller spreads are developed south of Cailliness Point [NX 147 351] and around the margin of Port Logan Bay [NX 098 407].

Alluvium

As the present drainage system developed the drift deposits occupying pre-existing valleys were partially reworked. The glacial sand and gravel spreads were incised and now stand as moundy terraces above recent alluvial terraces, notably in the valley of the Water of Luce. Up to three successively higher alluvial terraces have been noted there, relating to progressive lowering of the local base level. Elsewhere, patches of alluvial sand and gravel border many of the streams. An extensive spread bordering the Piltanton Burn [NX 125 565] may overlie glacial sands and/or raised beach deposits and is itself locally covered by blown sand. The interaction of stream erosion and deposition with wind-driven dune movement produces a constantly changing set of deposit inter-relationships.

Peat

On the high ground in the north-east of the Rhins of Galloway district extensive peat mosses have built up to a depth of several metres. However, peat growth now appears to have ceased or to be very slow and in most of the upland areas the peat deposits are now wasting. Spreads of peat, grading into peaty clay, fill hollows in many of the lower-lying areas. Some, such as Logan Moss [NX 093 438], probably originated in a lacustrine environment. Other low-lying peaty areas east of Stranraer [NX 092 605] and near West Freugh [NX 120 550] appear to have formed on raised beaches. Elsewhere within the Stranraer glacial sand and gravel spread, small pockets of peat and peaty clay commonly mark the position of kettle holes. Buried peat layers occur in many sections through glacial sand and gravel or alluvium.

THIRTEEN
Economic geology

METALLIFEROUS MINERALS

The only record of exploitation of metalliferous mineralisation in the Rhins of Galloway district is at the New Luce or Knockibae Mine, about 2.5 km north-east from the village of New Luce [NX 192 665]; lead and zinc were worked from a vein complex within Portpatrick Formation Ordovician greywacke. It was described by Wilson (1921) as follows: 'The mine appears to have been first opened up about the middle of the eighteenth century, and a few cwt of rich ore are said to have been obtained. A second attempt was made about 1790, but little appears to have been done. In 1866 a company was formed to work the mine, and reports were given ...(that)... the vein, which averages 3 ft in thickness, trends north-east, is associated with a line of movement, and hades to the west. The country-rock is hard greywacke, and the infilling consists mainly of calcite, with associated galena and zinc-blende. The vein has been opened up by an adit-level which has been driven a considerable distance along the course of the vein; a few small shafts have also been sunk'. It would appear that mineralisation has been concentrated into one of the NE–SW late-Caledonian sinistral wrench faults.

A mineralised fault plane also occurs in the northern part of the Rhins peninsula where a strike fault within the Corsewall Formation contains massive haematite. The mineralisation is seen at outcrop below high water mark on the Loch Ryan coast north of Lady Bay [NX 027 721] in a zone about 2 m across (BGS specimen MC 5393). Similar mineralisation was reported by Peach and Horne (1899) from within the same fault zone on the western Rhins coast [NW 963 691].

Mineralisation related to Caledonian intrusive rocks has been described in two BGS Mineral Reconnaissance Programme Reports: at Cairngarroch (Allen et al., 1981) and at Portencorkrie and the Mull of Galloway (Cooper et al., 1982). The following account of the mineralisation is largely derived from those reports and the intrusive suites themselves have been described in Chapter Eight.

At Cairngarroch (Figure 39) both the broadly granodioritic intrusive complex and the host Ordovician greywackes (Shinnel Formation) show, locally, intense hydrothermal alteration. Narrow zones of bleached rock are rich in calcite, chlorite and pyrite and contain minor amounts of chalcopyrite and pyrrhotite. Elsewhere, network fracturing and brecciation is accompanied by locally intense alteration to sericite or calcite with abundant pyrite in veins and sporadic disseminated chalcopyrite. Arsenopyrite is a rare accessory in wall-rock alteration adjacent to the intrusive complex and vein arsenopyrite has been shown to contain significant antimony and gold by Duller (1989) using microchemical techniques. Allen et al. (1981) determined a pervasive but patchy Cu-Fe-As-Mo mineralisation with copper values in the hydrothermally altered granodiorite locally exceeding 600 ppm. The mineralisation is accompanied by irregular barium, potassium and strontium enrichment. In its general characteristics the mineralisation and alteration around the Cairngarroch intrusive complex is reminiscent of a failed porphyry system and it is conceivable that copper enrichment might increase with depth.

The Portencorkrie diorite-grandiorite complex [NX 090 365] shows little sign of hydrothermal alteration but is cut by numerous quartz veins. These are particularly abundant along the northern margin of the complex with the host Hawick Group greywacke. Veins trend between north-west and NNW and cut both the marginal diorite facies of the intrusion and the thermally metamorphosed host greywackes. They are broadly parallel to one of the conjugate fault directions initiated in the later stages of Caledonian deformation. The vein-filling is principally quartz accompanied by calcite, epidote and sparse pyrite, chalcopyrite, galena and arsenopyrite; metal content of the vein material ranges up to 1.1 per cent Cu and 0.07 per cent Pb (Cooper et al., 1982). Green secondary copper minerals are visible adjacent to some veins and as thin veneers on nearby vein-parallel joint planes. One specimen from a vein 500 m NNW of Barncorkrie Farm [NX 093 362] contained the unusual secondary assemblage of paratacamite and connellite (Cameron and Lawson, 1979).

In the vicinity of the Mull of Galloway, the narrow neck of land separating East and West Tarbet [NX 142 309] is underlain by a sheared and altered microdiorite intrusion. The rock consists principally of quartz, carbonate, sericite and chlorite with common disseminated pyrite and rarer chalcopyrite. Quartz and carbonate are present in widespread veinlets which sporadically contain, in addition, baryte and pyrite. Rarely the veinlets increase to 20 cm in width and, in these examples, galena, possible sphalerite and green copper secondary minerals have been reported in a quartz gangue (Cooper et al., 1982). Overall, the altered igneous rock shows a patchy but significant enrichment in copper, arsenic and barium.

BULK MINERALS

Many small quarries have been opened in the past for the local supply of building materials and roadstone. These have generally worked Lower Palaeozoic lithologies, although Moore (1842) reported a quarry at Challoch [NX 022 637] working Carboniferous sandstone which would have been extremely soft and friable. Fine-grained and thinly bedded siltstone and shale, with cleavage sub-

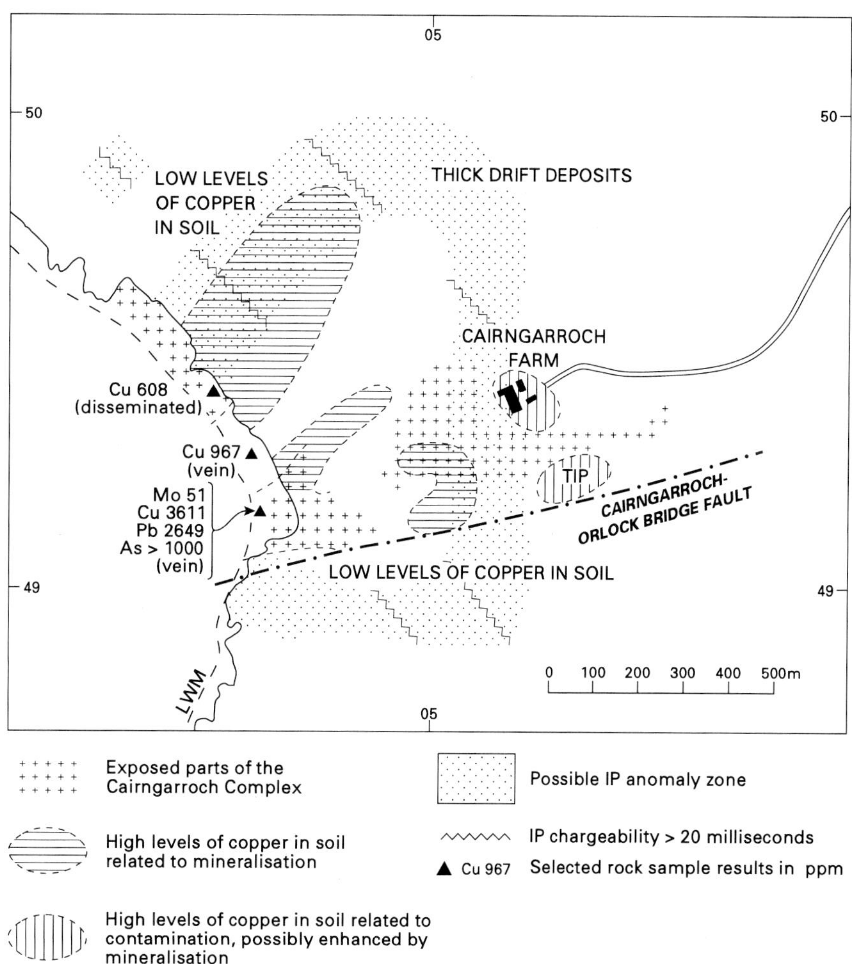

Figure 39 Summary of geochemical and geophysical data for the Cairngarroch mineralised zone. Modified from Allen et al. (1981).

parallel to bedding, have been worked for aggregate and poor-quality roofing slates at Cairnryan [NX 068 688] and at several localities in the Grennan area [NX 124 394]. At the time of writing (1992) there is only one commercially active quarry in the Rhins of Galloway district. At High Croach [NX 076 682] crushed rock aggregate is produced intermittently from greywackes of the Ordovician Kirkcolm Formation; much of the produce is shipped out by sea from the adjacent harbour of Cairnryan.

Sand and gravel resources have been widely exploited on a small scale to satisfy local demand. Within the glacial meltwater deposits of the Stranraer isthmus several sections were described by Cameron (1977) in an assessment of the considerable sand and gravel resources of the area. Two working (in 1992) pits north-east from Sandhead at Clayshant [NX 110 524] and at Sandmill [NX 105 516] exploit mainly raised beach material and the overlying blown sand.

REFERENCES

Most of the references listed below are held and available for consultation in the libraries of the British Geological Survey at Keyworth, Nottingham and Murchison House, Edinburgh. Copies of the references can be purchased from the Keyworth Library subject to the current copyright legislation.

ALLEN, P M, BIDE, P J, COOPER, D C, PARKER, M E, and HASLAM, H W. 1981. Copper-bearing intrusive rocks at Cairngarroch Bay, south-west Scotland. *Mineral Reconnaissance Report, Institute of Geological Sciences*, No. 39.

ANDERSON, T B. 1987. The onset and timing of Caledonian sinistral shear in County Down. *Journal of the Geological Society of London*, Vol. 144, 17–825.

— and OLIVER, G J H. 1986. The Orlock Bridge Fault: a major Late Caledonian sinistral fault in the Southern Uplands terrane, British Isles. *Transactions of the Royal Society of Edinburgh: Earth Sciences*, Vol. 77, 203–222.

ARMSTRONG, H A, CLARKSON, E N K, and OWEN, A W. 1990. A new Lower Ordovician conodont faunule from the Northern Belt of the Southern Uplands. *Scottish Journal of Geology*, Vol. 26, 47–52.

BALL, D F, and ROBINS, N S. 1985. Trial drilling in the New Red Sandstone of Dumfries and Galloway Region. *Hydrogeology in Scotland Report, British Geological Survey*, No. 85/4.

BARNES, R P. 1989. Geology of the Whithorn district. *Memoir of the British Geological Survey*, Sheet 2 (Scotland).

— ANDERSON, T B, and MCCURRY, J A. 1987. Along-strike variation in the stratigraphical and structural profile of the Southern Uplands Central Belt in Galloway and Down. *Journal of the Geological Society of London*, Vol. 144, 807–816.

— FLOYD, J D, and STONE, P. 1988. Big Scare — resurveyed after 110 years. *Report of the British Geological Survey*, Vol. 19, No. 2, 19–23.

— LINTERN, B C, and STONE, P. 1989. Timing and regional implications of deformation in the Southern Uplands of Scotland. *Journal of the Geological Society of London*, Vol. 146, 905–908.

— ROCK, N M S, and GASKARTH, J W. 1986. Late Caledonian dyke-swarms in Southern Scotland: new field, petrological and geochemical data for the Wigtown Peninsula, Galloway. *Geological Journal*, Vol. 21, 101–125.

BEAMISH, D, and SMYTHE, D B. 1986. Geophysical images of the deep crust: the Iapetus suture. *Journal of the Geological Society of London*, Vol. 143, 489–497.

BELL, A M. 1981. Vergence: an evaluation. *Journal of Structural Geology*, Vol. 3, 197–202.

BENNETT, J R P. 1982. Geophysical investigations. 88–89 *in* Geology of the country around Carrickfergus and Bangor. GRIFFITH, A E, and WILSON, H E. *Memoir of the Geological Survey of Northern Ireland*, Sheet 29.

BISHOP, W W, and COOPE, G R. 1977. Stratigraphical and faunal evidence for Lateglacial and Early Flandrian environments in south-west Scotland. 1–68 in *Studies in the Scottish Lateglacial environment.* GRAY, J M, and LOWE, J J (editors). (Oxford: Pergamon Press.)

BLUCK, B J. 1983. Role of the Midland Valley of Scotland in the Caledonian orogeny. *Transactions of the Royal Society of Edinburgh: Earth Sciences*, Vol. 74, 119–136.

— 1984. Pre-Carboniferous history of the Midland Valley of Scotland. *Transactions of the Royal Society of Edinburgh: Earth Sciences*, Vol. 75, 275–295.

BOTT, M H P. 1964. Gravity measurements in the north-eastern part of the Irish Sea. *Quarterly Journal of the Geological Society of London*, Vol. 120, 369–396.

BOUMA, A H. 1962. *Sedimentology of some flysch deposits: a graphic approach to interpretation.* (Amsterdam: Elsevier.)

BOULTON, G S, PEACOCK, J D, and SUTHERLAND, D G. 1991. Quaternary. 503–543 in *The geology of Scotland.* (3rd edition). CRAIG, G Y (editor). (London: The Geological Society.)

BREWER, J A, MATTHEWS, D H, WARNER, M R, HALL, J, SMYTHE, D J, and WHITTINGTON, R J. 1983. BIRPS deep seismic reflection studies of the British Caledonides — the WINCH profile. Nature, London. Vol. 305, 206–210.

BRITISH GEOLOGICAL SURVEY. 1992. Kirkcowan. Scotland Sheet 4W. Solid. 1:50 000. (Southampton: Ordnance Survey for British Geological Survey.)

BROOKFIELD, M E. 1978. Revision of the stratigraphy of Permian and supposed Permian rocks of southern Scotland. *Geologische Rundschau*, Vol. 67, 110–149.

BUTLER, R W H. 1982. The terminology of structures in thrust belts. *Journal of Structural Geology*, Vol. 4, 239–245.

CAMERON, I B. 1977. Sand and gravel resources of the Dumfries and Galloway Region of Scotland. *Report of the Institute of Geological Sciences*, No. 77/22.

— and LAWSON, R I. 1979. An occurrence of paratacamite in south-west Scotland. *Mineralogical Magazine*, Vol. 43, 547.

— STONE, P, and SMELLIE, J L. 1986. Geology of the country around Girvan. *Explanation of 1:50 000, British Geological Survey*, Sheet 7 (Scotland).

CARRUTHERS, R M. 1980. Detailed airborne surveys, 1978. An assessment of geophysical data from the Girvan–Ballantrae district. *Institute of Geological Sciences, Applied Geophysics Unit Report*, No.78.

CHALONER, W G, and COLLINSON, M E. 1986. An illustrated key to the commoner British Upper Carboniferous plant compression fossils. *Proceedings of the Geologists' Association*, Vol. 86, 1–44.

COOPER, D C, PARKER, M E, and ALLEN, P M. 1982. Investigations of small intrusions in southern Scotland. *Mineral Reconnaissance Programme Report Institute of Geological Sciences*, No. 58.

COWIE, J W, and BASSETT, M G. 1989. International Union of Geological Sciences 1989 Global Stratigraphic Chart. Episodes, Vol. 12, No 2, Supplement.

CRAIG, G Y, and WALTON, E K. 1959. Sequence and structure in the Silurian rocks of Kirkcudbrightshire. *Geological Magazine*, Vol. 96, 209–20.

DAVIES, P. 1990. The geology of the Rhins of Galloway, SW Scotland: the west coast between Killantringan Bay and Clanyard Bay. *British Geological Survey Technical Report*, WA/90/67.

DAY, G A, and SUNDERLAND, J. 1970. Cruise report for mv.'Surveyor' North Channel survey 70/4, *Institute of Geological Sciences, Marine Geophysics Unit Report*, No. 13.

DEWEY, J F. 1971. A model for the Lower Palaeozoic evolution of the southern margin of the Early Caledonides of Scotland and Ireland. *Scottish Journal of Geology*, Vol. 7, 220–240.

DICKINSON, W R, and SUCZEK, C A. 1979. Plate tectonics and sandstone compositions. *Bulletin of the American Association of Petroleum Geologists*, Vol. 63, 2164–2182.

DULLER, P R. 1989. The lithogeochemical and mineralogical setting of turbidite hosted arsenic-gold deposits in the Lower Palaeozoic of Scotland. Unpublished PhD thesis, Strathclyde University.

DUNNE, W M, and FERRILL, D A. 1988. Blind thrust systems. *Geology*, Vol. 16, 33–36.

EALES, M H. 1979. Structure of the Southern Uplands of Scotland. 269–273 *in* The Caledonides of the British Isles — reviewed. HARRIS, A L, HOLLAND, C H, and LEAKE, B E (editors). *Special Publication of the Geological Society of London*, No. 8.

EBERL, D D, SRODON, J, KRALIK, M, TAYLOR, B E, and PETERMAN, Z E. 1990. Ostwald ripening of clays and metamorphic minerals. *Science*, Vol. 248, 474–477.

ELDERS, C F. 1987. The provenance of granite boulders in conglomerates of the Northern and Central Belts of the Southern Uplands of Scotland. *Journal of the Geological Society of London*, Vol. 144, 853–863.

ELLES, G L. 1925. Characteristic assemblages of the graptolite zones of the British Isles. *Geological Magazine*, Vol. 62, 337–347.

— and WOOD, E M R. 1901–1918. A monograph of British graptolites. *Monographs of the Palaeontographical Society* [11 parts].

EVANS, J A, STONE, P, and FLOYD, J D. 1991. Isotopic characteristics of Ordovician greywacke provenance in the Southern Uplands of Scotland. 161–172 *in* Developments in sedimentary provenance studies. MORTON, A C and others (editors). *Special Publication of the Geological Society of London*, No. 57.

FERRILL, D A, and DUNNE, W M. 1989. Cover deformation above a blind duplex: an example from West Virginia, USA. *Journal of Structural Geology*, Vol. 11, 421–431.

FLOYD, J D. 1982. Stratigraphy of a flysch succession: the Ordovician of W. Nithsdale, SW Scotland. *Transactions of the Royal Society of Edinburgh: Earth Sciences*, Vol. 3, 1–9.

— and RUSHTON, A W A. 1993. Ashgill greywackes in the Southern Uplands: an extension of the Ordovician succession in the Northern Belt. *Transactions of the Royal Society of Edinburgh: Earth Sciences*, Vol. 84, 79–85.

— STONE, P, BARNES, R P, and LINTERN, B C. 1987. Constraints on the significance of the Orlock Bridge Fault within the Scottish Southern Uplands. *Transactions of the Royal Society of Edinburgh: Earth Sciences*, Vol. 78, 219–221.

— and TRENCH, A. 1989. Magnetic susceptibility contrasts in Ordovician greywackes of the Southern Uplands of Scotland. *Journal of the Geological Society of London*, Vol. 146, 77–83.

FULLER, J G C M. 1958. The petrology of the Carboniferous rocks near Stranraer, Wigtownshire. *Proceedings of the Geologists' Association*, Vol. 69, 166–174.

FYFE, T B, and WEIR, J A. 1976. The Ettrick Valley Thrust and the upper limit of the Moffat Shales in Craigmichan Scaurs (Dumfries and Galloway Region; Annandale and Eskdale District). *Scottish Journal of Geology*, Vol. 12, 93–102.

GAUSS, G. 1969. Records of wells in the area of Scottish one-inch Geological Sheets Kirkmaiden (1), Whithorn (2), Stranraer (3), Wigtown (4), Kirkcudbright (5) and Annan (6). *Institute of Geological Sciences Well Catalogue Series.*

GEIKIE, A, and IRVINE, D R. 1873. Explanation of Sheet 3: Western Wigtownshire. *Memoir of the Geological Survey, Scotland.*

GILL, J B. 1981. *Orogenic andesites and plate tectonics.* (Berlin: Springer.)

HALL, J, BREWER, J A, MATTHEWS, D H, and WARNER, M R. 1984. Crustal structure across the Caledonides from the 'WINCH' seismic reflection profile: influences on the evolution of the Midland Valley of Scotland. *Transactions of the Royal Society of Edinburgh: Earth Sciences*, Vol. 75, 97–109.

HALLIDAY, A N, STEPHENS, W E, and HARMON, R S. 1980. Rb, Sr and O isotopic relationships in 3 zoned Caledonian granitic plutons, Southern Uplands, Scotland: evidence for varied sources and hybridization of magmas. *Journal of the Geological Society of London*, Vol. 137, 329–348.

HARRISON, R K, STONE, P, CAMERON, I B, ELLIOT, R W, and HARDING, R R. 1987. Geology, petrology and geochemistry of Ailsa Craig, Ayrshire. *Report of the British Geological Survey*, Vol. 16, No.9.

HINXMAN, L W, and MACGREGOR, M. 1920. Special report on the mineral resources of Great Britain. 14. Refractory materials: Fireclay. *Memoir of the Geological Survey of Great Britain.*

HOLGATE, N. 1943. The Portencorkrie Complex of Wigtownshire. *Geological Magazine*, Vol. 80, 171–195.

HUGHES, R A. 1989. Llandeilo and Caradoc graptolites of the Builth and Shelve inliers. *Monographs of the Palaeontographical Society*, Vol. 141 (for 1987), No. 577.

INSTITUTE OF GEOLOGICAL SCIENCES. 1982. Isle of Man. Sheet 54°N-06°W. Solid. 1:250 000. (Southampton: Ordnance Survey for Institute of Geological Sciences.)

IRVINE, D R. 1872. Explanation of Sheet 1: Wigtownshire — Mull of Galloway. *Memoir of the Geological Survey, Scotland.*

JACKSON, A A. 1985. The area between Cairnryan and Gabsnout Burn, Galloway. *British Geological Survey Technical Report*, PDA2/85/4.

JARDINE, W G, and MORRISON, A. 1976. The archaeological significance of Holocene coastal deposits in south-western Scotland. 175–195 in *Geoarchaeology, Earth Science and the past.* DAVIDSON, D A, and SHACKLEY, M D (editors). (London: Duckworth.)

KELLEY, S, and BLUCK, B J. 1989. Detrital mineral ages from the Southern Uplands using ^{40}Ar-^{39}Ar laser probe. *Journal of the Geological Society of London*, Vol. 146, 401–403.

KELLING, G. 1961. The stratigraphy and structure of the Ordovician rocks of the Rhins of Galloway. *Quarterly Journal of the Geological Society of London*, Vol. 117, 37–75.

— 1962. The petrology and sedimentation of Upper Ordovician rocks in the Rhins of Galloway, south-west Scotland. *Transactions of the Royal Society of Edinburgh*, Vol. 65, 107–137.

— DAVIES, P, and HOLROYD, J. 1987. Style, scale and significance of sand bodies in the Northern and Central belts, southwest Southern Uplands. *Journal of the Geological Society of London*, Vol. 144, 787–806.

— and WELSH, W. 1970. The Loch Ryan fault. *Scottish Journal of Geology*, Vol. 6, 266–271.

KEMP, A E S, OLIVER, G J H, and BALDWIN, J R. 1985. Low grade metamorphism and accretion tectonics: Southern Uplands terrain, Scotland. *Mineralogical Magazine*, Vol. 49, 335–344.

KIMBELL, G S. 1991. An assessment of geophysical data from the Rhins of Galloway district, south-west Scotland. *British Geological Survey Technical Report*, WK/91/10.

— and STONE, P. 1992. Geophysical evidence for a concealed Caledonian intrusive body at Sandhead, Wigtownshire. *Scottish Journal of Geology*, Vol. 28, 19–25.

KNELLER, B, EDWARDS, D, MCCAFFREY, W, and MOORE, R. 1991. Oblique reflection of turbidity currents. *Geology*, Vol. 14, 250–252.

KNIPE, R J, CHAMBERLAIN, M I, PAGE, A, and NEEDHAM, D T. 1988. Structural histories in the SW Southern Uplands, Scotland. *Journal of the Geological Society of London*. Vol. 145, 679–684.

KUENEN, Ph H. 1953. Graded bedding, with observations on Lower Palaeozoic rocks of Britain: Part 2, Probable deep-water origin of some Southern Upland rocks. *Verhandelingen der Koninklijke Nederlandsche Akademie van Wetenschappen, Afdeeling Natuurkunde Eerste Reeks*, Part 20, No.3, 36–45.

LAMONT, A, and LINDSTRÖM, M. 1957. Arenigian and Llandeilian cherts identified in the Southern Uplands of Scotland by means of conodonts. *Transactions of the Edinburgh Geological Society*, Vol. 17, 60–70.

LAPWORTH, C. 1878. The Moffat Series. *Quarterly Journal of the Geological Society of London*, Vol. 34, 240–346.

LEGGETT, J K. 1987. The Southern Uplands as an accretionary prism: the importance of analogues in reconstructing palaeogeography. *Journal of the Geological Society of London*, Vol. 144, 737–752.

— MCKERROW, W S, and EALES, M H. 1979. The Southern Uplands of Scotland: a Lower Palaeozoic accretionary prism. *Journal of the Geological Society of London*, Vol. 136, 755–770.

— — and SOPER, N J. 1983. A model for the crustal evolution of southern Scotland. *Tectonics*, Vol. 2, 187–210.

LEMAITRE, R W. 1989. *A classification of igneous rocks and glossary of terms.* (Oxford: Blackwell Scientific Publications.)

LINDSTRÖM, M. 1958. Different phases of tectonic deformation in the Rhins of Galloway. *Nature, London*, Vol. 182, 48–49.

LINTERN, B C, BARNES, R P, and STONE, P. 1992. Discussion on Silurian and Early Devonian sinistral deformation of the Ratagain Granite, Scotland: constraints on the age of Caledonian movements on the Great Glen system. *Journal of the Geological Society of London*, Vol. 149, 858.

LYELL, C. 1839. On the occurrence of graptolites in the Slate of Galloway. *Proceedings of the Geological Society*, Vol. 3, 28.

MCCURRY, J A. 1990. The geology of the Rhins of Galloway south of the Portayew area. *British Geological Survey Technical Report*, WA/90/66.

— and ANDERSON, T B. 1989. Landward vergence in the Lower Palaeozoic, Southern Uplands-Longford-Down terrane, British Isles. *Geology*, Vol. 17, 630–633.

MACDONALD, R, THORPE, R S, GASKARTH, J W, and GRINDROD, A R. 1985. Multi-component origin of Caledonian lamprophyres of Northern England. *Mineralogical Magazine*, Vol. 49, 485–494.

MCKERROW, W S, DEWEY, J F, and SCOTESE, C R. 1991. The Ordovician and Silurian development of the Iapetus Ocean. 165–178 *in* The Murchison Symposium. BASSETT, M G, LANE, P D, and EDWARDS, D (editors). *Special Papers in Palaeontology*, No. 44.

— LAMBERT, R StJ, and COCKS, L R M. 1985. The Ordovician, Silurian and Devonian periods. 73–79 *in* The chronology of the geological record. SNELLING, N J (editor). *Memoir of the Geological Society of London*, No. 10.

— LEGGETT, J K, and EALES, M H. 1977. Imbricate thrust model of the Southern Uplands of Scotland. *Nature, London*, Vol. 267, 237–39.

MCLEAN, A C. 1978. Evolution of fault-controlled ensialic basins in northwestern Britain. 325–346 *in* Crustal evolution in northwesternBritain and adjacent regions. BOWES, D R, and LEAKE, B E (editors). *Geological Journal Special Issue*, No. 10.

— and DEEGAN, C E. 1978. The solid geology of the Clyde Sheet (55°N-06°W). *Report of the Institute of Geological Sciences*, No. 78/9.

MANSFIELD, J, and KENNETT, P. 1963. A gravity survey of the Stranraer sedimentary basin. *Proceedings of the Yorkshire Geological Society*, Vol. 34, 139–151.

MERRIMAN, R J, and ROBERTS, B. 1990. Metabentonites in the Moffat Shale Group, Southern Uplands of Scotland: geochemical evidence of ensialic marginal basin volcanism. *Geological Magazine*, Vol. 127, 259–271.

— — 1993. The low grade metamorphism of Lower Palaeozoic strata on the Rhins of Galloway, SW Scotland. *British Geological Survey Technical Report*, WG/92/40.

— — PEACOR, D R. and HIRONS, S R. In press. Strain-related differences in the crystal growth of white mica and chlorite: a TEM and XRD study of the development of metapelitic microfabrics in the Southern Uplands thrust terrane, Scotland. *Journal of Metamorphic Geology*.

MOORE, J C. 1842. On the rocks which form the west shore of the bay of Loch Ryan in Wigtownshire, NB. *Proceedings of the Geological Society of London*, Vol. 3, 277–278.

— 1849. On some fossiliferous beds in the Silurian rocks of Wigtownshire and Ayrshire. *Quarterly Journal of the Geological Society of London*, Vol. 5, 7–12.

— 1856. On the Silurian rocks of Wigtownshire. *Quarterly Journal of the Geological Society of London*, Vol. 12, 359–366.

MORRIS, J H. 1987. The Northern Belt of the Longford–Down Inlier, Ireland and Southern Uplands, Scotland: an Ordovician back-arc basin. *Journal of the Geological Society of London*, Vol. 144, 773–786.

MYKURA, W. 1965. The age of the lower part of the New Red Sandstone of south-west Scotland. *Scottish Journal of Geology*, Vol. 1, 9–18.

NEEDHAM, D T. 1993. The structure of the western part of the Southern Uplands of Scotland. *Journal of the Geological Society of London*, Vol. 150, 341–354.

OLIVER, G J H, and LEGGETT, J K. 1980. Metamorphism in an accretionary prism: prehnite-pumpellyite facies metamorphism of the Southern Uplands of Scotland. *Transactions of the Royal Society of Edinburgh: Earth Sciences*, Vol. 71, 235–246.

— and 7 others. 1984. Early Palaeozoic metamorphic history of the Midland Valley, Southern Uplands–Longford Down massif and the Lake District, British Isles. *Transactions of the Royal Society of Edinburgh: Earth Sciences*, Vol. 75, 245–258.

PEACH, B N, and HORNE, J. 1899. The Silurian rocks of Britain, 1: Scotland. *Memoir of the Geological Survey of the United Kingdom.*

PEARCE, J A. 1982. Trace element characteristics of lavas from destructive plate boundaries. 525–548 in *Andesites.* THORPE, R S (editor). (New York: Wiley.)

— 1983. Role of the sub-continental lithosphere in magma genesis at active continental margins. 230–249 in *Continental basalts and mantle xenoliths.* HAWKESWORTH, C J, and NORRY, M J (editors). (Nantwich, Cheshire: Shiva.)

PECCERILLO, A, and TAYLOR, S R. 1976. Geochemistry of Eocene calc-alkaline volcanic rocks from the Kastamonu area, northern Turkey. *Contributions to Mineralogy and Petrology,* Vol. 589, 63–81.

PICKERING, K T, STOW, D A V, WATSON, M P, and HISCOTT, R N. 1986. Deep water facies, processes and models: a review and classification scheme for modern and ancient sediments. *Earth Sciences Reviews,* Vol. 23, 75–174.

POWELL, D W. 1970. Magnetised rocks within the Lewisian of Western Scotland and under the Southern Uplands. *Scottish Journal of Geology,* Vol. 6, 353–69.

RICKARDS, R B. 1976. The sequence of Silurian graptolite zones in the British Isles. *Geological Journal,* Vol. 11, 153–188.

ROBERTS, B, MERRIMAN, R J, and PRATT, W. 1991. The influence of strain, lithology and stratigraphical depth on white mica (illite) crystallinity in mudrocks from the vicinity of the Corris Slate Belt, Wales; implication for the timing of metamorphism in the Welsh Basin. *Geological Magazine,* Vol. 128, 633–645.

ROBINS, N S, and BUCKLEY, D K. 1988. Characteristics of the Permian and Triassic aquifers of south-west Scotland. *Quarterly Journal of Engineering Geology, London,* Vol. 21, 329–335.

ROCK, N M S, GASKARTH, J W, and RUNDLE, C C. 1986. Late Caledonian dyke-swarms in southern Scotland: a regional zone of primitive K-rich lamprophyres and associated vents. *Journal of Geology,* Vol. 94, 505–522.

RUSHTON, A W A. 1990. Ordovician graptolite biostratigraphy in the Welsh Basin: a review. *Journal of the Geological Society of London,* Vol. 147, 611–614.

— and STONE, P. 1991. Terrigenous input to the Moffat Shale sequence, Southern Uplands. *Scottish Journal of Geology,* Vol. 27, 167–169.

RUST, B R. 1965. The stratigraphy and structure of the Whithorn area of Wigtownshire, Scotland. *Scottish Journal of Geology,* Vol. 1, 101–133.

SAMPLE, J C, and MOORE, J C. 1987. Structural style and kinematics of an underplated slate belt, Kodiak and adjacent islands, Alaska. *Bulletin of the Geological Society of America,* Vol. 99, 7–20.

SCRUTTON, C T, and MCCURRY, J A. 1987. The derivation, biostratigraphy and palaeobiogeographic significance of corals from Silurian deep-sea turbidite facies in the south-west Southern Uplands. *Scottish Journal of Geology,* Vol. 23, 49–64.

SHAND, P. 1989. Late Caledonian magmagenesis in southern Scotland. Unpublished PhD thesis, University of Birmingham.

SISSONS, J B. 1974. The Quaternary in Scotland: a review. *Scottish Journal of Geology,* Vol. 10, 311–337.

— 1983. Quaternary. 399–424 in *The geology of Scotland* (2nd edition). CRAIG, G Y (editor). (Edinburgh: Scottish Academic Press.)

STEPHENS, W C, and HALLIDAY, A N. 1984. Geochemical contrasts between late Caledonian granitoid plutons of northern, central and southern Scotland. *Transactions of the Royal Society of Edinburgh: Earth Sciences,* Vol. 75, 259–273.

STONE, P. 1988. The Permian successions at Ballantrae and Loch Ryan, south-west Scotland. *Report of the British Geological Survey,* Vol. 19, No. 2, 13–18.

— FLOYD, J D, BARNES, R P, and LINTERN, B C. 1987. A sequential back-arc and foreland basin thrust duplex model for the Southern Uplands of Scotland. *Journal of the Geological Society of London,* Vol. 144, 753–764.

— GREEN, P M, LINTERN, B C, PLANT, J A, and SIMPSON, P R. 1991. Geochemistry characterises provenance in southern Scotland. *Geology Today,* Vol. 7, 177–181.

— and SMELLIE, J L. 1988. *Classical areas of British geology: the Ballantrae area: description of the solid geology of parts of 1:25 000 sheets NX08, 18 and 19.* (London: HMSO for British Geological Survey.)

STRACHAN, I. 1971. A synoptic supplement to 'A monograph of British graptolites by Miss G L Elles and Miss E M R.Wood'. *Monographs of the Palaeontographical Society.*

STRINGER, P, and TREAGUS, J E. 1980. Non-axial planar S1 cleavage in the Hawick Rocks of the Galloway area, Southern Uplands, Scotland. *Journal of Structural Geology,* Vol. 2, 317–331.

— — 1981. Asymmetrical folding in the Hawick Rocks of the Galloway area, Southern Uplands. *Scottish Journal of Geology,* Vol. 17, 129–147.

STYLES, M T, STONE, P, and FLOYD, J D. 1989. Arc detritus in the Southern Uplands: mineralogical characterization of a 'missing' terrane. *Journal of the Geological Society of London,* Vol. 146, 397–400.

THIRLWALL, M F. 1988. Geochronology of late Caledonian magmatism in northern Britain. *Journal of the Geological Society of London,* Vol. 145, 951–968.

TINDLE, A G, MCGARVIE, D W, and WEBB, P C. 1988. The role of hybridisation and crystal fractionation in the evolution of the Cairnsmore of Carsphairn Intrusion, Southern Uplands of Scotland. *Journal of the Geological Society of London,* Vol. 145, 11–21.

— and PEARCE, J A. 1981. Petrogenetic modelling of in situ fractional crystallisation in the zoned Loch Doon pluton, Scotland. *Contributions to Mineralogy and Petrology,* Vol. 78, 196–207.

TULLY, M C. 1969. North Channel Irish Sea, Cruise Report — Project 69/7. *Marine Geophysics Unit Report Institute of Geological Sciences,* No. 10.

WALTON, E K. 1955. Silurian greywackes in Peeblesshire. *Proceedings of the Royal Society of Edinburgh,* Vol. B65, 327–357.

— 1961. Some aspects of the succession and structure in the Lower Palaeozoic rocks of the Southern Uplands of Scotland. *Geologische Rundschau,* Vol. 50, 63–77.

— 1983. Lower Palaeozoic — stratigraphy, structure and palaeogeography. 105–166 in *The geology of Scotland* (2nd edition). CRAIG, G Y (editor). (Edinburgh: Scottish Academic Press.)

— and OLIVER, G J H. 1991. Lower Palaeozoic — stratigraphy, structure and palaeogeography. 161–228 in *The geology of Scotland.* (3rd edition). CRAIG G Y (editor). (London: The Geological Society.)

WATSON, J V. 1984. The ending of the Caledonian orogeny in Scotland. *Journal of the Geological Society of London*, Vol. 141, 193–214.

WEBB, B. 1983. Imbricate structure in the Ettrick area, Southern Uplands. *Scottish Journal of Geology*, Vol. 19, 387–400.

WEIR, J A. 1968. Structural history of the Silurian rocks of the coast west of Gatehouse, Kirkcudbrightshire. *Scottish Journal of Geology*, Vol. 4, 31–52.

WELSH, W. 1964. The Ordovician rocks of north west Wigtownshire. Unpublished PhD thesis, University of Edinburgh.

WHITE, D E, BARRON, H F, BARNES, R P, and LINTERN, B C. 1992 [for 1991]. Biostratigraphy of late Llandovery (Telychian) and Wenlock turbiditic sequences in the SW Southern Uplands, Scotland. *Transactions of the Royal Society of Edinburgh: Earth Sciences*, Vol. 82, 297–322.

WILLIAMS, S H. 1982a. Upper Ordovician graptolites from the top of the Lower Hartfell Shale Formation (*D. clingani* and *P. linearis* zones) near Moffat, southern Scotland. *Transactions of the Royal Society of Edinburgh: Earth Sciences*, Vol. 72, 229–255.

— 1982b. The late Ordovician graptolite fauna of the Anceps Bands at Dob's Linn, southern Scotland. *Geologica et Palaeontologica*, Vol. 16, 29–56.

— 1983. The Ordovician–Silurian boundary graptolite fauna of Dob's Linn, southern Scotland. *Palaeontology*, Vol. 26, 605–639.

— 1987. Upper Ordovician graptolites from the *D. complanatus* Zone of the Moffat and Girvan districts and their significance for correlation. *Scottish Journal of Geology*, Vol. 23, 65–92.

WILSON, G V. 1921. Special reports on the mineral resources of Great Britain. Vol. XVII. The lead, zinc, copper and nickel ores of Scotland. *Memoir of the Geological Survey, Scotland.*

WRIGHT, J E, HULL, J H, MCQUILLAN, R, and ARNOLD, S E. 1971. Irish Sea investigations 1969–1970. *Report of the Institute of Geological Sciences*, No.71/19.

APPENDIX 1

BGS publications relevant to the Rhins of Galloway district

1. Maps at 1:10 000 scale, solid edition

The maps at 1:10 000 scale covering, wholly or in part, the solid rocks in the 1:50 000 sheet 1 and 3 are listed below with the names of the surveyors (P M Allen, R P Barnes, I B Cameron, P Davies, A A Jackson, J McCurry and P Stone) and the date of survey. They are derived from surveys between 1977 and 1989 but incorporate some older data.

The maps are not published but are available for consultation in the Library of the British Geological Survey, Murchison House, Edinburgh EH9 3LA. Dyeline copies can be purchased from the Sales Desk.

National Grid sheet		
NW 95 NE	Stone, Davies	1985–1987
NW 96 NE	Stone	1987
NW 96 SE	Stone	1987–1988
NW 97 SE	Stone	1987
NX 03 NE	Cameron, McCurry	1977, 1985–1986
NX 03 SE	Cameron, McCurry	1977, 1985–1986
NX 04 NE (with part of NW)	McCurry, Davies, Allen, Stone	1980, 1985–1986
NX 04 SE	McCurry, Davies, Stone	1985–1986
NX 05 NW	Stone	1987
NX 05 NE	Stone	1988
NX 05 SW (with part of NW 95 SE)	Stone, Davies	1985–1987
NX 05 SE	McCurry	1985–1986
NX 06 NW	Stone	1987
NX 06 NE	Stone	1986
NX 06 SW	Stone	1987
NX 06 SE	Stone	1986
NX 07 SW	Stone	1987
NX 07 SE (part only)	Jackson, Stone	1984, 1986
NX 13 NW	McCurry, Cameron	1977, 1985–1986
NX 13 SW	McCurry, Cameron	1977, 1985–1986
NX 14 NW	McCurry	1985–1986
NX 14 SW	McCurry	1985–1986
NX 15 NW	Stone	1989
NX 15 NE	Barnes	1982–1984
NX 16 NW	Jackson, Stone	1984, 1986–1987
NX 16 NE	Jackson, Stone	1984, 1987
NX 16 SW	Stone	1986
NX 16 SE	Jackson, Stone, Barnes	1983–4, 1986
NX 17 SW (part only)	Stone	1986–1987
NX 17 SE (part only)	Stone	1986–1987

2. Report Series

CAMERON, I B. 1977. Sand and gravel resources of the Dumfries and Galloway Region of Scotland. *Institute of Geological Sciences Report*, No. 77/22. 26pp.

STONE, P. 1988. The Permian successions at Ballantrae and Loch Ryan, south-west Scotland. *Report of the British Geological Survey*, Vol. 19, No. 2, 13–18.

3. Technical Report Series

DAVIES, P. 1990. The geology of the Rhinns of Galloway, SW Scotland: the west coast between Killantringan Bay and Clanyard Bay. *British Geological Survey Technical Report*, WA/90/67. 54pp.

JACKSON, A A. 1985. The area between Cairnryan and Gabsnout Burn, Galloway. *British Geological Survey Open File Report*, No. PDA2/85/4. 24pp.

KIMBELL, G S. 1991. As assessment of geophysical data from the Rhins of Galloway district, south-west Scotland. *British Geological Survey Technical Report*, WK/91/10.

MCCURRY, J. 1990. The geology of the Rhinns of Galloway, SW Scotland, south of the Portayew area. *British Geological Survey Technical Report*, WA/90/66. 23pp.

MERRIMAN, R J, and ROBERTS, B. 1993. The Low Grade Metamorphism of Lower Palaeozoic Strata on the Rhins of Galloway, SW Scotland. *British Geological Survey Technical Report*, WG/92/40.

4. Mineral Reconnaissance Programme Report Series

ALLEN, P M, BIDE, P J, COOPER, D C, PARKER, M E, and HASLAM, H W. 1981. Copper-bearing intrusive rocks at Cairngarroch Bay, south-west Scotland. *British Geological Survey Mineral Reconnaissance Programme Report*, No. 39. 20pp.

COOPER, D C, PARKER, M E, and ALLEN, P M. 1982. Investigations of small intrusions in southern Scotland. *British Geological Survey Mineral Reconnaissance Programme Report*, No. 58. 26pp.

APPENDIX 2

Faunal distribution summary

ORDOVICIAN–SILURIAN GRAPTOLITE LOCALITIES ON SCOTTISH SHEETS 1 AND 3

Sheet 3 (Ordovician)

Locality	NGR	BGS Internal Report No.	Biozone deduced
1. Finnarts Bay	NX 0515 7240 NX 0516 7215 NX 0517 7216	84/33.1 84/33.2 84/33.3	gracilis
2. Polymodie Burn	NX 0585 7020	85/95 87/46.1	gracilis
3. Cairnryan Quarry	NX 0683 6886	87/46.2 & 3 87/50.5	gracilis
4. Dounan Bay	 NW 9662 6866 NW 9668 6877 NW 9665 6875	87/50.1 87/420.5 87/420.6 88/245.1	'peltifer'
5. Slocknamorrow Bay	NW 9608 6658	87/420.4	gracilis or 'peltifer'
6. Portobello		87/50.2	gracilis-'peltifer'
7. 'Trap Arch'	c.NW 977 587	87/50.4	gracilis
8. Cable House	NW 9786 5813	87/420.2	gracilis or 'pelifer'
9. Cable House	NW 9804 5818	87/420.3, 3a 88/245.2 89/137.1	clingani
10. Killantringan Bay	NW 9829 5721 NW 9827 5722	88/233.1 88/245.3	linearis
11. Crailloch Burn	NX 0332 5936	87/50.6 89/137.2	gracilis
12. Crailloch Burn		89/137.2a	clingani
13. Cross Water of Luce		89/137.3	gracilis or 'peltifer'
14. Cross Water of Luce		89/137.3a	gracilis-clingani
15. Water of Luce 1	NX 1661 6644	85/88.2	
16. Valley of Luce	NX 1442 6709	85/88.3	gracilis
17. Valley of Luce	NX 1442 6709	85/88.4	gracilis or 'peltifer'
18. Water of Luce 4 & 6	NX 1521 6746	85/88.6 & 7	gracilis
19. Water of Luce 9	NX 1519 6750	85/88.9	gracilis
20. Water of Luce 10	NX 1517 6751	85/88.10	gracilis or possibly 'peltifer'
21. Water of Luce	NX 1517 6752	85/88.12	gracilis or possibly 'peltifer'
22. Water of Luce 14	NX 1527 6744	85/88.5	Llanvirn to wilsoni
23. Gabsnout Burn 2	NX 1828 6053	84/25.1	u.clingani or ?linearis
24. Gabsnout Burn 7	NX 1985 6118	84/25.6	clingani
25. Gabsnout Burn		87/50.10b	clingani
26. Gabsnout Burn 4	NX 1925 6090	84/25.3	linearis (?clingani)
27. Gabsnout Burn 5	NX 1924 6090	84/25.4	linearis
28. Gabsnout Burn		87/50.10a & b	linearis
29. Morroch Bay		88/227.1	gracilis
30. Morroch Bay		88/227.2	gracilis or 'peltifer'
31. Morroch Bay		88/227.3	gracilis
32. Morroch Bay		88/227.5	prob. wilsoni
33. Morroch Bay		88/227.6	poss. wilsoni?
34. Morroch Bay		88/227.7	clingani or linearis
35. Morroch Bay		88/227.8	gracilis or 'peltifer'
36. Morroch Bay		88/227.10	clingani
37. Morroch Bay		88/227.11	?clingani
38. Morroch Bay		88/227.12 88/227.13	clingani
39. Morroch Bay	NX 0140 5260	88/227.14 88/232.1–6	clingani
40. Colfin Burn		87/50.7	possibly wilsoni or clingani
41. Port of Spittal Bay	NX 0196 5210	87/46.4	linearis
42. Portayew Bay		87/50.8a	gracilis-'peltifer'
43. Portayew Bay	NX 0392 5024	87/50.8 88/233.2–4	clingani or linearis
44. Grennan Pt., or Dumbreddan Bay		87/50.8b	?clingani
45. Bay N. of Grennan Point	NX 0748 4384	92/322.7	persculptus

Sheet 1 (Ordovician)

Locality	NGR	BGS Internal Report No.	Biozone deduced
46. N end Clanyard Bay		87/49.7	Ordovician

Sheet 3 (Silurian)

Locality	NGR	BGS Internal Report No.	Biozone deduced
47. Strandfoot	NX 0522 48112	86/160.2, 87/46.5	atavus-acinaces
48. Strandfoot	NX 0526 4805	87/46.6	gregarius
49. N Float Bay	NX 0620 4724	89/398.2	cyphus
50. Castle Point	NX 0683 4455	87/46.8, 89/420.4	triangulatus
51. Hooies	NX 0681 4462	89/420.1 & 2	magnus

Locality	NGR	BGS Internal Report No.	Biozone deduced
52. Bay N of Grennan Point (N)	NX 0748 4384	92/322.9	atavus
53. Bay N of Grennan Point (N)	NX 0748 4384	92/322.8	acuminatus
54. Bay N of Grennan Point (centre)	NX 0751 4387	89/420.5	acuminatus
55. N of Grennan Point	NX 0755 4382	89/420.6	poss. atavus
56. N of Grennan Point	NX 0748 4376	92/322.2-4	convolutus
57. N Drumbeddan Bay	NX 0771 4372	92/322.1	convolutus
58. N Dumbreddan Bay		86/230.2	prob. cyphus
59. N Dumbreddan Bay	NX 0774 4374	89/420.7	triangulatus
60. N Dumbreddan Bay		86/230.1 & 3	magnus
61. Near Grennan Point	loc. uncertain	87/50.9	convolutus
Sheet 1 (Silurian)			
62. Cairnie Finnart	NX 0883 4146	87/47.1	turriculatus
63. Grennan Quarry		86/160, 87/49.1 & 2	crispus
64. Dunbuck		87/49.3	?crispus
65. N end Clanyard Bay	NX 1010 3812	87/47.9	atavus
66. N end Clanyard Bay		87/49.4	acinaces
67. N end Clanyard Bay	NX 1010 3812	87/47.6	cyphus
68. N end Clanyard Bay	NX 1010 3812	87/47.5	cyphus-triangulatus
69. N end Clanyard Bay		87/49.5	convolutus
70. N end Clanyard Bay	NX 1010 3812	87/47.4, 87/49.6	sedgwickii
71. N end Clanyard Bay	NX 1010 3812	90/76	basal turriculatus
72. S end Clanyard Bay	NX 0966 3768	89/282.2	cyphus
73. S end Clanyard Bay	NX 0966 3768	89/282.3 & 4	convolutus
74. Saddle	NX 0855 3676	89/282.5–7	convolutus
75. N of Laggantulloch Head		87/49.8	?cyphus

Localities	1	2	3	4	5	6	7	8	9	10	11	12	13	14	15	16	17	18	19	20	21	22	23	24	25	26	27	28	29	30	31	32	33	34	35	36	37	38	39	40	41	42	43	44	45	46
Amphigraptus radiatus																																		x												
Amplexograptus leptotheca				x		sp								sp?																					sp											
Amplexograptus perexcavatus																																x														
Climacograptus antiquus																	x																													
Climacograptus bicornis	x							x								x		x											x				x		x									x		
Climacograptus caudatus												x												x														x								
Climacograptus dorotheus																							?					x									x	?								
Climacograptus spiniferus																																							x				x			
Climacograptus styloideus																							x			x	cf																			
Climacograptus wilsoni																																x														
Climacograptus (s.l.) sp.	x	x		x	x	x			x	x	x				x					x	x				x									x				x	x		x		x			
Corynoides calicularis									x							sp		sp						x										sp	sp			sp	x							
Corynoides curtus												x											x		x														x							
Cryptograptus tricornis	sp?	x	x				x				x				x	sp	x	x	x	x									x	x	sp?				x			x	sp?			x				
Dicellograptus angulatus											sp					sp												sp					x						x							sp
Dicellograptus carruthersi																											x												sp							
Dicellograptus divaricatus s.l.			cf																																											
Dicellograptus divaricatus rigidus																		x		x									x																	
Dicellograptus flexuosus																							x			x							x			x	x	x	x							
Dicellograptus intortus															x			x	x	x									x																	
Dicellograptus moffatensis									?																														x				x			
Dicellograptus morrisi																																				x		x	x				?			
Dicellograptus patulosus?																				x																										
Dicellograptus pumilus																									x	x	x												x							
Dicellograptus salopiensis	cf												?					x	x	x	cf																									
Dicellograptus sextans	x	x																											x	x					x											
Dicellograptus sextans exilis	x	x	x	x		x	cf	?									x	x											x																	
Dicranograptus brevicaulis																					x																									
Dicranograptus furcatus																														x																
Dicranograptus furcatus minimus															x																											x				
Dicranograptus nicholsoni														cf					x													x														
Dicranograptus ramosus											x	x							cf										x									x	x					x		
Dicranograptus ramosus longicaulis									x																x			?																		
Dicranograptus ramosus spinifer		x		?														x																												
Dicranograptus rectus	x			x	x	x										x	x	x			x																									
Dicranograptus ziczac																															?							x								
Didymograptus serratulus															x																															
Didymograptus superstes	x	x	x				x				x				x	x		x	x	x											x											x				
Diplograptus cf. *compactus*																		x																												
Diplograptus foliaceus		x																?																												
Glossograptus hinksii							x									x	sp?	x														x			sp											
Glyptograptus? avitus																																													x	
'Glyptograptus' euglyphus	x	x		sp?			sp								sp		x	x		x	x										x															
Glyptograptus cf. *persculptus*																																													x	
Glyptograptus cf. *'venustus'*																																													x	
Hallograptus bimucronatus					x										sp																															
Hallograptus mucronatus		x	x																x	x									x																	
Lasiograptus costatus	sp?		cf														x	x																												
Lasiograptus harknessi																	x																			x		x	?	x						
Leptograptus flaccidus										x					sp?				sp?	sp			x			sp		x						x	sp				?		sp	sp?				
Leptograptus flaccidus spinifer																							x																							
Nemagraptus gracilis	sp?						sp								x	x	sp	x	x		sp								x																	
Nemagraptus pertenuis		x					x									cf																														
Neurograptus fibratus																								sp										x		x			sp?							
Neurograptus margaritatus																									x	x								x					x							
Normalograptus brevis																	x																													
Normalograptus miserabilis																										x																				
Normalograptus mohawkensis																																									x		x			
Normalograptus cf. *normalis*																																													x	
Normalograptus tubuliferus																												x													x					
Orthograptus amplexicaulis [group]																										x		x											x	x	x	x	x			
Orthograptus calcaratus acutus																x		x			x																									
Orthograptus calcaratus basilicus																																									x					
Orthograptus calcaratus vulgatus																																	x													
Orthograptus calcaratus [group]									x		?												x	x		x		x	x		?					x			x							
Orthograptus intermedius																																		x					?				x			
Orthograptus pageanus																																						cf	x				x			
Orthograptus pauperatus																																		x					x							
Orthograptus quadrimucronatus																																		x				x	x		x		x			
Orthograptus quadrimucronatus spinigerus																												x						x					x							
Orthograptus whitfieldi		?	sp	aff					sp				sp		sp			x											x	sp								sp	sp			x	sp			
Plegmatograptus nebula																																					x									
Plegmatograptus sp.																											?	?											?		x					
Pleurograptus linearis										?													sp					x																		
Pseudoclimacograptus modestus	sp?	x		sp							sp?			sp?		x		sp			sp																									
Pseudoclimacograptus scharenbergi						x											x		x	cf		x																								
Reteograptus geinitzianus						x																																	sp							
Thamnograptus capillaris											x										x																									
Thamnograptus scoticus																														x					?											
	1	2	3	4	5	6	7	8	9	10	11	12	13	14	15	16	17	18	19	20	21	22	23	24	25	26	27	28	29	30	31	32	33	34	35	36	37	38	39	40	41	42	43	44	45	46

Localities	47	48	49	50	51	52	53	54	55	56	57	58	59	60	61	62	63	64	65	66	67	68	69	70	71	72	73	74	75
cf. *Akidograptus ascensus*							x																						
Atavaograptus atavus	x					?			x			?								sp	x								
Atavaograptus gracilis						?			x																				
Atavaograptus strachani									?																				
Cephalograptus cometa																												x	
'Climacograptus' innotatus									x																				
Coronograptus cyphus			x																		x	x				cf			x
Coronograptus cyphus praematurus									x																				
Coronograptus gregarius				x	x					x	x		?									x				?	x	x	
Cystograptus vesiculosus									?										x	x	x								
Dimorphograptus confertus									x																				
Dimorphograptus decussatus decussatus									x																				
Dimorphograptus elongatus									?										x										
Dimorphograptus erectus	x								x																				
Dimorphograptus cf. *longissimus*	x																					x				x			
Dimorphograptus physophora																					x								
Diplograptus elongatus			x						cf																				
Diversograptus runcinatus?																x													
cf. *Glyptograptus? avitus*							x																						
Glyptograptus cf. *enodis*														x															
Glyptograptus aff. *enodis latus*									x																				
Glyptograptus incertus				cf											x									x					
Glyptograptus serratus																							x						
Glyptograptus sinuatus																						x							
Glyptograptus tamariscus				cf	x					x																		sp	cf
Glyptograptus sp							x																						
Lagarograptus acinaces																				x						aff			
Metaclimacograptus undulatus										x																			
Metaclimacograptus sp												x	x																
Monograptus argenteus					?					cf	cf																		
Monograptus austerus												x									x								
Monograptus capis																												x	
Monograptus clingani										x																	x		
Monograptus communis				x	x																						x		
Monograptus cf. *communis rostratus*				x																									
Monograptus convolutus										x					x								x				x		
Monograptus (s.l.) *crenularis*										x																			
Monograptus crispus																	x												
Monograptus decipiens											x				x														
Monograptus denticulatus																											x	x	
Monograptus difformis				x																		x							
Monograptus discus																	x												
'Monograptus' 'gemmatus'															x														
Monograptus involutus																									x				
Monograptus limatulus															x								x				x	x	
Monograptus lobiferus																							x						
Monograptus marri																	x	x											
Monograptus cf. *planus*																		x											
Monograptus priodon																	x	cf											
Monograptus proteus																x	?	x											
Monograptus pseudobecki?																		x											
Monograptus pseudoplanus				x	cf						aff																		
Monograptus revolutus				x																	x								
Monograptus sedgwickii																								x	x				
Monograptus sudburiae?					x																								
Monograptus triangulatus fimbriatus				x										cf															
Monograptus triangulatus separatus													x																
Monograptus triangulatus triangulatus					x										sl														
Monograptus (Diversograptus?) capillaris																									x				
triangulate monograptid		x																				x		x					
Normalograptus medius		?				x	x												x	x									
Normalograptus miserabilis	x		cf				x		cf																				
Normalograptus normalis		x	x				x												x	x	?								
Normalograptus rectangularis			x						x											x									x
cf. *Normalograptus scalaris*											x																		
Normalograptus sp.					x		?							x												x	?	x	
'Orthograptus' bellulus																							x			sp?	x		
'Orthograptus' cyperoides				x						x		cf									?								
'Orthograptus' insectiformis				x							cf										?								
'Orthograptus' mutabilis																													x
Parakidograptus acuminatus acuminatus							x	x																					
Petalograptus altissimus?																		x											
Petalograptus ovatoelongatus					x					sp																			
Petalograptus cf. *palmeus latus*														x															
Petalograptus palmeus palmeus															x										cf				
Petalograptus tenuis																								x					
Pribylograptus argutus				cf									cf														sp?	cf	
Pribylograptus cf. *incommodus*			x																										
Pribylograptus jonesi											?																		
Pribylograptus leptotheca															x														
Pribylograptus sandersoni																					x								
Pristiograptus concinnus					x					x																	sp?	sp	
Pristiograptus jaculum											x																		
Pristiograptus nudus																									x				
Metaclimacograptus hughesi			?	cf																									
Pseudoplegmatograptus? sp.																								x	x				
Rastrites abbreviatus																									x				
Rastrites cf. *approximatus geinitzi*					x																								
Rastrites longispinus													cf		x														
Rastrites peregrinus				sp	aff									x	sp												x	aff	
Rhaphidograptus toernquisti						x				x		sp									x								
Rhaphidograptus extenuatus																			x										
Streptograptus exiguus																	x	x											
Streptograptus plumosus																		x											
cf. *Streptograptus nanshanensis minutus*																									x				
Localities	47	48	49	50	51	52	53	54	55	56	57	58	59	60	61	62	63	64	65	66	67	68	69	70	71	72	73	74	75

APPENDIX 3

Representative modal and geochemical analyses of greywackes from the Rhins of Galloway district

		Quartz	Plagioclase	K-feldspar	Pyroxene	Hornblende	Mica	Opaques	Acid igneous rock clasts	Andesitic igneous rock clasts	Basaltic igneous rock clasts	Metamorphic rock clasts	Sedimentary rock clasts	Matrix
Leadhills Group														
Corsewall Formation:	S 78150	24.3	14.6	11.0	0.1	0.1	—	3.2	8.5	16.4	3.0	5.4	1.1	12.3
	S 81779	33.5	14.2	15.3	1.8	—	—	2.0	7.3	12.7	1.1	0.6	1.2	10.3
Kirkcolm Formation:	S 70796	36.8	9.8	7.1	—	—	4.3	1.1	6.7	3.3	1.5	1.0	5.3	23.1
	S 78154	32.0	7.4	—	—	—	2.7	2.0	19.4	3.0	4.8	1.7	7.3	19.7
	S 81781	43.2	12.2	1.0	—	—	2.1	1.7	4.6	3.4	1.7	1.4	3.5	25.2
Galdenoch Formation:	S 78105	25.5	7.6	7.5	5.1	3.8	—	0.4	10.4	22.5	1.9	0.6	1.5	13.2
Portpatrick Formation:	S 77091	22.3	11.2	10.7	2.0	1.7	—	0.6	17.9	12.7	4.2	0.9	6.0	9.8
	S 81780	25.1	15.8	12.1	0.8	0.1	—	3.4	8.2	13.7	3.7	3.1	1.9	12.1
Glenwhargen Formation:	S 81477	60.4	9.0	3.3	1.3	—	3.0	0.4	3.6	—	—	2.0	—	17.0
Gala Group unit 2:	S 81788	32.4	14.3	5.4	3.2	0.3	—	0.6	4.0	16.2	1.6	3.3	0.8	17.9
unit 4:	S 81782	45.2	13.1	10.3	—	—	4.1	0.6	5.6	5.6	2.1	1.1	0.8	11.5
unit 5:	S 80350	33.6	13.9	19.4	1.3	—	2.7	2.2	5.8	4.1	2.6	0.4	0.7	13.3
unit 6:	S 81787	43.9	16.2	17.0	—	—	5.7	1.2	3.6	—	1.0	0.3	1.8	9.3
unit 8:	S 78890	53.1	14.5	0.5	—	—	3.1	0.6	3.9	—	1.5	6.6	2.2	14.0
Hawick Group														
Carghidown Formation:	S 80345	30.1	14.6		—	—	8.4	1.3	5.3	0.2	—	1.6	0.5	38.0*
	S 81784	30.5	8.7		—	0.1	—	1.4	8.5	—	1.2	1.8	1.4	46.1*

	Leadhills Group												Gala Group tectonostratigraphic unit						Hawick Group
	Corsewall Formation		Kirkcolm Formation			Galdenoch Formation		Portpatrick Formation		Glenwhargen Formation		Shinnel Formation	2	4	5	6	7	8	Carghidown Formation
	S78150	S81779	S70796	S78154	S81781	S78105	S79770	S77091	S81780	S77090	S81477	S82626	S81788	S81782	S80350	S81787	S81783	S78890	S81784
SiO_2	60.42	59.91	66.89	68.04	67.85	65.96	58.04	65.56	56.72	67.52	75.51	63.91	59.38	70.47	67.74	69.76	67.58	75.20	56.49
Al_2O_3	13.04	13.36	12.93	13.69	10.81	13.36	12.52	13.29	15.59	6.33	9.55	14.41	14.12	10.51	11.60	12.16	11.78	10.42	8.74
TiO_2	1.15	1.21	0.95	0.95	0.85	0.80	1.23	0.69	0.90	0.34	0.72	0.75	0.92	0.75	0.77	0.71	0.68	0.70	0.59
Fe_2O_3*	8.42	7.61	6.52	6.88	5.60	6.06	8.34	6.09	7.81	1.97	3.57	5.88	7.67	5.05	5.54	5.00	5.96	4.31	4.78
MnO	0.125	0.094	0.069	0.068	0.062	0.095	0.145	0.094	0.125	0.057	0.045	0.079	0.104	0.059	0.071	0.074	0.060	0.045	0.112
MgO	6.22	6.77	3.73	2.84	3.02	3.41	5.88	4.01	5.47	1.12	1.82	3.96	4.51	3.26	3.18	2.79	3.35	2.00	5.06
CaO	1.35	2.32	0.87	0.44	3.21	2.48	4.21	2.47	5.29	10.23	2.88	1.84	6.87	1.55	2.72	1.45	2.21	1.17	8.10
Na_2O	3.09	3.26	2.17	2.97	1.63	3.21	2.86	3.13	3.50	1.78	1.91	3.67	2.35	1.98	2.67	2.84	1.70	2.07	1.47
K_2O	1.94	1.35	1.97	1.62	1.50	2.43	1.77	2.05	1.69	1.23	1.31	1.84	1.11	2.19	2.22	2.49	1.87	1.47	1.44
P_2O_5	0.18	0.17	0.17	0.15	0.15	0.19	0.40	0.12	0.18	0.07	0.13	0.20	0.19	0.17	0.19	0.18	0.14	0.12	0.12
LOI	4.58	4.10	3.96	3.05	5.01	2.86	4.86	2.81	3.14	8.63	2.61	3.49	3.50	3.62	3.64	2.92	4.95	2.78	13.27
Total	100.52	100.15	100.23	100.70	99.69	100.85	100.25	100.31	100.42	99.28	100.05	100.03	100.72	99.61	100.34	100.37	100.28	100.29	100.17
* total Fe as Fe_2O_3 LOI = loss on ignition																			
Ba	425	241	297	260	239	1407	830	631	396	414	183	383	169	418	578	534	220	253	102
Rb	31	24	55	49	50	49	36	45	40	21	34	48	33	57	54	59	64	49	48
Sr	311	231	56	78	130	1088	695	285	353	349	113	259	381	103	225	162	71	97	63
Y	22	23	26	25	27	25	32	18	17	13	20	18	20	22	21	23	24	24	23
Zr	128	119	258	213	328	233	355	147	109	307	248	168	184	330	285	263	200	229	229
Nb	6	6	13	14	12	11	13	5	4	6	11	8	6	10	9	10	10	11	7
Cu	36	82	27	43	30	25	63	22	40	7	16	30	36	21	51	25	13	19	90
Zn	65	68	57	60	69	69	71	59	73	27	51	67	72	55	44	59	65	48	27
Pb	16	6	11	1	9	27	66	14	10	11	13	11	11	32	5	7	6	15	5
Cr	154	308	149	111	131	146	162	236	137	73	56	155	104	246	179	138	90	66	115
Ni	54	140	68	60	47	49	52	55	46	24	22	82	41	72	60	65	37	31	50
V	200	204	98	105	85	111	183	127	179	27	56	106	155	87	103	81	79	60	58

Major oxides in %, trace elements in ppm.

Geochemical analyses by XRF at the British Geological Survey, Keyworth.
Analysts: P H Miles, A G Scothern, M N Ingham and A S Robertson.

* carbonate matrix

APPENDIX 4

Geochemical analyses of representative intrusive igneous rocks from the Rhins of Galloway district

	Pyroxene diorite		Central granodiorite		Hornblende-diorite		Porphyritic grano-diorite	Quartz-micro-diorite	Mica-lamprophyres Kersantites			Hornblende-lamprophyres Spessartites			Felsites and porphyrites		
SiO_2	58.60	59.42	66.43	68.01	59.80	62.64	63.70	57.04	52.22	51.30	52.31	53.53	61.15	51.87	58.87	63.31	58.26
Al_2O_3	16.54	16.25	15.48	15.81	16.65	17.35	15.52	17.30	14.86	12.63	13.33	14.91	15.55	14.62	16.87	15.05	14.40
TiO_2	0.88	0.79	0.49	0.54	0.76	0.94	0.62	0.93	1.24	0.80	0.94	0.73	0.73	1.18	0.70	0.55	0.60
Fe_2O_3	6.05	5.96	3.48	3.08	5.72	4.92	4.44	6.95	8.67	8.19	8.87	7.50	5.12	8.03	5.96	3.95	5.01
MnO	0.10	0.09	0.05	0.03	0.07	0.07	nd	nd	0.17	0.12	0.13	0.12	0.09	0.14	0.11	0.06	0.09
MgO	5.56	5.74	2.08	2.24	5.16	3.65	2.71	3.62	7.08	8.97	7.65	8.54	4.40	6.73	3.74	2.17	6.02
CaO	6.37	6.19	2.70	2.21	5.67	5.88	4.04	5.21	7.25	7.06	6.69	5.69	2.56	6.81	4.69	3.55	3.92
Na_2O	4.14	3.90	3.87	3.98	4.25	3.33	4.16	4.44	2.60	2.06	2.92	3.68	4.16	3.29	3.87	3.50	3.12
K_2O	2.31	2.34	4.08	4.39	2.48	1.37	3.49	1.98	3.51	4.95	3.17	2.08	3.12	2.59	2.58	3.60	2.74
P_2O_5	0.31	0.23	0.19	0.16	0.26	0.20	0.17	0.22	0.61	1.24	0.61	0.24	0.20	0.33	0.24	0.17	0.19
LOI									3.02	1.86	4.30	1.50	2.05	3.03	1.61	3.74	4.35
Ba	1130	1011	1147	1203	1022	336	973	763	1745	1616	2535	1102	995	1187	853	1011	1265
Rb	39	49	130	118	45	29	104	60	116	265	60	47	66	53	64	119	66
Sr	1074	788	596	548	853	555	1265	676	760	456	791	771	504	525	995	506	644
Y	13	16	16	18	14	16	20	20	24	20	20	14	19	24	20	22	15
Zr	134	127	207	215	97	113	230	122	162	126	134	150	164	155	149	244	146
Nb	6	8	13	12	6	8	nd	nd	10	7	7	10	9	10	8	13	8
Cu	43	39	52	39	100	27	608	54	nd	nd	nd	nd	nd	nd	nd	nd	nd
Zn	55	49	22	6	46	83	23	63	nd	nd	nd	nd	nd	nd	nd	nd	nd
Pb	18	18	17	15	16	15	<13	<13	nd	nd	nd	nd	nd	nd	nd	nd	nd
Cr	172	235	50	81	193	123	nd	nd	136	361	284	496	172	286	94	64	344
Ni	88	88	63	31	81	34	21	12	54	121	63	220	89	75	48	27	145
Co	172	30	nd	28	35	40	nd	nd	nd	nd	nd	nd	nd	nd	nd	nd	nd
V	136	125	70	87	133	161	nd	nd	195	190	213	142	119	199	119	84	116
Th	9	9	17	25	9	4	15	5	7.5	7.9	nd	5.7	nd	4.4	nd	nd	nd
La	28	19	31	41	18	11	nd	nd	28.6	14.6	nd	27.4	nd	20.3	nd	nd	nd
Ce	74	58	62	82	70	52	53	25	57.9	33.6	nd	53.7	nd	43.1	nd	nd	nd
Nd	35	28	25	30	26	22	nd	nd	31.0	nd	nd	25.0	nd	32.0	nd	nd	nd
Sm	5	4	4	4	4	4	nd	nd	4.7	4.8	nd	4.5	nd	4.9	nd	nd	nd
Eu	nd	nd	nd	nd	nd	nd	nd	nd	1.4	1.3	nd	1.4	nd	1.5	nd	nd	nd
Tb	nd	nd	nd	nd	nd	nd	nd	nd	0.8	0.6	nd	0.4	nd	0.7	nd	nd	nd
Yb	nd	nd	nd	nd	nd	nd	nd	nd	2.3	2.3	nd	1.4	nd	2.2	nd	nd	nd
Lu	nd	nd	nd	nd	nd	nd	nd	nd	0.4	0.3	nd	0.2	nd	0.3	nd	nd	nd
Hf	nd	nd	nd	nd	nd	nd	nd	nd	4.0	3.2	nd	3.8	nd	4.0	nd	nd	nd
Ta	nd	nd	nd	nd	nd	nd	nd	nd	nd	0.4	nd	0.5	nd	0.6	nd	nd	nd
	Portencorkrie Complex						Cairngarroch Complex		Dykes from the Rhins of Galloway								
	4	8	12	19	27	29			1	2	3	4	5	6	7	8	9

Portencorkrie analyses by XRF at the University of Aston, analyst J W Gaskarth.

Cairngarroch analyses by XRF at the British Geological Survey, Greys Inn Road Laboratory, analysts T K Smith and A Davies.

Lamprophyre, felsite and porphyrite analyses by XRF at the University of Aston, analyst J W Gaskarth. Additional data for some lamprophyres (Th to Ta only) by Instrumental Neutron Activation Analysis at the Hahn-Meitner Institute, Berlin, analyst P Möller.

LOI Loss on ignition
nd No data.

Specimen locality details:
Portencorkie Complex. See Figure 24.
Cairngarroch Complex. See Allen et al., 1981, fig. 5.
Dykes from the Rhins of Galloway.

1. NX 1085 3600 2. NX 1083 3276 3. NX 1088 3268
4. NX 0789 4526 5. NX 0610 4728 6. NX 0446 5142
7. NX 1300 3409 8. NX 0705 4946 9. NX 0465 5168

APPENDIX 5

Data and analytical details for Rb-Sr regression age of the Portencorkrie intrusion

Age 392 ± 19 Ma (2σ): see Figure 26c
Intercept 0.7053 ± 0.0001
MSWD 0.7

The Rb/Sr ratios were determined using a Philips automated X-ray spectrometer. The quoted ratios in the data table are averages of analyses of both sides of a rock-powder pellet. The Rb and Sr concentrations were estimated from the Molybdenum Compton scatter and have a precision of about ± 5% 1σ. These concentrations are not used in the age calculation.

The isotope composition of the samples was determined using a VG 354 multicollector mass spectrometer. This gave a value for the international standard NBS 987 of 0.710232 ± 27 (1σ) (20 determinations) during the period when the samples were analysed. The best fit line through the data was determined using a York-Williamson least squares regression with errors on both axes. The errors used in the regression are 0.5% 1σ on the Rb/Sr ratio and 0.01% 1σ on the $^{87}Sr/^{86}Sr$ ratio. The decay constant used for ^{87}Rb is 1.42* $10^{11}a^{-1}$ (Steiger and Jäger, 1977). The analyst was J A Evans.

STEIGER, R H, and JÄGER, E. 1977. Subcommission on geochronology: Convention on the use of decay constants in geo- and cosmochronology. *Earth and Planetary Science Letters*, Vol. 36, 359–362.

Specimen No.	Locality NGR	NIGL laboratory No.	Rb ppm	Sr ppm	$^{87}Rb/^{86}Sr$	$^{87}Sr/^{86}Sr$
		PC1	131	600	0.631	0.708745
		PC2	134	657	0.591	0.708752
		PC3	122	531	0.664	0.709023
S 64169	Closely spaced	PC4	119	475	0.727	0.709382
	around	PC5	121	626	0.558	0.708380
S64172	NX 0895 3510	PC6	122	646	0.545	0.708383
		PC7	111	575	0.559	0.708387
		PC8	118	692	0.495	0.708038
		PC10	132	588	0.650	0.708957
S 64233	NX 0884 3540	PA74	76.4	762	0.290	0.707009
S 64183	NX 0875 3482	PA80	109	632	0.500	0.708108
S 64188	NX 0895 3428	PA82	117	596	0.568	0.708538
S 64206	NX 0894 3405	PA83	71.5	776	0.267	0.706766
	NX 0905 3390	PA84	77.1	821	0.272	0.706824

Specimen numbers prefixed 'S' are registered in the BGS collection, Murchison House, Edinburgh.

Specimens with laboratory numbers prefixed 'PC' were collected by Dr J W Gaskarth, those prefixed 'PA' by Mr I B Cameron.

FOSSIL INDEX

Only graptolites mentioned in the main text are indexed here. The whole graptolite fauna, including species not cited in the text, is given in Appendix 2 on pp. 92, 93.

GENERAL INDEX

BRITISH GEOLOGICAL SURVEY

Keyworth, Nottingham NG12 5GG
(0115) 936 3100

Murchison House, West Mains Road, Edinburgh
EH9 3LA 0131-667 1000

London Information Office, Natural History Museum
Earth Galleries, Exhibition Road, London SW7 2DE
0171-589 4090

The full range of Survey publications is available through the Sales Desks at Keyworth and at Murchison House, Edinburgh, and in the BGS London Information Office in the Natural History Museum (Earth Galleries). The adjacent bookshop stocks the more popular books for sale over the counter. Most BGS books and reports can be bought from HMSO and through HMSO agents and retailers. Maps are listed in the BGS Map Catalogue, and can be bought together with books and reports through BGS-approved stockists and agents as well as direct from BGS.

The British Geological Survey carries out the geological survey of Great Britain and Northern Ireland (the latter as an agency service for the government of Northern Ireland), and of the surrounding continental shelf, as well as its basic research projects. It also undertakes programmes of British technical aid in geology in developing countries as arranged by the Overseas Development Administration.

The British Geological Survey is a component body of the Natural Environment Research Council.

HMSO publications are available from:

HMSO Publications Centre
(Mail, fax and telephone orders only)
PO Box 276, London SW8 5DT
Telephone orders 0171-873 9090
General enquiries 0171-873 0011
Queuing system in operation for both numbers
Fax orders 0171-873 8200

HMSO Bookshops
49 High Holborn, London WC1V 6HB
(counter service only)
0171-873 0011 Fax 0171-831 1326
68–69 Bull Street, Birmingham B4 6AD
0121-236 9696 Fax 0121-236 9699
33 Wine Street, Bristol BS1 2BQ
0117-9264306 Fax 0117-9294515
9 Princess Street, Manchester M60 8AS
0161-834 7201 Fax 0161-833 0634
16 Arthur Street, Belfast BT1 4GD
01232-238451 Fax 01232-235401
71 Lothian Road, Edinburgh EH3 9AZ
0131-228 4181 Fax 0131-229 2734
HMSO Oriel Bookshop,
The Friary, Cardiff CF1 4AA
01222-395548 Fax 01222-384347

HMSO's Accredited Agents
(see Yellow Pages)

And through good booksellers